Silver Platter

Ellin Berlin

Biography of Marie Louise Antoinette (Hungerford) mackay

Doubleday & Company, Inc.
Garden City, New York
1957

To My Grandchildren
Elizabeth Esther, Irving Berlin
and Mary Ellin Barrett

Contents

8 Contents

Silver Platter

Dear Granny—

My first memory of you is long ago—before either of the world wars—the year was 1906 or 1907. I think you were stopping at the Waldorf-Astoria. I shall find the exact date as I follow your story through family letters, through newspaper files, through memoirs. It can still be told as you would have told it to me, as you did tell it in part. You came back to the States in 1920, and I was married in 1926. If only I hadn't interrupted. If only I had listened. But, you see, I expect you saw then, that in those modern years of the 1920s it wasn't fun to listen. The fun was to tell. Who wanted to hear about the old Prince of Wales, a fat man in a homburg with a stickpin and a cigar? Our rotogravure showed us a much better prince. A nice new Prince of Wales.

But all this was later.

A grandmother was a new thing to me. My grandmother lived abroad. She was a lady from Europe. I almost don't remember. I remember a sweet powdery smell. I remember a smooth opaque skin and carefully coifed black hair. And I remember the big pearls in the lobes of your ears. I remember the pearls well because you offered me a pair of earrings if I would have my ears pierced. I refused the offer and you gave me a doll instead. You took me to Schwarz' to choose her. My sister must have refused the earrings too. She was there, I know. We drove back to Long Island afterward. And we watched when the car stopped in the dusk and the chauffeur got out to light the headlights.

I saw you again in 1909 in Paris. I must have visited you but I don't remember your apartment. I remember ours in the Astoria. The sitting room was upholstered in pale blue with white lace antimacassars. I do remember your house in London in the summer of 1913. It was the season, you told us, and that was why a London town house was polished and shining, with footmen in livery. New York houses in summer were wrapped in brown holland covers and a caretaker came slowly to answer the doorbell. The door of 6 Carlton House Terrace flew open as my sister touched the bell. I remember that she and our brother and I ran through the rooms, touching the statues and the pictures, and we pounded up and down the wide stone curve of the stairs. I remember the house but I don't really remember you again until 1920 when you came to live with us in America.

I remember that you were small. Your feet were tiny and arched. And your hair was alive. It was dark, streaked only a little with white. And your skin was soft and fine and white so that I could imagine how it must have been before the lines and wrinkles. Your eyes were big and startlingly blue. Startling because I expected an old lady to be all one color. Gray like a steel engraving or a knitted shawl. I could imagine what you had been but I couldn't really see it. I had felt it more clearly in that first meeting between us more than ten years before. It is hard to begin to know someone when she is seventy-seven. But we managed. We managed very well. It shouldn't be hard for me to tell your story. You told me a good deal. And the record is there for me to find.

I hope you will approve—you'd tell me quickly enough if you didn't. I can hear the click of your teeth. And I can see the change of color in your eyes when you unexpectedly spoke your mind. You were kind to me because you chose to be. Old age hadn't melted you. Your *loyalties and your hates weren't blurred with time. I suppose they grew stronger in your last years. You had lots of time in which to remember.*

Do you remember when Mr. Dey, Grandfather's confidential secretary, died? Father was so nervous about telling you. "Poor Mammy. This'll be an awful shock to her. Poor Mammy." He made me go to you with him. I can see him now walking up and down your room with that quick impatient walk of his. Then he sat on the edge of the chair beside you and spoke loudly. His nervousness made him speak too loudly. You frowned. You didn't like it when people shouted more loudly than your deafness required.

"Well, Mammy," he said, "well, Mammy. Now don't be nervous. The boy's fine. Nothing wrong in the family. Everything's fine. But I've sad news, Mammy. Very sad news."

You raised your heavily penciled brows and waited for him to continue.

"I'm sorry to have to tell you, Mammy. I know it will be a terrible blow to you. But poor old Mr. Dey passed away today."

Your brows were level and your voice was crisp as you answered. "Thirty years too late to suit me."

Your loves and your hates and your prejudices are still vivid to me. The Princess of Wales. You were proudest of your acquaintance with her. She was more than royalty. She was the elegance of an entire period. Mrs. Paran Stevens. She was kind to you when you returned to New York in the Centennial year. It was kindness you bargained for, but the others wouldn't bargain. And you gave her her due. You made her alive, dark, handsome, fashionable. And Theresa Fair. She was your friend of the old days. For her sake you were still angry with Jim Fair, though he was a handsome man, you said. You said he could charm the birds from the trees. And he was a clever man. Very clever. For her sake you liked the Fair girls, Tessie and Birdie. You were fond of Birdie for her own sake too. She was like you, small and dark-haired and quick. And if your boy, Willie, had lived he would have married her. Birdie would never have refused Willie. No one could have refused Willie. You hated your son-in-law. "He had," you said, "every vice save that of drink, which would have excused the others." He spoiled the life you had so carefully planned for your beloved daughter. Because of him you took pleasure in despising all Italians. When we drove together in the motor, if you saw

*laundry flapping between windows you announced with great posi-
tiveness and satisfaction, "Italians, of course!" Italians were shiftless,
they were dishonest, they were superstitious. You had stories to prove
it. You forgot your good Italian brother-in-law and remembered only
Ferdinand Colonna, who had defeated you. "Italians!" Your voice
was hard.*

*You were kind to my sister and my brother and me. You comforted
us when we were in disgrace. You watched us fall in love and you
gave your opinion if we asked for it. I don't know what you told the
others. With me you were interested and practical and always a little
detached.*

*You listened when I told you about Irving. And you said you en-
joyed Mr. Woollcott's book, where the story was better told. Woollc-
cott was very eloquent about the poverty of the tenement in which
Irving lived on Cherry Street. Did you remember Cherry Street? It
runs into Pearl, where you were born. Did you remember when you
lived nearby on Varick Street and Grand Street in little more comfort than Moses and Leah Baline were to know forty-five years later?*

*You went to the Fourth Music Box Revue with me. You wore all
your pearls to do me credit and you laughed heartily at Fanny Brice
and Bobby Clark. You commented on the full house with satisfaction.*

*We got to know each other well, you and I. Well enough, I think,
for me to tell your story. There was affection between us. Indeed, I
loved you. But love comes easily in the teens. The only person you
loved was my father. He was the only one left. And he was the
youngest of your children, so perhaps he was always the dearest.*

*You were Granny and Mrs. Mackay in my time. I heard only one
human being call you Louise. But I think I know what Louise was
like. My first impression of you was the true one: beneath the coronet
of dark hair, the firm curve of the white cheek was still beautiful.
And your charm worked with me as it had with all the others. If I
hadn't been charmed I should surely have been afraid of the needle
piercing my ears, and yet afraid to refuse the strange lady. But I felt
free to choose the doll and proud of the curious grown-up offer I had
rejected.*

I think I can tell your story.

*"If you don't get sentimental." I can hear the sound of your voice
as though you were speaking to me. You were annoyed by the visitors
who tried to embalm you as a saintly old lady. You didn't like being*

old and you never chose to make a virtue of it, nor would you wish any part of your history sweetened or altered. You had every right to be pleased with it as it was. So I shall try to set it down as you told it to me, as, at its end, I knew it, and as I find it on the record.

Chapter I

9 Grand Street

LOUISE DID NOT remember when they lived on Pearl Street. Before she was a year old her parents had moved. They had lived in so many places: on West Broadway, on Franklin Street, on Varick Street. Two years ago when she was going on six they had moved to the rooms in Grand Street. Louise could not remember 530 Pearl Street but she liked sometimes to walk part of the crooked length of the street where she was born. Pearl was a pretty name and it must once have been a pretty street. Fine ladies and gentlemen must have lived in the boardinghouse at the corner of Pearl and Cherry streets. The old-time elegance of the Franklin mansion could be imagined behind the veil of dirt and shabbiness.

Today she walked past St. John's Park, fashionable now as once the other streets had been. She looked through the railings at the frozen fountain. The little park was cold and deserted in December. In the spring ladies and gentlemen would take their keys and unlock the gate, and promenade across the enclosed green. Louise had left the last parcel of embroidery at the house of a lady who had a key to the park. In the summer the lady would take the air in her fine silk dress and her fine straw bonnet. She would carry a ruffled parasol. She would walk in the pretty, private park beneath the tall trees. The air would be sweet with flowers. The lady would stand in the shade beside the fountain. Louise, freed now of the last parcel, walked elegantly with mincing steps. She listened to the imagined sounds: silk rustling against dainty cloth-gaitered boots, feathers gently brushing the straw brim of a satin-lined bonnet. No, at this time of the year it would be velvet and fur; smooth and thick and quiet as snow. The only sound would be gold coins and the key to St. John's Park jingling in her purse.

The wind blew across the park and Louise ceased to be a fashionable, velvet-clad lady as she skipped ahead of the wind. She would take a turn on Broadway before she went home. Broadway was her favorite street. It was so lively. The carriages and the omnibuses made it dressy. Once, with her father, she had driven down Broadway in a hired carriage. The carriage had been lined with red velvet. It was like a lady's jewel box, only dustier. Louise wrinkled her nose at the memory of the smell. She pulled her nostrils taut. She must do nothing to make her nose more of a pug than it already was. Louise longed for a thin, pointed, aristocratic nose like the lady who lived in the big house in Washington Square. It was in the beautiful brick house that she had seen the velvet-lined jewel box. She had helped her mother carry the parcels and she had watched the trying on. The lady had opened the plain dark box, and under the pearls was the rich lining. That's how real ladies do, Louise thought as she remembered the box in the lady's hands, as she remembered, in her mother's hands, the swift needle moving through the fine embroidered linen. That's how they do: inside the plain dark wood the beautiful thick velvet, under the plain dress Mémé's finest embroidery.

Louise stood beside a pile of paving stones. They sheltered her from the wind. She watched a fleet of omnibuses swaying and lurching up the broad street like ships under heavy sail. Some were plain white. The best were bright with elaborate gold leaf. They reminded her of the beautifully ornamented steamers that in summer moved, majestic and top-heavy, up and down the river, beyond the tall masts of the ships. The masts were a forest of leafless trees that, summer and winter, stood tall around the city. In Trinity's tall spire the chimes rang clear and high above the proud ocean-going ships. On such a ship her father had sailed, once to the war and once to the West where the gold was. "And when I find it, we'll have our own carriage and pair. You'll see, Louise. You'll have everything." His laugh boomed, loud and confident, in the velvet-lined hack.

Louise considered walking west toward the river but that would make her too late. Mémé would worry and her grandmother would scold, birthday or no birthday. She ran to make up for the time already lost. There was less time than usual today, less daylit time anyway. December twenty-first was the shortest day of the year. It was lucky to be born on such an important day. Her birthday was the very turning point of the year. Eighteen fifty-one would not end officially for ten more days, but surely this was its true end. She held her head high. In her purse her birthday money jingled. It wasn't gold but it jingled loud. Let it clamor to be spent. She wouldn't spend it yet. She would save it for a darker, more ordinary day. Today she needed to buy herself no treat. There would be a fine supper tonight. Mémé and Grandmother would let her sit with them while they worked. She would hold the shiny colored silks and listen to their conversation. She would turn the illustrated pages of the *Lady's Book*. No one would send her into the dark bedroom early tonight. This was her day and they would let her make it last as long as she liked.

On the corner of Grand Street, Martin Duhme was standing outside his grocery shop. He beckoned to Louise. "Here, for your birthday, Louise, I hear you're eight years old. That's a fine age to be." He held out a fat red apple. He polished the smooth skin till it shone like red gold. "The best in the barrel for you. Such a fine birthday."

"Thank you. Oh, thank you, Mr. Duhme." She held the fruit delicately so as not to dull the shining surface.

As she climbed the narrow stairway of 9 Grand Street, Louise held the rosy apple close to her nose. Mr. Devlaeminck's chemist shop was closed. The hall was dark. On the second floor Mrs. Chevalier's door was closed too. On weekdays Mrs. Chevalier's washing overflowed in the hall. On Sunday no damp linen brushed sweatily against Louise's face as she crossed the narrow landing, but even on Sunday there was a stale smell of soapsuds and steamy dampness. Louise pressed her nose against the sweet, cool freshness of her birthday apple.

On the top floor, lamplight streamed through the open door to welcome her.

Mme. Visera held the lamp in her hand while Mrs. Hungerford cleared the worktable for supper.

"You shouldn't frighten your mother like this, Marie Louise," the old lady said sharply to her granddaughter. "It's wrong of you to linger late on the street and it's dangerous." Her French *R*s rolled angrily in her throat. Her voice was always more foreign when she was distressed.

"You shouldn't be frightened for me, Mémé." Louise untied the ribbons of her bonnet and held up her face for her mother's kiss. "I'm never afraid for me so why should you and Grandmother be?" She tossed her head as her mother put away the bonnet. "Be careful of it, Mémé. It's my beautiful birthday bonnet. It's like a true lady's bonnet. Why doesn't Grandmother make bonnets for the ladies?"

"We're lucky to have their embroidery to do. And see the dress I have done for the little girl in Washington Square." Mrs. Hungerford smoothed the changeable violet taffeta. "There are to be three rows of passementerie. I shall try to finish it after supper."

The last mouthful of the birthday pudding was eaten. The white cloth was folded and put away. The table was again spread with its working paraphernalia: silks and muslins and the silver shine of scissors and needles.

Louise sat between her mother and her grandmother and sorted the colored silks. This was pretty work but it was not so exciting as her father's. She could just remember her father's shop and the deep sound of the gentlemen's voices and the sweet smell of soap and pomade.

"What happened to Father's chair?" she asked.

"Daniel's chair? Why, your father never had a special chair. Some gentlemen are selfish that way but your father . . ."

"Her father was never one to sit long at home in any chair and well we know it, Eveline."

Louise persisted in her inquiry. "I mean the chair in the shop. What happened to it? What happened to all the beautiful things? The knives sharp as swords, the razors, I mean, and the big looking glass where the gentlemen could see how fine Father made them."

"We sold them with the business. There was no use keeping them when your father went West; he had no more use for them and, dear knows, neither had we."

"First he went to be a captain and then to be a rich millionaire and then he'll come to fetch us in our own carriage and pair. Mémé, tell me about his going to the war. Tell me about the time when I was one year old and he knew the mayor."

"Your father didn't precisely know Mayor Harper. But it was the election of '44 that first took him out of the barbershop. The Native American party. It had a fine sound. And there were parades with torches and banners. Mr. Harper was elected, my dear, and so was your father. He was elected one of the two constables in the fifth ward."

"And all the time he was a hairdresser too?"

"Yes, you see, barbering was never enough for him. He had a nice little business. But his heart wasn't in it. His heart was in those Native American meetings. His heart longed for a war and when it came . . ."

"Your father put down his razor and took up a sword," Mme. Visera said. "And your mother and I took up our needles and scissors."

"And tell about just before he got to be a captain."

Louise knew it all by heart. There had been public proclamations. All the great people of the city had a meeting. And the volunteers drilled. Every day one saw companies of young men riding or marching on Broadway. They looked so fine in their clean new uniforms, often they had flowers stuck in their gun barrels. After the news of General Taylor's battles, the Native Americans held a great meeting at Native American Hall on Broadway and Grand Street . . .

"And Father himself made a speech before all the people, didn't he, Mémé?"

"*Je n'en doute pas*," Mme. Visera said. "The embattled barber. He has never been a silent man, your Daniel, Eveline, and he talked himself right off to war."

"It is well for him that he has learned courage and endurance. He needs them in that wild western country. He needed them when our little Nito died."

Louise remembered the last birthday supper. She looked across the table. Nito had sat there. He had laughed and banged with his spoon on the empty plate. She remembered the brown eyes bright with merriment. He was hot from excitement and his hair curled damp on his forehead.

"Poor Daniel," Mrs. Hungerford said. "He had no time. It's bad enough when there is time, when there is apprehension to prepare the heart. But to learn suddenly in a letter that his son is dead. To learn from the slow letter that the child has been long dead while his father has pictured him alive."

"But Daniel was here so little after the boy was born. It's harder for you, Eveline."

"I think it makes it no easier to have less to remember. It may even make it harder." Mrs. Hungerford sighed. "Poor Daniel. I hope he's happy. I hope he's himself again. His gallant, dapper self. The embattled barber, as you said, Maman."

"I didn't say it to hurt you, Eveline. As for his hairdressing saloon, I wish he had stayed in it, not run away, first after glory, then after gold."

"I don't know that he'll find gold, Maman, but he found the glory he was looking for." Mrs. Hungerford put down her work and from a shelf she took an oblong leaflet bound in cream-colored paper. "Here, Louise, you may read it. For your birthday you may read the list of Father's battles."

Louise read the title page:

OFFICIAL
LIST OF OFFICERS
Who marched with the army under the Command
of
Major General Winfield Scott,
From Puebla Upon the City of Mexico,
The seventh, eighth, ninth and tenth of August, one thou-
sand eight hundred and forty-seven,
and
who were engaged in the battles of Mexico
Mexico
1848
American Star Print

Down the left margin of the pages marched the brave officers. Opposite each was the list of his battles. She turned to the New York Volunteers. She read the names. Colonel Ward B. Burnett, Lieutenant Colonel Charles Baxter, Major Burnham, Captain Taylor, Captain Hungerford.

She read the dates and the places where Captain Hungerford was employed. August 19, Contreras. August 20, Contreras and Churubusco. September 8, Coyaocan. September 12, near Chapultepec. September 13, Chapultepec and Garita de Belen. September 14, City of Mexico.

Tears flooded Louise's eyes.

"There, don't cry." Mrs. Hungerford took the book. "Though I know it's sad to think of the battles and of the brave men dead—on both sides, the poor brave men."

"I'm not crying because I'm sad. I'm crying because they were brave and I'm proud. Captain Daniel, the last of the Hungerfords. Weren't the Hungerfords once grand, important people? Weren't we grand in England, Mémé?"

"We've never been grand in America, that's sure. We've never been anything but poor in our lives and in all the lives of which I have any knowledge."

"But, Mémé, Father said, Father said . . . I remember he said that long ago we came from a castle in England."

"Yes. There was a story in his family. There's such a story in most families, I suppose. And if you get rich enough you can make other people accept the legend as fact."

"Don't you believe Father, Mémé?"

"Of course, dear. I believe he heard the story from his father and so believed it, and his father told it because he in his turn had heard it from his father. And you, Louise, believe anything you like if it's a comfort and a pride to you. Pretend there was really a castle in England."

"I don't want to pretend. I want to know exactly how things are. I want to know what to believe."

"My dear, it's not my story nor Grandmother's. It's your father's, and he hurts no one if he chooses to believe it." Mrs. Hungerford's dark head bent more closely over her work.

"I choose like Father," Louise said. "I choose to be from a castle."

"Very well, my child. It's not important. Your father himself is what's important. It's because of him you have the right to hold your curly head as high as you do."

"And what news have we, Eveline, of the brave captain?" Mme. Visera asked. "I saw you had a letter today, but you mentioned no news."

"There isn't much news. The gold isn't right in San Francisco. It's in the mountains and the rivers, though Daniel hasn't found any yet.

But he has prospects. He hopes to send for us soon to join him in Downieville."

"Downieville," Louise repeated. "Downieville isn't a pretty name. It doesn't sound as exciting as San Francisco."

"It's on the Yuba River. Don't you like that, Louise?" Mrs. Hungerford asked. "Don't you think 'Yuba' has a fine wild western sound?"

"Will it be sunny and warm like the picture in the *Lady's Book*? Let me show you, Mémé, here above the poem. Will it be like the poem?

> *Know'st thou the land where citron-apples bloom*
> *And oranges like gold in leafy gloom——*"

"I don't know. I think not, in the mountains. Your father speaks of the pines. Sweet-smelling pines and clear air. You'll like that, Louise."

"I'd like to see lemons and oranges growing. But I'd like pine trees too and the fierce rushing river. I'd love to see the gold when it's big and smooth and thick before it gets made into money and jewelry and things."

"There I agree with you, Marie Louise," Mme. Visera said. "I, too, should like to see the color of California gold."

"There's a beautiful picture in the *Lady's Book* of a cloak the color of gold. It's very dressy. Let me show you, Grandmother. It's made all of velvet the color of gold and richly trimmed with Siberian sable. A fashionable lady wore it to a ball in Philadelphia. Let me show you."

"No, Louise." Mrs. Hungerford closed the *Lady's Book*. "It's time now for sleep."

Before she fell asleep in the narrow low bed beside her mother's, Louise thought of the town and the river. Neither name pleased her at first. Yuba was too harsh. Downieville was too plain; it lacked the foreign flourish of San Francisco. Downieville, Downieville. Perhaps it would do. It had a soft sound. Soft as down, people said. Downieville. Soft, soft as the velvet and furs she would wear when the gold was found and she drove with her father, the captain, in their own carriage and pair.

Chapter II

The Road to Downieville

EIGHTEEN FIFTY-FOUR was the year of the journey. The road to Downieville was long. Even the beginning of the journey was long. The advertisements had promised that the sea voyage from New York to Aspinwall would take only a week. But storms delayed the vessel, and the Atlantic journey took almost a fortnight.

The ship had loomed tall and safe in the smooth harbor. Louise had stepped confidently on board the quiet steamer. She had exclaimed with pleasure at the tiny cabin. The metal cylinders of the life preservers had hinted excitingly at a danger in which she did not believe. She had climbed to the snug little bunk that was to be hers. She had laughed down at her mother and cried, "It'll be exciting up here. A lot more exciting than that old trundle bed."

Now in the storm she huddled beside her mother in the swinging, creaking saloon. She kept her eyes on the floor not to see the wider swing of the horizon as it rose and fell sickeningly beyond the portholes. When night came and the lamps were lit she hid her face against her mother's shoulder to shut out the brightness of the hot, plush-lined room that floated so insecurely on the heavily moving darkness. No one could be brave in the misery of seasickness. "Oh,

Mémé." Louise was too sick to be brave. She clung to her mother. "Oh, Mémé, why didn't he just come home and have the barbershop again?"

"Hush, Louise. You'll be better soon."

"I'll never be better. Why did he have to go all that far away to have a drugstore? People go to California for gold, not for a drugstore. Why didn't Father just come home?"

Mme. Visera spoke through pale lips. "Daniel Hungerford would never come home if there were anyplace else to go."

Mrs. Hungerford pushed the black curls back from Louise's forehead. "Be quiet, dear. Grandmother doesn't feel well either. Perhaps the rough weather will end soon. Try to sleep, Louise. It's cooler here than in the cabin."

Louise moaned and shut her eyes. Only a fool would judge a ship by its snug appearance in a harbor. They looked tall and handsome in a harbor, but only a fool would put to sea in one of the nasty, rolling things.

On the morning of the thirteenth day they reached Aspinwall. The small landing boat glided smoothly across the bay. The white houses were low on the shore. Above them the steep bluffs of the harbor were thickly, vividly green. Louise had never thought that green could have so many shades. Flowered vines garlanded the trees.

The dark rolling misery was forgotten. Forgotten, too, was the discomfort of the last hot days when the cramped little ship moved slowly on the glaring surface of the southern sea.

The discomfort had been a small thing. The smooth turquoise sea had promised the beginning of journey's end. The passengers had mocked in song at the danger past. Returning miners had started the singing and the others had joined them. Only the words were strange; the tunes were familiar. "Pop Goes the Weasel," the music said. The new words were not hard to learn.

> You go aboard a leaky boat
> And sail for San Francisco.
> You've got to pump to keep her afloat.
> You have that by jingo!
> The engine soon begins to squeak,
> But nary thing to oil her;
> Impossible to stop the leak.
> Rip goes the boiler!

Louise looked back at the ship. Once again it appeared safe and solid. She sang her farewell.

> *"'Pork and beans' they can't afford*
> *To second-cabin passengers.*
> *The cook has tumbled overboard*
> *With forty pounds of sassengers.*
> *The engineer, a little tight,*
> *Bragging on the mail line,*
> *Finally gets into a fight.*
> *Rip goes the engine!"*

"Louise," Mrs. Hungerford said firmly. "Stop. That isn't a nice song for a little girl. Forget the ship. Look at the shore before us."

Louise stared into the brilliance. She stretched her eyes wide so that if she were dreaming she would wake. She closed her eyes and opened them quickly. The bright landscape was still there.

"And look, Mémé, look, Grandmother, it is the land—look." She could see them now close at hand, the pale gold fruit and the deeper orange. "Oh, Mémé, it is the land where citron-apples bloom. And oranges like gold."

The passengers streamed through the noisy streets. Louise could not see over the tall bodies that jostled against her.

Still hurrying, still pushing, the passengers climbed aboard the train. Mrs. Hungerford found Louise a place beside a window.

"This is nice, Mémé." Louise sat back in the cane seat.

Through the window she watched the incredible landscape unroll. This was certainly an unusual trip on the cars. A trip on the cars should be through a neat countryside, through tidy villages. This railway train plunged into the jungle. It climbed on frail wooden bridges across yawning chasms. Sometimes the jungle, close and tall, hemmed in the narrow track and shut out the sky. It was a jungle blooming with flowers and fruit. The trees were strangely shaped, with strong vines growing from the ends of the branches and pulling them earthward. The birds, too, were strange to see. Some were smaller than the tiniest New York sparrow; others were big with heavy, ungainly bills that must make flying very difficult. And their plumage was bright with unexpected colors. Crimson and yellow and blue.

The train stopped to take on wood for the engine. When it started again the rain began, thick gray rain that hid all the landscape.

Louise turned contentedly from the invisible landscape to watch her fellow passengers. There were only a few ladies and they looked the same as ladies anywhere, but the gentlemen were interesting to listen to and to watch. They spoke so many languages: French and Spanish and German. She recognized German because that was what Mr. Duhme's mother spoke. But besides those known languages, there were queer guttural tongues that Louise had never heard before. And the gentlemen had such varied ideas of what to wear to the West. Some were neatly dressed in sober broadcloth and fine linen. Others were in their shirt sleeves, and bright red shirt sleeves at that. They were almost all equipped with a variety of weapons: pistols and knives and tall rifles. A revolver and a bowie knife looked very fine and fierce against the back of a red flannel shirt. Some of them were playing cards. Then the singing began again. The card game must have suggested the song, Louise thought sleepily. Her foot beat the quick time against the cane seat.

> "A gambler's life I do admire,
> > Du-da, du-da.
> The best of rum they do require,
> > Du-da, du-da.
> The poker sharks begin to pout,
> > Du-da, du-da.
> I played all night and cleaned them out,
> > Du-da, du-da, da.

> "I'm bound to play all night,
> I'm bound to play all day;
> I bet my money on the ace and king,
> Who dare bet on the trey?"

The rain fell steadily. The train stopped for a long time. Something was wrong with the loud-voiced little engine. When they went on toward the summit it was late in the afternoon.

Only half awake, Louise felt her mother's cool hand on her forehead. She heard a man's voice. "Not feverish, is she, ma'am? Even nowadays the isthmus isn't a good place, fever, cholera . . ."

Louise jerked upright. She relaxed as she heard her mother's quick calm reply. "No, no fever. She's not ill. Only tired, I think. Listen to the singing now, Louise. Listen to the tune anyway. You've gone to sleep to that tune, many a time.

> *"Way down upon the Swanee River*
> *Far, far away."*

The men's strong voices drowned Mrs. Hungerford's light soprano.

> *"Away up the Yuba River*
> *Far up in the mines*
> *There's where I've been mining, ever*
> *Since we dug our rockers out of pines;*
> *All up and down the digger nation*
> *Many times I've roamed,*
> *All dirt and rags, besides starvation,*
> *Hair that seemed it never had been combed.*

> *"All the mines look hard and dreary*
> *Everywhere I roam;*
> *Oh, miners, how my heart grows weary,*
> *Ne'er a cent and far away from home."*

When they reached the summit it was too late to start the mule journey to Panama. The passengers found quarters in the Halfway House.

"It's a rough-looking place," Mme. Visera said. "But I'm glad to be out of that noisy car."

"One can't expect too much, Maman, so far from civilization. Not that this isn't civilized; it's just different." Mrs. Hungerford glanced anxiously from Louise to the dark-skinned figures lounging in the doorway.

Louise looked up interestedly at the strangers. The women's flounced and flowered dresses were cut low like evening gowns. They wore hats made of palm leaves, not so pretty as the white straws of the men. Perhaps by day the finely woven straw would appear soiled, but in the lamplight it shone white as silk. Louise peered more closely. She giggled with pleasure at an unexpected sight. The women as well as the men were smoking little black cigars.

Mrs. Hungerford touched her daughter's shoulder warningly.

"We'd best go inside, dear. Stay close to me."

"I'm not afraid, Mémé. On the ship I was only afraid because I was sick. I'm not afraid. This is interesting."

"Of course we're not afraid, dear, but we must hurry if we are to obtain a place to sleep."

They were given three cots in a small cabin. Beyond the door and windows of the room was the noise of men's voices, loud voices that became angry voices as the night progressed. Somewhere a long way off a group of men were singing. They were too far away for her to distinguish the words. Only the remembered air was clear. She tried to recall the words she had learned on board ship.

> *If a rowdy meet a rowdy*
> *Going through the street,*
> *If a rowdy . . . if a rowdy . . .*

It was no use. She couldn't think of the new words. The old words sang in her head. The old words sang a lullaby to the distant music.

> *If a body meet a body*
> *Coming through the rye . . .*

The next day the company set off on muleback for Panama. The way was steep. It seemed dangerous to Louise, but her mule was calm and sure-footed. She set her chin firmly. She would not be out-done in courage by a mule. Her skin grew sore as it rubbed against the animal's hide and the leather of the saddle. She kept herself from flinching. Soon they would be in Panama.

Panama was more romantic than Aspinwall. It was an old city. Its castle must have been built with pirates' gold. In the evening light the cathedral and the balconied houses were beautiful to behold.

In the morning the city appeared shabby and dusty, but Louise scarcely saw it. She was too eager for her first sight of the steamer which was to take them to San Francisco.

The very first afternoon on board the *John L. Stevens* Louise found a friend. She stood with her elders on the deck in the warm sunny shelter of one of the two big smokestacks. A woman with two children approached them. The little boy was very small. Even the little girl was rather young, not much more than six years old, Louise thought. She had a grave face and light brown wavy hair.

The little girl's name was Louise Meier, and she and her mother and her baby brother were on their way to Downieville.

Louise Hungerford laughed with pleasure. The same name and the same destination. "Almost the same name. My whole name is Marie Louise Antoinette, but nobody calls me that. Even Grandmother just says Marie Louise."

"I'm Louise Althea and I have a doll." Louise Althea withdrew her hand from a fold of her skirt and held out a small India-rubber doll. "You can hold her."

"You can call me Marie Louise and I'll call you Louise Althea. Then we'll know which we are."

The ladies withdrew and left them to their play.

A ten-year-old boy watched them. "You're sillies," he announced. "You're sillies with your big silly names. Marie Louise," he called in a taunting falsetto. "And Louise Althea. Little Louise Althea. Little baby Louise Althea."

"You hush up," Marie Louise said fiercely. "You hush up and go away and leave her alone. This is our place to play."

"Who made it yours? Who said so?"

"I made it and I say so." The black brows met in a dark level line on the white forehead.

The boy looked from the menacing frown to the clenched fist.

He withdrew but he bided his time. When Marie Louise's back was turned he snatched the doll from Louise Althea. He danced a war dance as he tore the doll's one garment to shreds. Still dancing and grimacing horribly he bit off the doll's nose. Marie Louise flung herself on him. His cries brought Mrs. Hungerford and Mrs. Meier running. Together they managed to pull Marie Louise from her victim. In her hand was the mutilated doll. Blood streamed from the boy's face.

"You poor child." Mrs. Meier wiped the bleeding face while Mrs. Hungerford held her daughter.

"He's not a poor child," Marie Louise said severely. "Look what he did to Louise Althea's doll. Look how she's crying."

"But, Louise," Mrs. Hungerford said, "even if he was naughty, even if he was ungentlemanly, that's no reason for you to demean yourself. I've always hoped you were a little lady."

"But, Mémé, even a lady has to fight back. She just has to."

"When the little boy returns you must say you're sorry."

"I'm not and I won't." She thrust out her chin and stood stiff and unyielding within her mother's encircling arm. "He won't dare come back. You'll see. He won't dare."

Louise Althea looked admiringly at her protector. "You're brave," she said. "That boy was bigger than you."

"He's not any older. And everybody can't be tall. Just the same I wish I was. I'm small for my age."

"You're tall enough. And you're pretty. My mother says you're the prettiest little girl she ever saw."

"My nose turns up too much."

"Oh, Louise, suppose you had bit that boy's nose right off."

"It would have served him right. I believe in serving people right."

San Francisco was a thousand times more exciting than Aspinwall or Panama. Here was no American town, too newly made. Here was no crumbling Spanish town waiting for the bright creeping destruction of the jungle. Here was a city. Every street had the excitement of Broadway. All the steep, crowded streets were filled with strange sights: a gentleman with feathers in his hat and in his white shirt a big diamond flashing in the sunlight; another gentleman with a squirrel tail in his hat and on his shirt a carved and jeweled breast pin; a miner in a red calico shirt, swinging a pistol in one hand and a bag of gold dust in the other; a Chinese in oddly cut clothes with a straw hat like a basket, and a heavily laden bamboo pole balanced on his narrow shoulders.

This was not like New York. Even in the few hours Louise could see that San Francisco was not in the least like New York. New York was a sedate and settled city where people lived and walked in their appointed places. Here were no nice little blocks of quietly respectable houses, no carefully tended private parks locked against the unfashionable intruder. All of this city belonged to everyone. The fast-moving crowds walked quickly up and down the streets or they rode or drove in fine painted carriages. And those who sat in the carriages were not always suitably dressed for such elegant vehicles. In a satin-upholstered carriage sat a rough, bearded man, wearing a dirty blue shirt and mud-stained trousers and boots. He waved to the little girls. He opened a sack beside him and poured gold dust into his hand. He held the sack high so that the falling dust made a golden cascade for the children to see.

The few hours in San Francisco were quickly gone. There was no

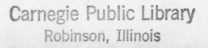

time to look at the sights long enough to remember them clearly: the gamblers; Mrs. Meier said that the jeweled gentlemen with furs and feathers in their hats were gamblers; the miners; the Americans in bright Spanish clothes riding gaudily saddled horses; the Spaniards, more quietly dressed, more elegantly boned, moving, aloof as ghosts, through the city of which they had been the masters; the silent smooth-footed Chinese, clad in soft blue calico or in rich silk; behind the glass of shopwindows were brilliant Chinese materials, shawls embroidered in a thousand colors, thickly crusted with the fantastic shapes of flowers and birds; in a jeweler's window gleaming piles of gold dust; everywhere the glint and sound of gold. Mémé had said there was no gold in San Francisco, but Louise saw it and heard it. It seemed as though the ringing gold chimed above the clamor of the noisy city, chimed clearer than the turning wheels and the horses' hoofs and the voices of the many-tongued people.

The last of the ships in which they traveled was a Hudson River steamer brought West because of the need for ships of all kinds. The white paint was soiled and the gold leaf was chipped, but the steamer retained a faded eastern elegance. In the scarlet-upholstered saloon Louise felt a pang of homesickness. Perhaps she would never see the Hudson again, never sail in such a steamer when, new and gleaming, it progressed with stately grace on the broad bosom of its native river beneath the cool gray Palisades.

Louise looked at her mother's pale face. Mrs. Hungerford's fingers twisted and untwisted the silk fringe of her mantle.

"Mémé." Louise touched her mother's restless hand. "Mémé, are you frightened? Are you frightened of going to Downieville?"

"No, dear." Mrs. Hungerford's hand held Louise's in a warm steady clasp. "No, dear, of course I'm not afraid. I'm only tired. It's a long journey."

"I am too, Mémé." Louise sank comfortably against her mother's shoulder. Her hand touched the smooth satin upholstery. Of course she was tired. But there was nothing to be afraid of. A stranger in New York might feel afraid. A stranger might feel homesick and afraid in any place where everyone else was at home. But on this journey, in this place, no one need feel homesick, since all the people were strangers. Louise patted the slippery satin. She laughed and lifted her face to her mother's. "I always wanted a trip on a Hudson River boat, Mémé."

At Marysville the last stage of the journey began. The children rode on burros, their elders on muleback. Their belongings, in trunks and bales and boxes, were tied on the backs of other mules. Louise rode behind her friend Louise Althea. Just ahead of them Louise could see the bureau that Mrs. Meier had brought all the way from Ohio. A bureau jogging along a mountain trail on muleback should be an unexpected thing to see. Louise was astonished to find it a comforting, homely sight. She wished the Hungerfords might have brought a solid possession like that, but the Hungerfords' few household belongings had been sold to help pay for the journey. Now they were on the last seventy miles of the thousands that had all been part of the road to Downieville.

Louise's bones and muscles ached from the long hours in the saddle. Her face and hands were coated with harsh red dust from the dry trail. Her throat and nostrils were sore and dry. Up and up the trail they climbed. Then she heard the sudden surge of hopefulness and joy in the voices ahead. As her burro brought her to the rise, cheerfulness bubbled from her lips in a laugh. A healing triumph softened the ache in her bones, comforted the soreness of her flesh. There far below them was Downieville. The Yuba was like a ribbon flowing. The Yuba was a silver ribbon; it was not as she had sometimes fearfully imagined it, wild and dark, flecked with gold. It twisted and turned and splashed against the gray boulders that choked its bed. It flowed swiftly, but the water was clear in the sunshine, green and cool beneath the pines.

Now that the end was in sight the trail was no longer weary. Someone began to sing a song Louise knew. She lifted her voice with the company:

> "Oh, Susanna, don't you cry for me.
> I'm off to California with a washbowl on my knee."

The travelers' spirits were high. As they clung to their mules on the rocky trail, they sang. When the town was hidden by a twist in the wooded path they still sang, because at last they had seen it and soon they would see it again. To the familiar tune they sang words for a new country:

> "Oh, California, we'll see you by and by
> If we have luck and if we don't
> Why bless you, don't you cry."

When the mule train came to a slow stop Louise was too tired to lift herself the short distance from the burro's back to the ground. Her fingers were too stiff to untangle themselves from the reins.

A gentle hand unloosed her hands from the leather. Strong arms lifted her from the hard chafing saddle. She looked up at the laughing handsome face. How could she ever have feared in the secret dark that absence would make him a stranger? The war and the West hadn't changed him. Just so had he laughed and held her when he lifted her down from the precarious height of the barber chair in the old shop on West Broadway.

"Well, Louise, here you are at last. It's been a long time."

She clung to his shoulder.

"I promised to come for you in a carriage. Remember that, Louise?"

She nodded her head and pressed it against the cloth of his coat.

"But that might have taken too long, dearie. It's better this way."

"Much better." She rubbed her face against the smooth broadcloth. His coat against her cheek was softer and better than the richest velvet that ever upholstered a carriage.

He put her gently down in the dusty street. "Mémé and Grandmother are waiting up ahead in front of the St. Charles. We're going to walk. Our house is not far."

Louise walked proudly beside her father. She held herself straight to match his soldierly bearing. She walked proudly and confidently home beside him.

Chapter III

•••—➤◉◄—•••

Strange Seasons

IN THAT FIRST summer Louise lived by day in Downieville and by night in New York. At night she found her way back to the ease of accustomed places. The sun shone on Mr. Duhme's rich display. Mrs. Chevalier sang on the landing as she hung up her wash. The handle of polished brass turned in the paneled door as the white-capped maid took the package of embroidery from the child's hand. In the morning the bright light startled her from familiar sleep into strange waking. Morning did not come like this on Grand Street. The waking days were filled with astonishment.

Years later Louise would not clearly place in time the events of that first summer. The separate days and hours would appear to her bright and complete like unstrung beads. She would have no familiar chain of memory to hold the moments in sequence. The first years would always be bound together in a matter-of-fact, remembered chronicle. I was ten, I was nine, I was eight, I was seven. In each orderly year that's how it was. The first western summer would be shattered by strangeness into brilliant particles that her mind, looking back, would never reassemble into a patterned whole.

The first summer, the first fall, the first winter, the first spring until summer again. The first summer? The second? Her memory would never be quite sure. The seasons, like the summer that began them, would never be remembered in certainty. Winter storm or summer sun darkening or lighting the scene might place an hour in its approximate time. She would never see that year whole, never be sure if it was a year or less or more. She would remember only the bright separate day or hour.

The singsong voice rose and fell and then was silent as the stream of water from the pursed lips sprayed the clean white linen. The children walked slowly toward the sunny patch of green between the washhouse and the river. One of the Chinese smiled at them before he refilled his mouth with water from the vessel beside him. Encouraged, the children moved close to watch the interesting process. With great deftness the Chinese squirted water evenly over the shirt as he ironed it into perfect smoothness.

The Chinese put down the steaming vessel. From the grass he took two pans, each small enough to serve in a doll's kitchen. "Missees play."

The children sat quietly in the warm sun, sheltered from the wind by the washhouse. They watched the rhythmic pattern of copper moving over linen under the steady arching spray. Behind them was more noisy work; splashing and rinsing and beating of clothes, and loud unintelligible talk. Washing was less exacting of attention than ironing and it was considerably rougher. Louise Althea cried out as a flying button stung her cheek.

Marie Louise touched her hand. "Don't be afraid, Louise Althea, they don't mean to hurt you. But it's getting late—I'll take you home."

Night fell quickly in the mountain valley. The sun was still shining for the people below when Downieville was in the dark of late twilight. Louise wrapped a shawl around her shoulders and ran out on to the stoop. Men were shouting and horses' hoofs were pounding. As they came closer, she could hear the padding of lightly running feet. She shrank against the railing. It was better, after dark, to be quiet and let the running feet go by.

The crowd was in front of the house now. Two figures ran toward the steps. "Hey, Dan."

Louise let go her breath in relief as she recognized the voice. "I'll call him, Mr. McDonald. He's inside."

Calvin McDonald pushed a trembling Chinese before him. "It's Ah Yang, our typo. They're out hunting Chinamen for licenses and they rounded him up with the drove."

Before the door closed safely behind them another man crossed the threshold. He called over his shoulder, "Round 'em up in front of the St. Charles, boys, and start searching. I'll bring this one along." He strode into the Hungerford house. "What do you think you're doing, McDonald, interfering with me in the discharge of my lawful duties?"

McDonald kept his hand protectingly on Ah Yang's shoulder. "The collector's business is disagreeable enough without a bystander interfering to make it harder, though I think the legislature might find some means of getting the foreign miners' tax paid besides the knock-down-and-drag-out system."

"Save it for the *Citizen*, McDonald, and hand over our celestial friend."

"I'm not handing him over. This is Ah Yang. Works for the *Citizen*."

"How you can tell 'em apart beats me. Of course the Chinamen say we Americans all look alike, but I guess I'm the exception. When I'm out collecting, John Chinaman notes my coming from afar and absents himself. That's why we hunt him at night. I'll tell you one thing about the legislature, Mac, it ought to be doing more than taxing. It ought to run the moonfaced creatures out of the mines entirely. These semibarbarians have no more right in California than blackbirds in a field of corn."

"Maybe," McDonald said. "But Ah Yang's my bird and he's staying with me. Don't you worry, Ding Dong, I'm your friend."

As the door closed behind his pursuer, a smile broke the frozen stillness of Ah Yang's face. He babbled in Chinese to his protector. Louise turned away. It had been less pitiful when Ah Yang had stood silent behind the mask of his immovable alien features. He hadn't seemed quite like a person then. His joyful gratitude, even though it was expressed in an unknown tongue, was something she recognized. So a child looked and spoke when unexpectedly released from unjust punishment.

"Don't you worry about all this, Louise." McDonald patted her cheek. "Look at my friend here and cheer up. Behold a happy Chinaman."

"I saw a lot of happy Chinamen at the washhouse. But tonight

I heard them crying out. I think those men were hurting them. I couldn't see. It was too dark, but I could hear."

Her father put his arm around her. "Run along now to your mother and help her with the washing up."

In the warm little kitchen Louise stood close to her mother. As she dried the dishes she looked up at the iron saucepans on the stove. Iron was not so pretty a metal as copper. She shivered a little in the warmth. The light running feet had been frightened. The light feet trying to outrun the heavy thudding horses. Ah Yang had been afraid but now Ah Yang was safe. By now Ah Yang would feel quite safe. He would be talking quietly with Mr. McDonald. He would be calm now and he would remember to speak English. Louise concentrated her mind on the cup in her hand. It was better not to think about Ah Yang at all. It was better to forget the frightened running feet and the cries of pain.

The children were playing beside the river behind Emanuel Meier's house. They dipped their hands in the swift water. They scooped up the small pebbles.

"Let's play we're miners. You can be the Live Yankee, Louise Althea, and Julius can be the Badger Company and I'll be the Knickerbocker because that's for New York. The pebbles can be nuggets."

Each child accumulated a small pile of pebbles on the grass. Dresses and hair were spattered with mud in the eager search for gold.

Louise Althea gave a cry of joy. "I have one. I have a really one. I scooped deep and I have a really one." Fearful of losing her treasure, she stepped back from the river's edge. Carefully she straightened her clenched fingers and held out her hand to Marie Louise and Julius. The small rough nugget shone in the sun.

Marie Louise touched it longingly. "Hold it tight, Louise Althea. Hold it tight and we'll take it to your father down at the store and he'll let us take it to Green and Purdy. You can have a beautiful thing made of it."

With some difficulty the girls persuaded Julius to give up the Badger Mining Company.

"Come on, Julius." Marie Louise dried his hands on the grass. "Come with us. Maybe Mémé will let us take you to the Sign of the

Pestle and Mortar for soda, or maybe your father will give you candy from the big jar."

Julius smiled and nodded agreement. Carefully he closed his hand on a smooth pebble. "My gold. My gold for candy at the store."

As they walked down the street with Julius between them, Marie Louise and Louise Althea discussed the treasure-trove. "Of course you can keep it, Louise Althea. It's perfectly all right to take gold out of the river, especially right beside your own house. They just won't let you dig under other people's houses. Judge Bob Taylor was telling Father about a man who dug up the sidewalk in front of his house. Judge Taylor was awful angry. He said he's going to bring the man into court, he said it was illicit to dig up people's sidewalks. But the river's all right."

The street was quiet and empty in the afternoon sun. The children could look their fill at the alluring displays in the shopwindows. S. W. Langton and Bro. had a fine assortment of books.

"*The Haunted Priory, or The Fortune of the House of Rayo*. That sounds good," Marie Louise said. "And the *Waverly Novels*. I'd like those. I mean I'd like them to read. I wouldn't have any brown books, though, if I had a room just for books. I'd have red, and blue like that Byron, and green maybe."

"But, Marie Louise, nobody has a room just for books."

"Yes, they do. I saw one once in a lady's house in New York. It was very pretty. Well, not pretty exactly, but handsome and fine."

They passed the shiny newly painted sign of the Sierra Drugstore. Beside it was Friedlander's rich display of materials, recently imported to the mountains. The materials were neatly labeled. Marie Louise read the names aloud. "French gingham. German gingham. American gingham. Did you ever think there were so many kinds of gingham? Figured *robe de laine,* bombazine, silk brocade, cashmere. And look at the laces and ribbons. And the fancy silk vests. But I guess we better cross the street to your father's," Marie Louise said regretfully. "His store is pretty too," she added hastily.

A small group of men were standing outside the saloon beside Craycroft's Mill. Suddenly the small group grew large. Above the shouts of laughter and encouragement, the noise of shrill barking came from within the fast-enlarging circle. The circumference of the circle swelled out into the street. The children were pushed back against the door of Friedlander's. They clung to each other. The shuffling feet of the crowd stirred up the dust. It blew against the children's faces and choked their nostrils. The air was loud now. Above the men's deep voices, through the open doors of the saloon, came the hurdy-gurdy music of the singing women, and over all was the shrill barking, the piercing animal cry of pain received and inflicted. Two pigs, which had been rooting quietly in the street, fled in terror. They pushed against the children in their escape. Julius fell. Marie Louise lifted him crying to his feet. The crowd and the hideous noise and the smell of dust and blood were close against the children. One voice rose louder than the rest. In a split moment of silence words rang out, "Son of a bitch, you——" And there was the quick hard crack of a blow. Then the roar was louder than before. A knife's blade flashed high in the air.

Mr. Friedlander drew the children inside his store and closed the door. Marie Louise steadied her shaking hand in a fold of her dress. "We're all right, thank you, Mr. Friedlander."

"No one's all right when they start fighting. You children wait here until it's over, then I'll take you across to Meier's."

Mr. Friedlander pushed the iron bolt in place. "Come along with me. I'll show you some pretty dresses I got up from the Bay."

The children admired particularly a fine satin ball gown. Its rich swinging skirt was caught with blue velvet bowknots and artificial flowers. "The Empress of France herself has nothing finer," Mr. Friedlander said proudly. "Your mother should see that dress, Mamie."

Marie Louise smiled. She and Louise Althea were inseparable companions. Their full names were too long for informal use, and the neighbors, in order to distinguish Marie Louise from her playmate, Americanized Marie and called her Mamie. Louise liked her Downieville nickname. It had a friendly sound, as though the strange town were welcoming her.

"Of course," Mr. Friedlander continued, "no one can equal her embroidery or Madame's bonnets. It's a great thing for Meier to have her and Madame making for him. We have so many ladies in Downieville nowadays, and naturally they want fashionable hats like the ladies at the Bay. And that's what they get at Meier's. Mrs. Sutter herself could go driving in her carriage à la fancy, wearing one of your grandmother's elegant creations. And now I think"—Mr. Friedlander cocked his head on one side to listen—"and now I think everything's quiet, at least in this part of town. I'll see you safe across the street."

The street was almost empty. Dust still swirled high at the windy corner by the bridge where the heavy feet had passed. Under a cloud of flies lay the bloody carcass of a dog.

Opposite Craycroft's was the Meier store. Its shelves were piled with an interestingly varied assortment of goods: cigars and playing cards, miners' tools and revolving pistols and cans of fruit. Apricots gleamed in brandy. A big glass jar was bright as a rainbow with candies, glistening black licorice and red and white peppermints and multicolored fruit balls. Best of all on the counter Louise liked the scale that waited to weigh the gold dust. It was strong and heavy and yet so lightly balanced that the gentlest touch set it swaying silently. "Weigh your nugget on that, Louise Althea. Can she weigh it on that, Mr. Meier? And can she take it to Green and Purdy's and see the beautiful thing that can be made of it?"

Breathlessly the children told of the rich discovery.

Mr. Meier hesitated over the expedition to the jewelers. "There was some fighting just now. Maybe you children better stay here."

"Oh, please, Mr. Meier. There's always fighting. And they wouldn't hurt us."

"She's right there, Emanuel," Mr. Friedlander said. "The worst of the rowdies wouldn't touch a child."

"I suppose you'll be safe enough," Mr. Meier grumbled. "Safe as you ever can be in these parts. You may go, Marie Louise, if you take Louise Althea and Julius straight home from Green and Purdy's. But you oughtn't really to go about alone when the town's upset."

"If we go to the Pestle and Mortar for a soda, Father will take us home."

"I've an errand that way," Mr. Friedlander said. "I'll hand them over to the captain."

In the window of Green and Purdy were several pieces of gold jewelry. "You can have a brooch, Louise Althea. You can have a dear little brooch like that."

"I think I'd like beads. I'd like a string of round gold beads."

"Oh no. You haven't enough gold for beads and anyway they're too plain for gold you've mined yourself. Precious metal from your own mine ought to get made into something memorable. I'd have earrings. I'd have carved earrings."

"Well, if you say, I'll have earrings. But now I want some soda water. I'm awful thirsty. I felt sick before and now I'm thirsty."

Marie Louise's throat was dry as she swallowed hard against the memory of nausea. "Father will give us good soda. It said in the paper, Captain Hungerford's soda at his drugstore is hard to beat. Give him a trial." She giggled in pleased anticipation. "We'll give him a trial."

The Pestle and Mortar was not as large nor as newly painted as the Sierra Drugstore. But Marie Louise sipped her soda in proud contentment. She shared a saucer of ice cream with Louise Althea and Julius. New paint and gold lettering weren't everything. A proud name was a lot. "At the Sign of the Pestle and Mortar" was a fine proud name. The other stores in Downieville had plain names. S. W. Langdon and Bro., J. Meier, A. S. McMillan and Co. Daniel Hungerford would never choose even a name in an ordinary way. Marie Louise Antoinette for his daughter. It was too long to say but it was nice to have. And "At the Sign of the Pestle and Mortar" for his establishment. Fine proud names both. She licked the last cold drops from the spoon. The clean taste of vanilla was sweet against her tongue.

The Yuba was frozen solid. The trails and the wagon road were blocked deep with snow. All travel was stopped except for Langton's express messengers on snowshoes. Downieville lay still under snow and ice. The streets were empty even of animal cries. Neither pigs nor cattle strayed noisily in search of food.

From the river came the shrill laughter of children as they slid on a wide patch of ice cleared for their pleasure. Louise's cheeks were as red as the shawl that was wrapped around her head and shoulders. Out of breath, she paused on the edge of the bank. Mrs. Meier was summoning Louise Althea and Julius. The quick winter dark was covering the town. Louise walked up Main Street. The children's voices were silent now. Beyond the quiet town she could hear the rush of the mountain winds. Beneath the rush was a deep roar. She recognized the steadily increasing, menacing sound of an avalanche rolling from the Buttes, growing as it came, ever larger, ever swifter. Such an avalanche had swept away two cabins the night before last. The occupant of one of the dwellings had been lucky. He had been found, injured but alive, in his bed, sixty feet from where his house had stood. The man who lived in the other cabin had not been so fortunate. His crushed body would not be found until the snows melted. Louise ran in the fast-falling dark. Surely cold, bruising, smothering death could not reach the heart of the town. Still she hurried to be safe within the shelter of her father's house. The inner canvas walls were frail, she knew. But the wooden outside walls were strong. Surely they were strong enough to withstand the icy mass of rock and snow. And surely even the biggest avalanche would exhaust its power when the steep height that gave it birth was left far behind.

The kitchen door was open. She approached the warmth. Her father was speaking. She stopped to listen to the sonorous sentences.

"It is with pleasure and pride that I receive this beautiful memento of your appreciation. Your kindness will by me be remembered with gratitude and it shall, if opportunity ever offers, no, ever presents, be my incentive to such conduct as may be worthy—no, deserving, I think—as may be deserving of such a mark of your consideration. Something along those lines don't you think, Eveline? I'll just go into the parlor and jot down my ideas. I promised Mac I'd let him have a record of my remarks."

Louise followed her father into the small chilly room.

"I'll just light the stove, Eveline."

"Oh, Daniel, no. Fuel is so high."

"And this is a high occasion, my dear." When the stove was alight he turned and saw Louise. "A truly high occasion, dearie," he said. "The Sierra Guards are to present me with a sword. You must never forget this night, Louise."

Already she remembered it. Before it happened she remembered it. The captain stood proud and tall. The military sash was bright around his waist. Soon she would see the soldiers and the officers drilling before him. Soon they would acclaim him. It would be fine, it would be like a steel engraving in one of Mr. Langton's books. It would be like Mémé's description of the gallant companies marching eagerly in the streets of New York in '47. Louise would remember. It was clear and vivid in her mind. The tall officer waiting proudly for the honor. Behind him on the wall were the two commissions. One from New York State, the other from California. Each in turn commissioning Daniel Hungerford captain. Soon there would be a third framed parchment: "Know Ye that reposing special trust and confidence in the Fidelity, Integrity, and Patriotism of D. E. Hungerford——" Mr. Harlow Cossett had told her. "Not a word, now, Mamie. It's a surprise for Dan. He doesn't know but he's going to be head of the whole shebang. Major of all the companies in the Sierra County Battalion. We're so sure of it in the Guards that we're putting 'Major' on the inscription." Tonight in the old Masonic hall over Craycroft's saloon she would witness the spendid presentation.

Mrs. Hungerford hurried Louise past the noisy doorway of the saloon. Above the singing and the tap of dancing feet, she heard them call. "Pretty proud night for you, isn't it, Mamie? Congratulations, Dan. Glad you made the riffle." Louise inclined her head. Tonight she was Marie Louise Antoinette. She trod as proudly on the steep wooden stairs as ever royal ladies did on marble steps.

The hall was finely decorated with American flags. The company stood at attention. Their quiet filled her ears. She no longer noticed the raucous noise from below.

The uniforms were not yet as she would remember them. The company had been formed only three months ago. Not all had uniforms. Many wore sashes over civilian clothes. Later they would have uniforms, and she would so remember them. Lieutenant Wetherell, Sergeant Proctor, Sergeant Spear. Poor young William Spear. She would remember him in his uniform.

Judge Robert Taylor stepped forward. He spoke solemnly. Tears filled Louise's eyes as she listened to the elegant, balanced sentences.

"This blade is of true steel. Hereafter, as before, be true as steel to your friends and to your country. The blade is bright, so were your own brave deeds upon the battlefields of Mexico." The judge held a magnificent gold-hilted sword in its scabbard. "The hilt of this good sword is bound with silver, firmly bound; may it be long years before 'the silver cord' of your life may be loosened 'or the pitcher broken at the fountain or the wheel broken at the cistern.' The scabbard is gilded with the glow of the most precious of metals; so may your own deeds untarnished glow with golden light, while you shall remain on this terrestrial camping-ground. And, when at last you shall march forward at the great roll call hereafter, may your field of duty be in a land whose golden brilliancy shall be undimmed forever."

The gilded scabbard flickered uncertainly through mist. Louise held back her head and blinked her wet lashes. She watched the people listening to her father. She could learn the words by heart, her father had written them down. They were almost the same as they had been when he practiced in the kitchen. No, the end was different. The last words were now:

"I accept this splendid sword from the Sierra Guards, and here, in the presence of this assemblage, I dedicate it to the service of my country, subject to its calls, whether it be on foreign shore, defending her rights, punishing her wrongs, or upon our soil, repelling an invading foe, or, worst of all that can befall a nation, a civil strife, threatening her nationality—to any and all of which I most sacredly volunteer its good steel, trusting in the God of Battles for strength to wield its bright blade in the cause of liberty and the rights of man, justice, and the honor of my country."

When they reached home the small stove had warmed the parlor. Captain Hungerford sat down to write his notes for the *Citizen*. Mrs. Hungerford fetched her work. "Maman is asleep. It would have been unwise for her to go out in this weather and besides some of your remarks might have distressed her."

"In heaven's name, Eveline, what was there to distress her?"

"Wars or the promise of wars. You don't really think, Daniel— you spoke of foreign foes and civil strife but you don't really think——"

"It's not for a soldier to think, my dear. It's for him to hear the call of duty and obey."

"Your duty is here. Maman is getting on and Louise is growing up. She needs her father. And I——"

Louise looked up from the scabbard. "Oh, Father, it says Major Hungerford. In the inscription it says 'Major Daniel E. Hungerford, From the Sierra Guards, January 8, 1855. Vera Cruz, Cerro Gordo, Contreras, Chapultepec, Garita de Belen. Our Volunteers were there.' Isn't it beautiful, Mémé? Isn't it brave and beautiful?"

"Yes, my dear."

"It should have a beautiful case, Father. The sword should have a beautiful glass case and lie on a bed of crimson velvet."

"But not yet, dearie. A soldier's sword isn't put away until he's old. And I'm not that—not yet, I'm not."

"But the sword's too handsome to be harmed in a battle."

"And you, too, Daniel," Mrs. Hungerford murmured. "Too handsome and too dear and too necessary to us. The years alone in New York were hard."

"I know, my dear. I know. And even here you do more than you should. Why are you working tonight? Does Meier drive you as hard as that?"

"Oh no. I asked for extra work. We need it. Mr. Friedlander was kind about credit so I could get Louise a few warm things for the winter. But they must be paid for."

"A lot of things to be paid for, Eveline. Come spring, Doc Aikin and I must do a bit of renovating at the Sign of the Pestle and Mortar. Might even be the practical thing to get the work started in the slow season."

"But, Daniel——"

"Got to be, my dear. Can't let Cochran and Carr get ahead of us at the Sierra Drugstore."

"But, Daniel, there's so much expense. I'm glad for you to be captain of the Sierra Guards and now major of the battalion, but all that has cost us a lot of money. I try, dear knows I try. I go to McMillan's for our groceries."

"The quick-sales and small-profits chap? Clever slogan he uses: A nimble sixpence being better than a slow shilling."

"All coins are nimble when you haven't enough of them." Mrs. Hungerford took up her work again.

"Any day, Eveline, if I get a proper stake together. If the drugstore prospers and I get a stake together, I may make a strike. You know how it is in the mines, Eveline. You can strike it rich any day."

Louise sat with the sword in her lap. She moved the blade gently in the scabbard. Someday the proud inscription and the steel blade bound with silver cord to the golden hilt would lie in state on fine velvet beneath the gilt-edged glass. Someday. Louise caressed the hilt. Someday when the strike was made, when the gold was found.

It was dark when Louise went to bed. It was queer for it to be dark so early on a summer night, she would think later, remembering. But it wasn't summer when she lay in bed.

The bedroom was divided from the parlor by a double partition of cloth papered to appear solid. The frail wall did not shut out the voices.

Her father and Dr. Aikin spoke of a winter day.

"And you were at Kanaka Flat on Tuesday, Doc, when it happened?"

"I rode in by chance. Had business on the flat. They were just cutting Woods down for the second time. They strung him up once, you know, then let him down, and he still wouldn't tell what he'd done with the stolen money. So they hanged him again. He was near dead when the money was found in the hollow of a tree. I thought for sure he was a goner when they cut him down the second time. Better if he had been, perhaps. Anyway, the mob scattered. Most of 'em off to Gates and Davidson's for the reward. I fixed Woods up as well as I could and he dragged himself away. But not far. Unfortunately not far. He found his partner, fellow named York. York came on the scene and accosted Pete McEvay. You remember Pete, Dan?"

"Tough customer."

"The leader of this particular lynch mob anyway. Oh, I know rough justice is sometimes necessary—but even so, in this case justice had been pretty rough. Hanging a man twice. Anyhow there were words between York and McEvay. Pete didn't expect trouble. Some of the mob were still around. And he struck York a blow. Before Pete's fellows could move, York drew a knife on him and cut him so his bowels hung out. Nothing I could do for the poor fellow. He lingered a while, but there was nothing. We got York away. He's safe in the Downieville jail awaiting the pleasure of the court or the committee."

"You've reason to feel harshly on the subject of the Vigilance Committee, Doc, but there've been times when we've needed 'em."

"Sure, Dan. But we've always needed courts of justice more. That mob today was smaller than the one in July of '51. That's all the difference."

"But if Woods was found a thief——"

"Maybe Juanita was a deliberate cold-blooded murderess. I don't know. Certainly her judges never knew. Or those who judged them. Yet Downieville was shamed before all the world for lynching a woman. Look at the facts, Dan. Both Cannan and his friend were the worse for wear the morning of the fifth. We all were. We don't have Fourth of July celebrations like that any more. You can be certain they both had terrible heads on them when Cannan accosted the Spanish woman. But what actually was said, no one will ever know. Cannan, if he wanted to tell the truth, couldn't. He was dead with a knife in his heart. His companion couldn't tell us. He didn't understand a word of Spanish. It may have been the truth that Mc-Murray tried to tell, but they shut him up fast enough. We'll never know the rights or the wrongs of the crime. But the wrong of what followed we know and knew then, Dan."

"You knew, Doc. I tried to see your side because you were my friend. But I was with the others. I saw poor Jack Cannan, a white man, one of our own, dead at the hands of a half-breed whore and I went as crazy as the rest. I can remember our carrying his bleeding body into town. She was dragged after him. I remember the day."

"We all remember the day, clear as yesterday, Dan. Those who wouldn't save her and those who couldn't. We all remember the sun beating down on the plaza. And her standing with her hands tied and the bruise darkening on her cheek. Her man was intent only on his own safety. Even before the trial was over and he was let go, she must have known she was alone. She was bruised and dirty but she held her head high, and so we remember her as right handsome."

"Remember, Doc, her hair fell half over her face. Her hands were tied and she couldn't push it away. She was a pretty woman, dirty and disheveled and all, and she was young."

"So we saw her, young and pretty. More excitement in hanging a woman if she's young and pretty."

In the cold dark as Louise listened the two voices fused into one. The voice of a tale told from a book, the voice heard in a dream. She was within the book, within the dream. The angry mob swept her with them as they carried the murderess and her victim to the place of justice.

They stood Juanita on the wooden speaker's stand that had been erected for yesterday's Fourth of July celebration. The rail was decorated in red, white, and blue. Flags flew on the plaza. The Spanish woman, her hands bound, swayed as her captors left her alone. She steadied her body against the flag-draped railing.

Below in the plaza, the voices were loud. "Hang her. Hang her. Give her a fair trial. Hang her. Give her a fair trial and then hang her."

Cannan's body was placed in the tent that had been used for refreshments the day before. After Dr. Carr had made his examination he stepped to the entrance of the tent. He described the fatal wound. The knife had cut Jack Cannan's heart in two. The mob pushed into the tent. The cries were deeper and angrier as they told what they had seen.

A judge and a prosecutor and a jury were quickly assembled.

"Prisoner needs a lawyer," someone shouted. "Got to give her a fair trial. Get her a lawyer."

A bespectacled young man moved forward.

"You a lawyer? Willing to appear for the prisoner? Your name?"

"Thayer. I'm new here from the East."

A shout of laughter greeted him. "Have to be new not to be a friend of Jack Cannan's." The growling voices rose again into a roar.

The noise subsided as the prosecutor unfolded the story. Jack Cannan, their friend, lay foully murdered at the hands of the Spanish woman. He had visited her the night before and either finding his advances unwelcome or changing his own mind he had withdrawn. If Jack Cannan had not returned in the morning he would still be alive but he *had* returned to apologize for his unwelcome advances, if they had been unwelcome—the jury must judge of that. Dr. Carr would tell on the stand how those amends were accepted. Dr. Carr would describe the fearful wound which the woman, without provocation, had inflicted. The jury would view the body for themselves.

It was hard to hear above the angry shouting. Juanita seemed not to hear. She stared straight before her, not looking at the man beside her. When young Mr. Thayer spoke to her she inclined her head politely. Her face was blank as a deaf woman's. An interpreter was brought. They spoke softly together while the prosecutor thundered to the approving roar of the crowd.

The prosecutor's case was complete. "And now my learned young friend for the defense."

A barrel was brought that "my learned young friend" might stand high and be seen and heard by all.

Thayer spoke with passion to the jury and to the mob. "Remember the women you love, remember the women who bore you. Do not shed the blood of this poor creature. This is not a trial. Let this woman be held somewhere in custody until she can be tried in a court of law and her innocence or her guilt established. I beg you stain not your hands and your honor. For the sake of those——"

The crowd drowned his voice. "Guilty! Guilty! Hang her. Guilty! Get the trial over and hang her."

When the cries had subsided Thayer started again. This time he spoke more quietly. He called his first witness and questioned him in a matter-of-fact voice.

"Mr. McMurray, you were in the vicinity of the defendant's cabin this morning?"

"I was."

"At what distance were you from the cabin?"

"Well, er, I'd say, well——"

"Approximately, Mr. McMurray."

"Not far. Less than a stone's throw."

"You were within earshot of the deceased and the defendant?"

"Oh sure, I heard 'em."

"Mr. McMurray, you speak and understand Spanish?"

"Sure. I was for more than a year down in——"

"I ask you." Thayer spoke quickly. The crowd was growing restless. "What was the nature of the apology made to the defendant by the deceased?"

"What Jack said, you mean? Why he called her a prostitute. Used quite a few Spanish phrases, but they all meant the same. Well, she flared up and——"

The roaring voice of the mob silenced the witness. Rough hands pulled the barrel from under Thayer's feet. Cyrus Aikin lifted him to his feet. Thayer spoke in a low voice to the doctor. "I'll see to it, Thayer, but you better get and get quick."

Voices nearby echoed the doctor's words. "He's right, young fellow, git while the gitting's good." Willing hands pushed Thayer to the edge of the crowd and held him there helpless.

"Since the defense rests," the judge began. "Yes, Aikin. Do you want to be heard?"

"If your honor permits."

The crowd watched the doctor and the judge. They could not hear the words. Then Dr. Aikin went up to the prisoner and led her down from the stand into Foster's cabin. The crowd did not protest. This was no young whippersnapper fresh from the Atlantic states. This was Doc Aikin whom they knew. They watched and waited.

When Juanita returned to the stand her hands were unbound; her hair and her dress were smoothed into a semblance of order.

Dr. Aikin stood beside her. As he spoke, every man in the plaza was silent.

"You cannot hang the woman. She is more than three months

pregnant. Whatever her fault, you cannot deprive her unborn child of life."

For a moment no one spoke. Then the prosecutor beckoned to Dr. Carr. "With your honor's permission, I suggest that Dr. Carr and Dr. Kibbe confirm Dr. Aikin's opinion. In a case as grave as this one man's opinion is not enough."

The crowd waited while Juanita was again taken into the cabin. The silence was complete when Dr. Kibbe and Dr. Carr emerged. Dr. Carr spoke. "We find that we are not in agreement with Dr. Aikin. He is mistaken. The woman is not with child. Justice can proceed."

The pent-up roar, released, shook the frail structure on which Juanita stood. The judge could be seen addressing the jury and they could be seen to answer, but only those close by could hear the verdict of guilty, the sentence of hanging before sundown.

The words passed swiftly through the crowd. Again Juanita was seized and carried to her cabin.

"Before sundown," they shouted. "Gives you an hour to prepare."

They led her into her cabin and left her alone within. They stood guard around the four walls and left her unattended. No one knew what she did in the hour they gave her. If she asked for a priest, they did not hear. If she searched for a hidden weapon to anticipate their sentence, she did not find it.

When the hour was up they saw that she had done what living women do when they have an hour to prepare at the end of the day. Juanita had discarded her soiled garments for her feast-day dress. She had brushed and braided her black hair and piled it high on her head beneath a Spanish comb. She stood before them, calm and neatly dressed as though she were a living woman, not swinging dead, in their eyes, from the Jersey bridge. Perhaps because she was already dead they led her quietly to her scaffold. They watched in silence as she climbed steadily to the place of execution. She adjusted the rope around her neck and while her hands were again being bound behind her she spoke. There were many translations of her words, but most agreed that she had said she had no defense of her crime save that she had been made very angry by Cannan and would do the same thing again if she were to be spared and again insulted. She spoke calmly and cheerfully as though she alone of all the company did not know she was a dead woman swinging from a rope.

Whether she jumped bravely or was pushed no one ever clearly
remembered. Suddenly the picture they had thirstily watched for
an hour in their minds was before their eyes. The dead woman hung
from the rope. She swung in a slow circle above the river. The sun
was setting. Soon one would be unable to see the distorted, blackened face beneath the braids of shining hair.

"I think she jumped, Doc," Captain Hungerford said. "I understand a bit of Spanish and when she spoke like that and jumped
so bravely, I came over queer. Like the whole thing had been a
dream. A lot felt the same. Not a man, hardly, spoke on the way back.
I couldn't even hurry, though I wanted to get to you and get you
out of town ahead of the mob."

"You got me away and I stayed away long enough."

"It's all forgotten and forgiven now, Doc."

"Forgiven? You mean my medical opinion?"

"Sure. We all understand. We know how you felt. You were de-
sirous of saving the woman. We don't hold it against you as a doctor."

"No one's ever asked me about it since. Not even you, Dan, have
asked if what I said was true. But I'll tell you. She was pregnant.
More than three months gone. Downieville lynched a child along
with the woman."

Silence fell between the men. In the dark Louise listened. She
heard their footsteps and the door closing behind them. She was left
alone in the winter dark. The dark and the cold were real, not the
summer day. The July day was over long ago. She raised herself in
bed to feel the cold, to see the dark, to hear the silence. These were
reality. The hot sunlight and the raucous voices were an evil dream.

Louise sat close to her mother and hugged herself to shut out the
chill air which the small stove could not warm. The white clapboard
walls of the church, newly painted in the fall, were fine to see but
they were not much protection against the December cold.

Louise watched Father Dalton as he walked from the altar to the
pulpit. She hoped he would not preach too long. He was only two
years out of All Hallows College in 'Dublin and he was pleasing to
listen to. In summer it had been nice to sit in the cool shade of the
church while the rich Irish voice spoke vividly of ancient holy times.

Father Dalton brought the gospel stories alive as Father Deyaert had never done.

Father Dalton was popular all over the mines. "The Father practices what he preaches," they said, and in many a gold strike the disputing parties had called on him to settle the claims and had abided by his decision. So popular a man must be thoughtful as well as just, Louise decided. He would surely not keep people longer than he had to on a cold day. Surely he wouldn't even on a great feast day.

Father Dalton looked down on his congregation. He was a tall, broad-shouldered young man. His dark eyes were bright, almost merry, under the wide deep brow beneath the unruly shock of black hair.

He told them that this was indeed a great day of joy. Last year, he reminded them, His Holiness had defined the doctrine of Our Lady's Immaculate Conception. He would not preach to them, Father Dalton said. It was too cold a day for them to have to be listening to his words. He would just read them Archbishop Alemany's pastoral letter on the subject. True, he had read it to them at his first sermon in Downieville in April, but it would do even those who had listened without distraction no harm to hear the glorious proclamation again. "And since this building in which we are gathered is to be consecrated as the Church of the Immaculate Conception, it is fitting that we assembled here should listen to the archbishop as he quotes the words of Pius IX. 'We declare, pronounce and define that the doctrine which holds that the Blessed Virgin Mary at the first instant of her conception by a singular privilege and grace of the Omnipotent God, in virtue of the merits of Jesus Christ——'"

Louise imagined the archbishop in his handsome study in Sacramento. On the hand that held the pen would be the ring of his office. It would be a fine quill pen, snowy white, worthy to copy the words of Pope Pius.

As Father Dalton finished the letter, a grander image stood before her.

"Addressing her," Father Dalton read, "with Cardinal Hugo in those words of Judith, fifteenth chapter, tenth verse. 'Thou art the glory of Jerusalem, thou art the joy of Israel, thou art the honor of our people.'"

In his rich crimson robes, with a jeweled cross on a gold chain around his neck, Cardinal Hugo dazzled Louise's mind. The cardinal was higher than an archbishop. He was a prince of the Church. She held her head high, as though she stood before the College of Cardinals. Hers was a church with princes. And that was as it should be. There had been not just humble shepherds but kings, too, traveling to Bethlehem. Traveling in humility, Mémé always said, in schooled humility that the shepherds hadn't had to learn. And Mémé also pointed out that the princes of the Church were not vainglorious, but humble servants of God. Even so, Louise thought proudly, they were princes, and their humility was by choice, not by imposition. Her lips moved with Cardinal Hugo's, "'Thou art the glory of Jerusalem, thou art the joy of Israel, thou art the honor of our people.'" It was a fine and pleasant thing to join in a prayer a prince had chosen.

It seemed odd to return to the weekday town. One expected Sunday to be waiting outside the church. Louise and her mother stopped before the courthouse. Captain Hungerford was climbing the steps.

"Why, Daniel! I thought you were at the Pestle and Mortar."

"Just a little matter of business."

Louise followed her mother into the courthouse. Justice of the Peace Harris was standing inside the doorway.

"Now, Dan. No earthly use coming to me. Talk to Snyder. He swore out the action and I had to have the summons served."

"But, Pap, you know Aikin and I are just suffering from a temporary financial embarrassment. Snyder and Brothers knows perfectly well we're good for the amount. It's a trifling sum."

"Can't be much embarrassed if you can call sixty-five dollars a trifling sum." Garland Harris laughed explosively. "Struck it rich, have you, Dan?"

"No, but I expect to——"

"We all expect to, Dan. Meantime Snyder'd like to see the color of your money."

"He will—don't you worry, Pap."

"I ain't worrying." Harris laughed again. "It's Snyder. And he's figuring to have you and the Doc do a little worrying too."

"We're not worrying about sixty-five dollars. Snyder'll get his money," Captain Hungerford said shortly. "Aikin and I will be here on the sixteenth."

"Good enough, Dan." Harris turned to Louise and Mrs. Hungerford. "How are you, Mamie? Ma'am, forgive me for laughing at the captain but he always strikes me funny."

The loud laughter followed them down the steps. Louise walked silently beside her parents. She kept her eyes from her mother's face. She could not shut out the anxious voice.

"Oh, Daniel. Another action for debt."

"Now, Eveline, don't worry. We'll find the money. We had to have the Pestle and Mortar fixed up. Snyder promised to wait. I don't know why he's suddenly so anxious about his money."

"Where will you find it? I can't ask Mr. Meier to advance any more."

"The Union Mining Company looks pretty hopeful. I——"

"Then you went in with them?"

"It looks pretty good, my dear."

"We haven't the money for all these things."

"And we never will have the money unless I have the courage to gamble when I see a good thing. If this is as good as I think, Pap Harris will be laughing out of the other side of his mouth. He doesn't laugh. He brays like one of his own Pike County Missouri mules."

"I'm sorry, Daniel. I didn't mean—— It's not your fault. Don't mind Garland Harris. He's only a poor ignorant fellow. It will be all right. We'll find the money."

There were other times, in the summer, in the fall. Other times less clearly remembered shadowed the uncertain seasons. N. J. Shearwood versus W. G. Still, Wm. A. Jackson and D. E. Hungerford, members of the Union Mining Co. Action for Amount due on Book Account for Blacksmith Work done. "Versus" meant "against," that Louise learned. And with D. E. Hungerford—always with him, never against him—was her mother. That, too, she learned. The gray shadow would lift, the mocking echo of the braying laughter would be stilled as Mémé spoke cheerfully and affectionately. "We'll manage, Daniel."

The seasons met and overlapped as Louise learned to know the town which once had been only a name heard in a distant lamplit room. Soon she would be thirteen. She was growing up in the narrow town in the deep river valley. Its streets were familiar to her feet. Downieville was now the place she knew.

She grew accustomed to the burning heat of the summer and to the long winter cold. She learned to know the violence of the elements: the crushing mass of snow and ice moving swiftly, inexorably from the Buttes; the surface of the earth trembling in the windless quiet of a summer day; fire flaming in the night, threatening the flimsy wooden structures.

She learned to know the violence of man. It must, even in the old days, have surrounded her. New York was not free of brutality and murder. Often the Californians spoke of eastern crime. They said angrily that there was no difference. Human nature was human nature in any grand eastern city as in the diggings. Perhaps the difference was that here violence was close at hand. Even a child must know. She must see. She must hear. Nothing was hid in the narrow town, nothing was muffled by the frail walls.

The dark violence was not all. It waited beneath the surface, as the tremors beneath the fair land, as the cold death in the serene snow-clad heights. It waited but it was not all. There were friends here. There was the warmth of being enclosed in a small community.

There was hope here. Hope is natural to youth. In this young country the faces and the voices reflected and echoed the hope that was expectation in Louise's heart. And there was courage, this she knew. Only brave men would come so far to follow a dream. Only brave men would endure so cheerfully the hard years of hope deferred.

There was safety here. In the little town, as in the great city, was the circle of safety. Here, as there, the lamp shone strong and bright on the worktable. The quiet evening hour was the hour Louise had always known. While her mother sewed, her father told of his hopes. The drugstore was but a stopgap. Any day, Eveline, any day. Any day the golden strike would be made. Louise listened as one listens to a fairy tale. She believed a little as, at twelve, one still believes a little the fairy tale. Someday the gold; someday the cotton frock turned to a satin ball gown; someday the shabby little house become a great marble palace; someday the velvet-lined carriage.

Chapter IV

····——◉——····

Educated at Benicia

UNTIL THE LETTER came, Louise had not believed in St. Catherine's. Though she knew the advertisement by heart, the academy in Benicia had no reality for her.

"St. Catherine's Female Academy, Benicia, Cal., near the residences of Judges Heydenfeldt and Hastings. This institution is conducted by the Sisters of St. Dominic, of whom some are from the States and others from Mexico and France, and they are prepared to teach in English, Spanish and French the branches usually taught in similar well conducted establishments. The yearly session of eleven months commences on the first Monday in September."

The Downieville schoolhouse stood solid and new with its white paint and its freshly shingled roof. The little wooden school was her school. Her father was one of those who had made its continued existence possible. She remembered the night of the benefit.

The Downieville Theater had been crowded for the amateur performance of *The Golden Farmer.*

"Do you remember, Father, Judge Taylor as Jemmy Twitcher? He was so funny. Every time he spoke, it made me laugh—even before he spoke, in that funny little old white hat with the crepe around it."

"I remember, Louise, and glad we all were to offer the benefit and save the school. The town was in arrears to the teachers. We cleared seven hundred dollars that evening. We were a pretty fine company. Almost as good as the Kents, eh, dearie?"

"Oh yes. I never knew plain people could be actors. I'd like to be an actress. A real actress."

The bells rang on the bridles of the mules, the red and yellow tassels swung cheerfully in the sunshine when the gay company wound in gala procession down the trail into town. Even when they traveled, actresses were not plainly dressed. And on the stage, richly clad, they stood in elegantly appointed rooms. They gestured nobly and spoke in grand and rounded phrases. Louise saw herself instead of Mrs. Kent in the final act of *The Lady of Lyons*. "That voice? Thou art——"

"Thy husband."

Her father's voice interrupted the scene. "An actress? Perhaps someday."

"Oh, Daniel."

"Let her dream, Eveline. This'd be a mighty narrow dusty town without dreams. And for you, Louise, someday, whether it be this dream or another—— But now about the academy at Benicia. Do you want to go?"

The little schoolhouse was easy. It was known. Mr. Cowden was kind. The children were her friends. In Benicia, Louise would be a stranger. And to arrive in January, to arrive at the half term, would make her a stranger alone.

"Well, dearie? Your mother and I shan't force you to go against your will."

"But, Mémé, it costs so much."

"I know. I know. Two hundred and fifty dollars payable half yearly in advance. And you must be properly outfitted." Mrs. Hungerford sighed as she read the requirements. "'Each pupil must be provided with sufficient bedding, two pairs of sheets, two pillowcases, neat and sufficient clothing, knife, fork, spoon, goblet, four napkins, four towels, basin, combs, brushes, etc.' It will mount up. This seems an extravagance."

"But, Eveline, you said . . ."

"It seems an extravagance, but this time, since you've found the money for the half year, I'll not say no. They can teach you, Louise. Education is worth having at any cost."

"But, Mémé, I won't learn much more than I can here." Louise repeated the words she knew by heart. " 'Tuition in the following branches: Reading, Writing, Arithmetic, Grammar, Geography, History, Composition, Natural Philosophy, Plain Sewing, Marking, Embroidery, Beadwork . . .' Mr. Cowden can teach me all the lessons except maybe natural philosophy, that sounds hard. And you teach me to sew and to speak French and Spanish like you and Grandmother. At St. Catherine's, French and Spanish are each fifteen dollars extra quarterly."

"Mr. Cowden is a good teacher and Maman and I do what we can, but we cannot give you what the Dominicans can give."

"They can make you a lady, Louise," Major Hungerford said. "And the other pupils will be ladies, too, little ladies."

Louise looked at her mother. "Like the little lady in Washington Square, Mémé? Like the young ladies in the house on St. John's Park?"

"Yes, Louise, like that. Are you afraid? Your father and I don't want you to feel you must go if you are afraid."

"But, Eveline . . ."

"Let her decide. She's almost thirteen. It's young to go away from home but it's old enough to decide. She knows the strength of her own heart best."

"And as for the young ladies she speaks of, Eveline, let me remind you that the Hungerfords of Farleigh Castle are——"

"But Farleigh Castle was a long time ago and——"

"Not too long, Eveline. I remember well my father telling me it would be a simple matter to establish our connection."

"Those other children need establish nothing. They come from fine homes in San Francisco. They come from prominent Spanish and American families."

"And my family, Eveline? Do you doubt?"

Mrs. Hungerford laid her hand on her husband's. "No, Daniel. Only Farleigh Castle is in the past. The drugstore and this little house are here and now."

"And you have called me a snob, Eveline."

"It's not I. It's the children from the Bay. They'll have more than you, Louise. I'll outfit you as nicely as I can. There isn't much time, but several ladies have offered to help with the sewing. Only, my child, you must consider. You are proud. Fashionable society is not easy on the proud intruder. New as it is and small as it is, San Francisco cannot be very different from New York. I saw the fashionable ladies of New York and their children when I sewed for them. Think, Louise. We can still write Reverend Mother Goemaere and say we have changed our minds."

Louise looked down at her plain frock. It was clean and carefully mended. She remembered the little girl in Washington Square. Her dress was of silk merino, banded with fine embroidery. Around her neck was a delicate necklace of coral.

Louise lifted her head and looked at her mother. "Can Mother Goemaere teach me to be a lady?"

"Louise, dearie," Major Hungerford said. "Any daughter of mine, and of course of your dear mother's, is born a lady, but there are certain refinements, certain little touches in voice, in manner, in deportment."

"Can she teach me all that, Mémé?"

"Yes, Louise. And they have a library such as the Downieville school cannot aspire to. And there will be music and art. You can learn to play the piano and to draw."

"But will they teach me to be a young lady, Mémé, a young lady exactly like the others so no one can tell the difference?"

"Yes, my child, if that is what you want to learn." Mrs. Hungerford's voice was gentle. "They can teach best what you most want to learn."

"I like it here. I like to be home." Her voice trembled. "Wherever we've gone, I've never not been home."

"Then, Louise, my darling, stay here with us. Mr. Cowden and Grandmother and I will do our best. Your father will understand."

"No, Mémé." Louise's voice was steady again. She held her head back and smiled. "I want to go to Benicia; I want to learn to be a lady."

The ladies of Downieville helped to prepare Louise's outfit for St. Catherine's. Louise sat with them and sewed. She listened gratefully to their talk. Even though she grew to be a different sort of lady she would never forget the kind neighbors. She listened to the variously accented voices. There was Mrs. Galloway's soft brogue and Mme. Annette Petrement's Rs, rolling as richly as Grandmother Visera's. Mrs. Genung's German accent reminded Louise of Mrs. Duhme. And Mrs. Genung was kind like Mrs. Duhme. It was good of Mrs. Genung to neglect her newly acquired dressmaking establishment on Jersey Flat in order to help with the clothes for Benicia. The American voices, too, were different one from another. None seemed to Louise as distinguished as the New York voices heard long ago. The ladies in the fine houses in New York had all spoken alike, as though they were actresses in one company. But the New York ladies did not have such noble, deep accents as Mrs. Kent and Miss Edwin. The New York voices were crisp and a little flat. In the great houses the light voices had been quick and high-pitched. They had not been shrill. They had been gently modulated and yet authoritative. And they had all sounded alike, as if the houses had each been part of one establishment, as if the fine ladies had been sisters. Louise tried to remember the brisk penetrating tones. She tried to hear again the details of the city's peculiar accent: the slight elegant distortion of certain vowels, the elimination of an *R* in one word and its exaggeration in another. Perhaps at Benicia some of the nuns would be from New York State. Mother Goemaere was Belgian. She would speak like Grandmother, or perhaps like Mémé, with just a faint French accent touching lightly the English words. One of the nuns would surely be from New York. And Louise could listen and learn.

It was late at night when Louise reached Benicia.

She stood beside her father as he spoke with Mother Goemaere. Within the smooth white frame of her veil the nun's strongly carved features were like those of a soldier, Louise decided, like those of a dedicated, crusading soldier.

"Marie Louise Antoinette, is it? A long name for such a little girl." A sudden smile softened the harsh lines between nose and mouth. The deep-set eyes looked for a moment with kindness at the child. "It's a pretty French name." The nun opened a red ledger and took up her pen and wrote: *Marie Louise Antoinette Hungerford de Downville. Entrée le 15 Janvier 1857. Agée de 13 ans.* "There, you see, my child. You are one of our children now."

Louise looked admiringly at the writing. She determined to learn to write like that, with fine flourishes and elegantly pointed letters.

"Now, Louise. It is Louise you are called at home?"

"Yes, Reverend Mother."

"We want you to feel that this, too, is your home. For many months. For many years, we hope. Come, Louise, you will go now with Sister Aloysia O'Neill. Sister Louisa, our children call her."

"Run along, dearie." Major Hungerford kissed her. "You're in good hands."

"Yes, Father, I know." Weariness enveloped her. She stumbled on the threshold. Sister Louisa took her hand. "Poor child, you're tired after the long days of travel, but it's just as well. You'll sleep sound. And tomorrow you'll be at home with us. Our children feel at home with us very quickly."

"Yes, Sister. Your voice." Louise spoke sleepily. "Your voice is like —is like——"

"My voice?" Sister Louisa laughed. "I grew up in Ohio. Is that what you mean? Are your folks from Ohio?"

"No, just Mrs. Meier." Louise clung to the young nun's warm, friendly hand. "You talk like Mrs. Meier. She's my neighbor, my kindest neighbor."

The small frame building in the hollow below the hill was sheltered from the winter winds. The Spanish girls from the south complained of the cold. They stayed indoors as much as the nuns would let them. To Louise the short winter was mild. She remembered the long Downieville winters and rejoiced in the warmth of the sun. In February and March the Sierras were deep in snow, while at Benicia in the early afternoon there was spring in the sun-drenched air. Underfoot the grass was green and there were flowers. The chill fog that rolled in from the bay on most evenings was no colder than an early autumn rain.

Louise lingered in the sun. She lifted her face and moved her arms lazily in the soft warm air.

Sister Louisa touched her shoulder. "Come, Louise. The bell will ring soon for vespers. You mustn't be late."

"It's hard to leave it, Sister Louisa. After the winters I'm used to it's so lovely to feel the sun, to feel the days stretching into spring. You don't know."

"I don't know your mountain town. But I knew long cold winters in Ohio. I sometimes think it must be like this in Virginia where I was born. Californians say theirs is the golden state, and I'm inclined to agree. Even your Sierras, Louise, cold as they are, have a certain grandeur."

"Yes. They're grand, but I like this better." Beyond the hill lay the gentle curve of the shore. Louise stared into the distance.

"You like it here?" the nun asked.

"I love it, Sister Louisa. It's so quiet and peaceful."

"Yes. I fancy that in the mines——" Sister Louisa hesitated. "You have made a place for yourself with your fellow pupils and with us."

"Thank you, Sister." It had not been too hard, Louise thought. Thanks to the ladies of Downieville, she had made a proper first impression. Even the girls from the Bay approved of the new pupil's outfit.

"You are full of fun, my child. And you have accomplishments."

"Thanks to Mémé, Sister." It had been an asset to Louise to speak French and Spanish. It had been an asset to be able to embroider. It was fortunate that she had watched and listened during the lamplit evenings.

"You have the accomplishments you brought with you. But are you learning?"

Louise heard a warning note in the nun's voice. "Why, Sister, I——"

"You're quick, Louise, and you're observant. You pick up as much from your schoolmates as from us. But your studies . . . I hesitate to speak. You're young, it's hard to study seriously when one is young. But I think you should use this opportunity."

"One can't do everything. I think I shall get a premium for my silk embroidery, and Reverend Mother said perhaps I'll be in the French dialogue at the closing exercises."

"Yes, these ladylike talents are charming in themselves and they impress your schoolmates but——" Again the nun paused. "There are other accomplishments, my child. Other values. Scholastic values—spiritual values. I don't ask you to concentrate on them entirely. But keep in the middle. That's what I tell the novices, keep in the middle."

"I'll try, Sister Louisa. I'll study harder next year. I'll be more used to St. Catherine's then. I'll be more used to it and I'll do better. You've no idea of the change."

Neither the nuns nor the pupils had any idea of the difference between Benicia and the mountain town. Louise knew that even if she wished to she could not tell. They took for granted the quiet shelter within a peaceful town. They took for granted the orderly routine of their days. Their days were set to music: in the morning and in the afternoon and in the evening the choral music marked the pious divisions of the day. They could never imagine the turbulence, the violence. The climate of their lives was too different. They would listen if she chose to speak but they could not imagine or believe. She might as well try to describe the deep snowbound winters and the burning summers to a child who had lived always in a seasonless subtropical zone.

Sister Louisa might understand, Louise thought. Sister Louisa was young and pretty but she was clever. And the clear blue eyes were kind. "You see, Sister, it's so different here from Downieville. You'll see, Sister. You'll see, next year."

"I hope so, Louise. But make the most of this year. That's all any of us have: this year. Don't let it slip away from you, unused."

"I won't, Sister." Louise knew that to older people, even to young and pretty older people, time was swift. Often Mémé would speak of the shortness of a period of time that to Louise seemed endless. "Only three years ago," Mémé would say as if the years had been days or months. To older people the years must be alike as days and in their changelessness they must go quickly by. And to nuns, the smooth, undifferentiated years must be even more alike. Louise felt a sudden rush of pity for the young nun whose unalterable years lay swift and sure before her. She looked up to see her pity mirrored in Sister Louisa's eyes.

Sister Louisa could not know that already Louise was learning. To dwell in this cool serenity was to learn a way of life. At St. Catherine's, Louise was learning a way of life she had never known. This lesson she would not forget.

In May the long spring reached its fullness. The first day of May was inaugurated with stately ceremony. The new statue of the Blessed Virgin, lately sent from the mother house in Paris, was carried, in singing procession, through the grounds. After the procession the Queen of the May was crowned. Louise listened to the queen as she accepted the honor.

Perhaps someday she would stand like that. Perhaps in her last year they would choose her. She would hold her head high beneath the crown of flowers and she, too, would speak in proud humility.

After May the school year moved slowly through long hot days to its end. The closing exercises were held on the last day of July. Louise had her small share of honor. She listened to the piano recital. Next year if she practiced faithfully she, too, might play for the assembled guests. Next year she would surely be in the French dialogue. Two older girls from the Bay had been chosen this year. But Louise had her small share. She had won a premium for her silk embroidery and she sang in the chorus.

She looked down into the audience until she found her father. He was sitting at the back of the room. He seemed gravely interested in the proceedings. He must be pleased to have her in the French chorus. He must be proud that she had won a premium.

After the exercises there was little time for farewells. "We have a long journey before us, Louise," her father reminded her. There was no time. Suddenly Louise understood how her elders felt. The slow year had moved placidly through the cool spring into the warmth of long summer days. Now the end was here. As she looked back, the months were brief as so many weeks or days.

"Good-by until September. Good-by until next year." Next year, they all said. This year was swiftly, unexpectedly gone. But only a month away the next year waited peacefully. Next year there would be time.

Louise bade Mother Goemaere good-by in French. There was no English word for *au revoir* and Louise was proud to speak in French. *"Au revoir, ma mère, au revoir."*

As Louise journeyed home, the thought of next year grew remote. The immediate joy of homecoming filled her heart.

Mrs. Hungerford was waiting when they arrived. She was sitting behind the worktable. So Louise had always imagined her when they were separated. It was good to have the picture true.

Major Hungerford helped Mme. Visera to bring Louise's supper. "I'll not have anything just now, Eveline. There's a meeting of the guards. If you'll forgive me——"

This, too, was part of the picture Louise had often watched as she waited for sleep in Benicia: her mother sitting at her work and her father going about his soldierly business.

"I've thought of it so often, Mémé. I've imagined it just like this."

"Then you're glad to be home, my darling? Even though you liked the academy, you were a little homesick there?"

"Only at first, Mémé. And even then I could picture you and comfort myself. I could always imagine you just as you were."

"Benicia is so far away, Louise. Wouldn't you perhaps rather stay here?"

"Oh no, Mémé. You were right about St. Catherine's."

"I hoped——"

Louise stared at her mother. "You sound, Mémé, as if—I'm going back to St. Catherine's, aren't I? I'm going back next year?"

"Oh, Louise, I—but we'll talk of this in the morning."

"Talk of what? Tell me now, Mémé."

"Yes, I'll tell you now. It's best to say the hard thing quickly. Your father gave you no hint?"

Louise shook her head.

"It's not his fault. He tried. He's so ambitious for you, he loves you so much that he tried. Though he couldn't afford it, he tried."

"You mean he can't find the money for another year? But the nuns would wait. Surely they would wait."

"They have waited."

"But he had the money. Don't you remember, Mémé? You said that since he'd found the money for the half year——"

"I know, but it turned out not quite like that. When he took you to Benicia he could pay only fifty dollars. Nevertheless, Mother Goemaere permitted you to stay. You mustn't blame the nuns, Louise. Things are not easy for them. Founding a new school is an expensive business. And the school must not fail. Mother Goemaere must think first of the school. Your father and I did our best but we have had unexpected expenses. Grandmother has not been well and times have been hard here. Meier's store has been in difficulties. There has been a long-drawn-out suit between Emanuel and the others. And your father has had legal troubles too."

"That old Justice Harris. He aways hated Father."

"Your father has thought him unfair, but his position is difficult. In March your father and Dr. Aikin were fined forty-five dollars because they hadn't been able to pay the license fee to the county for selling drugs and medicine. Your father resented the heavy fine. Mr. William Spear took his part and they quarreled with Garland Harris. Blows were struck."

"Good!"

"It wasn't good. He had them arrested for breaking the peace. And there was another fine to pay."

"I don't blame them one bit. Justice Harris is a hateful wicked man."

"I don't blame your father, Louise. It was hard to have a fine added to the license fee. I only tell you so that you'll know why it's been so difficult to make the payments to the convent. We couldn't send anything until the first of April. We sent ten dollars then and twenty-five on the sixteenth. And in June we scraped together two more payments, one for thirty dollars and one for twenty. We managed the tuition for the half year and a little more. But not enough more. There are extras. Washing is extra and so are French and Spanish and music. Your father is so proud of you. He was determined you should have every advantage St. Catherine's offered. We still owe the Dominicans eighteen dollars."

"Oh, Mémé. Surely between now and September. Eighteen dollars isn't——"

"We can't spare it. And we should have to pay not only that but an advance on your tuition for next year. There's no way we can manage it. We can't go any deeper into debt. Mother Goemaere was kind. Your father explained our situation. She didn't press for payment. She understood our difficulties."

"Then I can't go back? Not ever?"

"Perhaps someday, Louise. Your father has been unlucky. But luck turns. Perhaps someday."

"Perhaps someday," Louise repeated. The fairy tale was no use. No magic wand would transform the shabby house. No velvet-lined carriage would carry them away. The steep mountain walls would hold them prisoners forever.

"I'm sorry, my darling. I know you hoped for next year."

"I hoped for next year," Louise repeated mechanically. She had not hoped. She had been sure. This year and next year had been more real than the summer month between the years. The month between would have been the dream, the waiting serenity of Benicia would have been the reality.

The angry realization of disappointment blazed in her eyes as she looked at her mother. The anger ebbed. Mémé's face was pale. Her eyes were heavy. For the first time Louise saw a streak of white in the dark hair.

"Oh, Mémé, I'm sorry." She stretched out her hand to touch the fingers weary with work.

"Poor child, poor child. But at least you've had the half year. Was it worth the disappointment?"

"Oh yes," Louise answered instantly. "It was worth it. I learned some things, and the others I can go on learning. By remembering, I can go on learning."

Mrs. Hungerford put down her sewing. She pressed her hand against her eyes. "I won't do any more tonight. And you must be tired after the long journey. Go on to bed, Louise. I'll clear these things away."

"Let me help."

"If you like." Mrs. Hungerford leaned her head wearily in her hands.

"There, Mémé. All done. All neat and tidy. And now quietly to bed not to wake Grandmother."

"Poor Maman. She's become so old in these last months. It's hard to watch."

"Come, Mémé. Everything's hard when you're tired."

Mrs. Hungerford sat motionless.

"Aren't you coming, Mémé?"

"Yes, Louise. There's one thing more you must know. But this I hope will be joyful news." Mrs. Hungerford pushed back her chair and got heavily to her feet. "As you see, I'm expecting. It's to be in October."

"Oh, Mémé." Louise looked unbelievingly at her mother's altered figure.

"Are you glad, my darling? Is it a shock learning it like this, Louise? I didn't want to tell you in a letter."

Louise gripped the edge of the table to steady herself. "It's a surprise, Mémé."

"I know, my darling, after all these years. I was surprised myself." Mrs. Hungerford laughed uncertainly. "But I'm glad. I'm glad for your father. He mourned so bitterly when Nito died. I hope the new baby may be a son, another Daniel." She drew Louise into the warm circle of her arm and held her. "Don't mind, Louise. You and Nito were my first babies. None can take your place or his. And you can share this new baby. He will have two mothers. Dear knows, I'm almost old enough to be his grandmother. You will love him, won't you, Louise?"

"Yes, Mémé."

"Kiss me then. And remember you are the child of my youth. The new baby can't take your place. He can only share it a little."

Safe in her bed in the dark, Louise gave in to the tears she had suppressed before her mother. She muffled the sound of her sobs in the pillow. When the sobs subsided she lay motionless with hot burning eyes. The new baby would take Nito's place. Nito would have nothing left but his name carved on stone in Greenwood Cemetery: Our Little Nito. Daniel D. Nito wouldn't even have his name. The new baby would take that too. He would be young Daniel. He would be the pride of her father's heart. His coming would change everything. He would not take her place, Mémé had said. But his place would fill the house. Unexpected expenses, Mémé had said when she spoke of the payments to the convent. The coming of the baby was the unexpected expense. Louise clenched her hands and swallowed hard. She mustn't hate a baby. That would be a sin. Such a sin would be difficult to confess to Father Delahunty. She remembered Mémé's tired face. She remembered the tired swollen body. She pressed her lips tight together to keep anger unspoken. Even alone in the dark she must not whisper the angry words. If it hadn't been for the interloper, her father would have found a way to send her back. Somehow he would have sent her back to Benicia. Now he would cease to think of her. The new baby would be the young lord of the house. Her father's pride would be in him.

Through the thin walls Louise heard her father return. He opened her door a crack. "Asleep, dearie?"

She did not answer. She lay still. Her eyelids trembling, she watched the door close gently. Her eyes burned. No healing tears would flow. The night was warm, but her body trembled as if with cold. She held her shaking hands against her sides and stared with wide dry eyes into the dark.

Louise grew accustomed to being at home again. This summer was like all the summers. Day after day the sun beat down on the narrow town. The fine red dust floated in the still air or blew with the hot winds. Beneath the high bridges the waters of the Yuba were low and sluggish. Through the open doors of the saloons music blared.

Late at night Louise could hear through her window the raucous tumult of the town. She heard the shouting, drunken voices. She heard the tireless singing of the hurdy-gurdy women. She remembered the quiet of Benicia. She did not speak often of St. Catherine's, not even to Louise Althea, but at night she remembered the peaceful quiet. She remembered the gentle, low-pitched voices. Sister Louisa had been so cross if a girl whistled in the corridors. "A lady does not whistle. She does not swing her arms when she walks. She does not run when she enters a room." So many things a lady does not do. Louise wondered if she would be able to remember them all. She would remember the nuns: Sister Louisa, young and pretty, old Sister Francis Stafford with her plaintive English voice, and Sister Dominica Arguello. Sister Dominica was old, too, and ill. Once she had been the most beautiful girl in Yerba Buena, the white-skinned, raven-haired Maria de la Concepcion Arguello, the betrothed of the Russian Count Rezanov. Sister Dominica still moved with grace. She walked with the assurance of remembered beauty. It was not hard to believe the sad romantic story of Mother Goemaere's first novice.

> "If a rowdy meet a rowdy
> Going down the street . . ."

The words came loud and clear through the window. Men's voices were joined with the women's. Louise held her hands to her ears. She would not listen. She would remember the other voices: Mother Goemaere, Sister Louisa, Sister Dominica, Sister Francis Stafford, Sister Joseph Dillon, Sister Raymond Murphy. She would remember the other music.

> *Lucis Creator optime*
> *Lucem dierum proferens.*

She would carefully remember the other music.

The voices would not be shut out. Shouting, laughing, singing, they were in the street outside Louise's window.

> "If a rowdy will be rowdy
> Ride him on a rail,
> Tar the rowdy, feather rowdy,
> Take him off to jail."

Louise spent the night of the second of October at the Meiers'. She did not speak of the baby to Louise Althea. Louise Althea was too young to know about a baby ahead. Louise wished that she were too young to know. If she didn't know she wouldn't be frightened for

Mémé. She had heard Mrs. Kibbe and Mrs. Meier talking to Dr. Aikin. "At her age we never know," they said. "After such a long interval we can only hope." Until she heard them, Louise had not been afraid for Mémé. Now, lying awake beside Louise Althea, she remembered Mémé's pale face. She remembered the streak of white in her hair. Mémé wasn't old but perhaps she was old to have a baby. Dr. Aikin had looked worried. Her father had hardly spoken as he confided her to Mrs. Meier's care. Frightened for Mémé, frightened by her ignorance of the danger that threatened, Louise lay waiting for the morning. If only she knew what was happening, if only she understood, it would be easier to lie in the dark and wait.

In the morning Mrs. Kibbe came for her. "I've good news for you, Mamie. You have a lovely little baby sister. Your mother's well, she wants to see you."

"A sister? There must be some mistake."

"That's what the poor major thinks, I'm afraid." Mrs. Kibbe laughed. "But she's a fine healthy child. Come and see her, Mamie."

When Louise reached the house Mrs. Hungerford was asleep. "We won't disturb her," Mrs. Kibbe said. "But you can see Baby. She's in here with Madame."

"Watch her for me, Marie Louise," Mme. Visera said, "while Mrs. Kibbe and I get the house in order."

Louise was left alone with the baby. She looked down at the mottled wrinkled face. Poor little thing. It was very ugly. And no one was pleased with it.

"I'm pleased," she whispered. "I wouldn't have been pleased with the boy. But I'm pleased with you. I'm not afraid of you."

Very carefully she slipped her arm under the small body swathed in knitted blankets. She held the bundle on her lap. "They're disappointed, but I'm not. You're funny-looking." She laughed softly. "But someday you'll be pretty. Someday you'll be a pretty little girl. By the time I'm a grown-up lady you'll be a little girl."

The small face turned a darker red. The mouth stretched wide as the infant roared. The thin red arms freed themselves angrily from the covering.

"Hush, please hush." Louise tucked the blankets back in place. "Don't be frightened. Poor little thing, don't be frightened. Poor little thing, they haven't even a name for you. They never thought of anything but Daniel, but they'll think of something pretty. Perhaps they'll let me choose. Oh, hush. Please do. Shall I sing?

> "*Way down upon the Swanee River*
> *Far, far away . . .*"

The baby grew quiet as Louise finished the song. Louise sat motionless not to disturb it. Someday she would teach it all she had learned at Benicia. She would teach it to play the piano and to sing. She would teach it to behave like a lady: not to run in the house, not to whistle.

The baby whimpered.

"Hush, Baby. Someday you'll have everything. When I get to be a lady I'll see that you have everything. You shall have a fine silk dress and a necklace of coral beads—— When I am a grown lady you shall have everything." Gently and steadily she rocked the baby in her arms.

Chapter V

···━◉━···

Fire in the Night

THE FIRST OF January, 1858, was a peaceful day. After the noisy night-long celebration of the New Year, Downieville was quiet, deep in snow. In the early evening the streets were silent.

Louise sat with her parents. In a corner of the room Ada Elmire slept in the padded basket that was her cradle.

Mrs. Hungerford looked at the newspaper cutting which her husband proudly handed to her.

"The Napa County *Reporter* has reprinted the article from the Sierra *Democrat*. Read it, Eveline."

" 'Major D. E. Hungerford yesterday forwarded to Brigadier Gen. Clarke, Commander of the Pacific Division, a proposition to raise a battalion of volunteers for the war in case troops should be desired for operations in Utah . . .' But that was early in December, Daniel. Perhaps, after all, General Clarke won't accept your offer."

"You must prepare yourself, Eveline. There may be war at any time. The Mormons have burned Major Russell's wagon train and they have threatened that if one of the Saints should be killed, they will demolish the whole United States Army. They are in open rebellion. Brigham Young's proclamation was a declaration of war.

For all his fine talk of constitutional rights, it's war he intends. He has forbidden all armed forces of any description to come into the territory. He means the United States Army and that's treason. A man cannot stand by . . ."

"He can. Certainly, you can. If there has to be a war, let the United States Army fight it. You have a family."

"Well, my dear, it may not be necessary for us to go. Brigham Young and his self-styled Saints may abandon their untenable position. But if not, the Sierra Guards are ready. For three years we have drilled to be ready for just such an emergency."

"But for you to go off now when things are looking better."

"Yes, the Doc and I are just about out of the woods. The drugstore is flourishing and I have a nice little dental practice." He stopped speaking and walked restlessly up and down the small room. "Oh, Eveline, the world is larger than this narrow town. A man feels caged, trapped in smallness."

"But it's our town. We are known here, we have friends."

"You'd still have my interest in the Pestle and Mortar. Doc Aikin's a fair dealer. And besides . . ." His shoulders sagged. He sank wearily into his chair. "I may as well admit it out loud. You have no real cause for alarm. General Clarke doesn't want us. There's been plenty of time for a reply and he hasn't sent one. I was hoping. That's all. Hoping."

"Hoping for a war?"

"Yes. Hoping for a war. Selling ice cream and drugs, plugging holes in decayed teeth. That's no life for a soldier. I might as well be back in the barbershop on West Broadway. I might as well have never gone to the Mexican War. Soldiering's all I'm fit for. I've had no luck with the mines. That would have been different. But I wasn't born to be a petty tradesman. I can't expect a woman to understand, not even you, Eveline."

"I understand." As she spoke Mrs. Hungerford drew a bright thread swiftly through soft silk. "I understand. For you this isn't any better than the old life. In spite of the Guards, in spite of the free mountain air, it isn't any better for you than Grand Street and West Broadway."

"I've a good life with you and the children. Only a man gets restless. A man loses heart."

"Of course he does. If your chance comes, Dan, take it. I managed before, I can again. And Louise is growing up. She can help me."

"She'd be proud to help, wouldn't you, dearie? Proud to help your mother if your father was called to battle."

"I'd be proud." Louise bent her head close over her work to see if her stitches were even. "I'm proud now. I help with the sewing and I look after Ada."

The clanging of the bell broke the silence. The jangling bell was the sound of danger. It was the sound that persisted, unchanged, through the tumult of the night. The weary clamor of the bell was the sound Louise would remember, the hopeless metallic cry for help that continued after all help had vainly come.

There had been other fires. In the very first summer there had been fires in the night. But their destruction had been limited to two or three houses. On this New Year's night all of Downieville was in flames. The old-timers told of the fire of '52. Louise had listened to the tale of horror without imagining its reality. Now she heard. Now she saw. Now, as she ran, she felt the hot scorching wind. She knew the gasping panic as her heart pounded to escape.

Major Hungerford led his family through the streets bright as day. The flames were all around them. Burning embers fell like rain. The cries of fear and pain and anger mingled in a chorus of terror. The bell clanged in fierce jangling dissonance.

Louise was with the group that got across the river to Jersey Flat before the bridge went. The men must return to fight the fire. They told the women to climb high on the hill. Unless the wind changed, the hillside would be a safe refuge.

Mrs. Hungerford gave Ada to Louise to hold. "I must get Grandmother to shelter; keep walking up and down just here. I'll come back for you."

Louise hugged Ada to her. She paced up and down on the edge of the crowd. Below her the fire burned steadily. The Jersey bridge was outlined in flames before it fell to destruction.

"If only the wind doesn't change," a shrill voice cried. "If only it doesn't change we'll be safe."

"We'll be safe, but Downieville's done for."

"The town's not done for." Louise recognized the cheerful voice of Mrs. Pond, the Congregationalist minister's wife. "They built after the fire of '52. We'll build again."

The voices were lost in the general clamor. Louise stared down into the burning town. The flames, reflected in the snow, seemed to leap beyond the confines of the valley, to climb the frozen hills.

She stamped her numb feet on the hard snow. She hugged Ada close, grateful for the warmth of the small body. The baby whimpered.

"Hush," Louise whispered. "Mémé will come for us soon."

Louise moved deeper into the crowd. She must keep Ada warm. "Poor little thing," she murmured. "Don't be afraid." She smiled at her foolishness. The baby knew nothing of fear. If we have luck, Louise thought, Ada need never know.

The women had made a fire in the stove of a deserted cabin. The children and the old people huddled close to its warmth. Outside, sheltered from the wind by the cabin wall, another fire was built.

Louise, with Ada in her arms, sat beside her grandmother. Mrs. Pond and Mrs. Hungerford and Mrs. Kibbe dressed the burns of those who had been hurt.

The stove quickly heated the little room. Comforted by the warmth, Louise let her head droop on her grandmother's shoulder. Except for her arms, her body relaxed. As she slumped in drowsiness she did not loose her hold of the baby. She lost count of time.

In the end, at dawn, she must have slept profoundly. Suddenly the red glow of the stove was dimmed by daylight. Around her the women were moving and talking.

The old people and the children, it was decided, should remain here in the warmth, in the care of Mrs. Kibbe and Mrs. Hungerford. Those who could be of use would go back to town. Someone would return to the cabin with food.

Louise and little Orrilla Kibbe walked to the edge of the clearing and looked down. The wind had stopped. Heavy smoke floated above the ruins of the town. Here and there a narrow flame darted. By daylight the pale flames were hard to see from the hilltop. As their eyes grew accustomed to the distance and to the haze, the children saw the black unrecognizable skeletons of buildings they had known. Sometimes a thin flame licked a dark outline. The outline changed as the mass of timber twisted and fell.

"Don't look any more, children." Mrs. Kibbe drew them back toward the cabin. "It's a bad thing to stand afar off and look at desolation. It's easier to bear when you can help. Come inside now."

Louise lingered for a moment behind Orrilla and Mrs. Kibbe. She forced herself to look away and follow them. This was desolation; she repeated aloud the unfamiliar biblical-sounding word. Afterward, whenever she heard the word she would remember her first glimpse of its meaning: the green and pleasant town burned to black ruin beneath the white unyielding mountain walls.

She would remember, too, the small details of destruction which she saw later as she walked with her mother through the burned-out streets: a small lake of molten glass, bright with all the colors of the rainbow; nails welded together by the fierce heat into the shape of the keg that had contained them, the charred fleshless skeleton of a dog.

She would remember the lonely look of the buildings which had escaped: the courthouse propped up on its tall, ungainly steps; the St. Charles Hotel, its white-columned elegance blackened by smoke but otherwise unhurt; the Catholic church on the hillside seeming, above the ruins, white as marble, its steeple tall as Trinity's spire.

She would remember the jagged broken shape of the blackened wall that was all that was left of the flourishing Pestle and Mortar.

She would never clearly recall the swift days of reconstruction. Every building that was left was used to shelter the homeless. The Hungerfords slept in Meier's store. Both families had lost their dwellings.

On the bitter cold January day it was impossible to imagine the rebuilding, impossible to believe in spring and a town made new.

Chapter VI

·••—◦●◦—••·

Summer

EIGHTEEN FIFTY-EIGHT had been a sad year. Louise was glad it was over and 1859 well begun. The new year might be a better year.

The fire had been the beginning of misfortune. Mme. Visera had never recovered from the chill she had caught that night. A blessed release, Mrs. Hungerford had said. "We must not grieve. She has felt herself failing, feared herself useless to those she loved."

Louise did not feel the deep sorrow which Mrs. Hungerford so firmly denied even while its marks were plainly visible on her face. Grandmother had been old always. One naturally expected that the old would someday die, and they must expect it too. Louise remembered her grandmother as old, always old, but Mémé must remember her long ago. She must remember her pretty young French mother. She must remember the lighthearted young matron and she must imagine Louise Paris before she married. She must have been gay, the young Louise, before the merriment turned sharp with age on her tongue. She must have been pretty, since Mémé was said to take after her. In the lamplight Mémé looked tired. Louise shivered. For a moment she was frightened. For a moment she imagined her mother old. For a moment she imagined the unendurable sequence of time.

"What is it, Louise? Are you sad about Maman?"

Mrs. Hungerford touched her daughter's cold hand gently as she took her work to examine it. "You've lots of years, Louise, and so have I. I'm only thirty-six, which may seem a great age to you but is not really frighteningly old. Believe me. Now let me see the dress for little George Kibbe. You're doing it very nicely. Mrs. Kibbe will be pleased. You're a great help to me. And, dear knows, I need help without Mr. Meier at the store."

Louise took back the dress. That was another thing that had happened in the dreary year. The Meiers had moved away. There were other children. There was Orrilla Kibbe. Orrilla was too young. Louise Althea had been too young, Louise supposed. They must, now that she was a young lady, have grown apart, and yet Louise Althea had not seemed too young. Since the first days in Downieville, they had been friends. Since before Downieville. Now the old friends were moving away. To Utah Territory, to the Northwest. Major Downie had gone to British Columbia to try again to make his fortune. He had been kind to Louise. She would miss him. Most of all she would miss Louise Althea.

"It's hard on you, Mémé, having the Meiers move away."

"Yes, my darling. Hard on all of us. I wish your father and Dr. Aikin had been able to rebuild the drugstore."

"Perhaps he could be a doctor, Mémé."

"He'd like that. But it's not possible. We have a great many doctors now. Dr. Kibbe, Dr. Carr, that young Dr. Bryant. And they are graduates. Dr. Carr from the Baltimore Alms House Hospital. Dr. Bryant from the College of Physicians and Surgeons in New York. Even though Dr. Bryant has been kind to your father, teaching him what he can at the hospital, it's no use."

"Isn't Dr. Bryant young to be in charge of the new hospital? And so lately come here too. I should have thought Dr. Carr or Dr. Kibbe."

"Your father says he's a very clever young man."

"Anybody home?" Major Hungerford's voice rang loud and confident.

Louise and her mother looked at each other. It was a long time since they had heard that hearty tone.

"Dr. Bryant walked over with me from Jersey Flat. I don't think you've met my ladies, Doctor. Mrs. Hungerford and my little daughter, Louise."

"Your servant, ma'am." The tall young man bowed over Mrs. Hungerford's hand with old-fashioned grace.

"The doctor has been telling me about a very interesting business proposition, my dear."

"Oh, Daniel."

"Mrs. Hungerford's a little nervous of new business propositions. But this one's sound enough, only as I told the doctor, I have other commitments at present."

"It's a golden opportunity, ma'am, or I shouldn't have mentioned it to the major. We're forming a company to be called 'The California and Utah Camel Association.' You know there are plans afoot to import the ship of the desert for use on our western plains."

"No. I hadn't heard."

"I know ladies don't care for business as a rule. But this is so romantic a venture—practical, too, or I wouldn't touch it. I think you and your little girl will be interested. Jefferson Davis was the first to see the possibilities. You know of him, of course, Major."

"I know the name. Though just at the moment, I don't quite place . . ."

"He's the senator. He was Secretary of War in Pierce's cabinet. All through that administration and since, he's been urging upon the army the use of camels for military purposes. Edward Fitzgerald Beale's expedition was the realization of Jefferson Davis' dream. In one year Beale led his party from the Gulf of Mexico to the Pacific and back again through practically unknown country, infested with hostile Indians. He tested the value of the camel, marked a new road to the Pacific, and traveled four thousand miles without losing a man of his company. Such an achievement is thrilling for a patriotic American to contemplate, ma'am. But we must also look at the practical aspect, the commercial possibilities. The camel is far superior to the mule. He can go for long periods without water. He can subsist on the wild and bitter desert plants. He can carry a load up to a thousand pounds. The commercial picture is plain, eh, Major? Lieutenant Beale says he looks forward to the day when every mail route across the continent will be conducted and worked altogether by this noble and economical beast. Even though you can't come in with us at this time, sir, I'd like to have you read some extracts from Beale's report."

"I'd like to, though, as I say, I have commitments."

"There's a lot of interest in the camel. There was an item in the

Sacramento *Union* only the other day." Dr. Bryant took a newspaper cutting from his pocket. "'The camel at Los Angeles. Some of the U. S. camels have arrived and set all the inhabitants agog. They were very quiet and tractable, walking off quite briskly with the heaviest loads.'

"Can't you visualize the prospect, ma'am? Can't you see its scope? From the Far East to our western plains. Isn't it a perfect example of the old world serving the needs of the new? This is truly Young America. Young America in action!"

As he talked, Dr. Bryant's dark eyes flashed and his slim white hands moved expressively. Louise listened and watched. If only her father wouldn't speak of her as if she were a child, she thought angrily. If only she weren't so short. Her ridiculously small stature made her appear a perfect baby.

"From what you tell me, my boy, the military usefulness of the camel has been proved beyond question, but of the commercial prospect I'm less certain—of the immediate prospect, that is."

"Never doubt it, sir. And we shall be pioneers in the field. There lies our advantage. The California and Utah Camel Association will be the first in this rich field and we shall reap a fortune. A fortune, Major! But I mustn't tire your good lady. Forgive us, ma'am."

"You don't tire us, Doctor." Louise spoke quickly before her mother could answer. "I'm very much interested. When I was at school—I was educated at Benicia—we studied the Crusades, so I know something of the customs of the East."

"And what do you think of my plan?"

"I don't know that the opinion of a girl only sixteen is worth very much, but your plan sounds clever and romantic."

"And practical? You see that our scheme is practical, don't you, Miss Louise?" he asked eagerly.

"I don't know." Louise struggled to maintain her mature and sober air, but her voice trembled. "I can't help it, Dr. Bryant, it's funny. To think of the old-timers swinging down the trail or the new road on camelback. And the Chinamen—though they would look more suitable. And I can see Mr. Langton's express messenger with a turban round his head, leading a camel laden with packages." She laughed helplessly. "I'm sorry, Doctor, I'm sure it's practical but it does seem funny."

"I don't mind your laughing, Miss Louise. I'm grateful for your opinion."

"She's a little young to have an opinion on a business matter," Mrs. Hungerford said gently. "She won't be sixteen until the end of December."

"Still, I value her opinion." Dr. Bryant's eyes were fixed on Louise. "I should like to know more of your views, Miss Louise. I have some books and articles on the camel which might interest you. We're pretty well settled. We shall capitalize at twelve thousand dollars. John Ager, John Cooper, and I are to be trustees. Several are already interested: Sam Langton, William Tennant, James Kane and others. It shouldn't be too difficult to find a hundred and twenty subscribers at a hundred dollars a share."

"I can see you are organizing on a sound business basis."

"Thank you, Major. And have I your permission to call on the ladies, sir?"

"Of course, my boy. I'm delighted. Delighted."

"And you, ma'am?"

"We shall be pleased, Doctor. Though I fear you will find ours a very quiet little household."

"Thank you. I shall take advantage of your gracious permission. And now, ma'am, sir, if you'll permit me to take my leave." He bowed and was gone.

"Fine young fellow," Major Hungerford said. "Every inch a graduate. And a gentleman. Just as I told you, Eveline. I knew he'd make a fine impression."

"You didn't tell us he was so handsome, Daniel."

"Didn't I? Well, that's of no importance. Brains are what count and the lad's chock full of them. Now for my news."

"Is it good news?"

"I think so. I think it's very good. I've taken a lease on that empty store on Main Street. And I'm going back to my old trade. Hungerford's Tonsorial Parlor. How does that strike you? I can combine it with my dental work and minor medical treatment. Cupping, bleeding—that sort of thing."

"Have you the money?"

"I've arranged a small loan. Don't look like that, Eveline. This is a business I understand. And Downieville needs a first-rate hairdressing establishment."

While her parents talked Louise thought about the young doctor. His tall, elegant carriage suited his eastern voice and manner. He was clever, her father had said. He must be clever to have been put in charge of the county hospital. She smiled as she imagined a camel moving flat-footed on the trail, with a red-shirted miner balanced precariously on the swaying hump. Perhaps the scheme was practical. Her father seemed to think so. Certainly it was romantic. She could understand why it appealed to the dark-eyed stranger.

She looked with dismay at the crooked end of her seam. That came of dreaming. And it would do her no good to dream of the handsome stranger. He was young for a doctor but he was old for her, too old and too clever. She sighed and set carefully to work to finish her seam.

TONSORIAL!
Hungerford and Co.
Having Opened A New And Completely Arranged
Hair Dressing & Shaving Saloon
Respectfully announce to the public that their facilities for performing all work pertaining to their profession are unsurpassed. Haircutting, Curling, Frizzing, Shampooing, and Shaving done in an artistic manner.

They have also provided facilities for Cupping, Leeching and Bleeding, Teeth Extracting, etc.; and each operation will be performed by an experienced hand.

M. Naas' celebrated India Zampoony used for Shampooing.

Hungerford & Co.
Main Street, Downieville

Major Hungerford cut the advertisement from the *Citizen* and showed it to his wife and daughter.

"Mighty fine, I think, my dears."

"Mighty fine, Daniel."

"Mighty fine, sir." Dr. Bryant stood in the doorway. "Forgive my making my first call a morning one, ma'am, but I hoped the major might permit me to escort his ladies to the grand opening."

"Nothing grand about it, son, just open for business. Indeed the ladies helped me put the finishing touches to the place yesterday."

"Then I'll go along with you, Major, and be your first customer.

I'll bring you a report, ma'am, on how business looks. You and Miss Louise are as well not to venture out. The snow's piled pretty high."

"Come along then, my boy."

"I'll just leave this book if I may. It's one of the ones I mentioned, Miss Louise. George P. Marsh on *The Camel*. He lived many years in the Turkish Empire and he knows his subject thoroughly. I think it will interest you."

Louise studied the dark brown volume. *The Camel. His Organization Habits and Uses Considered with Reference to His Introduction into the United States*. Over two hundred pages, eighteen chapters, and four appendixes. At least there was an index. Perhaps it would help her. *Burden of Camel. Callosities of Camel. Camel Adapted to Desert*. She turned the page. *Foot, Adaption of the Various Surfaces. French Dromedary Regiment. Furniture of the Camel. Gad-fly Annoys Camel*. "I should think it might!" She laughed out loud.

"Louise, you mustn't make fun of the poor young doctor. He takes this camel venture of his seriously."

"Don't you, Mémé?"

"Oh, my dear, I don't know. I suppose it's no worse than many others. No worse than most mining claims. And since he brought you the book, you must show a little interest. After all, he is a friend of your father's."

"Yes, Mémé."

"I've things to do in the kitchen. You can help me presently."

"Yes, Mémé."

Louise examined the book. It was difficult not to laugh as she read. However useful, the camel was a comical beast. It was romantic only as an adjunct to Bedouins and palm trees. Two hundred pages about its anatomy and habits was too much. Still, she must read at least enough to sound intelligent. She skimmed the chapter headings: "Species and Breeds," "The Caravan." That might be interesting.

"For the purposes of general observation, camel-riding is the most advantageous of all possible means of conveyance. The slowness and regularity of your rate of progress, the elevation of your seat, which gives you a wide range of vision, and (no trifling matter in the parched desert) secures you the full benefit of every breeze that blows, and your entire exemption from the necessity of guiding or even watching the movements of your beast, affords you the greatest facilities for studying the aspect of the country, and enjoying the unrivalled sublimity of the mountain ranges which in the Arabian and most other deserts, you so often skirt or traverse. With a special attendant too, whom you can call upon to pick up a stone, or gather some curious plant . . ."

Louise was deep in an imagined journey when Dr. Bryant returned. She looked at him with shining eyes.

"Oh, Doctor. At first I thought it funny, a whole book about camels. I still do, it's so solemn. But some of it's wonderful where it tells about camel paths, thousands of years old, making a pattern in the desert. See, here." She pointed to the paragraph.

He drew a chair beside her and read as she held the book. "It's romantic to think of oneself riding in a caravan through ancient lands, but I want to show you the practical aspect as applied to America— where he speaks of the peculiar adaptation of the Bactrian camel to our trans-Mississippian territory—let me show you."

As he took the book, their fingers accidentally touched and were still. Louise was the first to speak. "I know where you mean. It's in the part about the United States." Her hand shook as she hastily turned the pages. "Here it is. Chapter Seventeen. 'Introduction of the Camel into the United States.'" She gave him the book.

He read: "'The question of the practicability and advantages of introducing the camel into the United States is a topic of much interest and importance.'"

Though the topic was of no interest to her, she listened eagerly.

"'Among those who are practically familiar with the habits and properties of the camel, and who have studied the physical conditions of our territory west of the Mississippi there is I believe little or no difference of opinion on the subject; and I am persuaded that the ultimate success of judicious and persevering effort is certain, and will be attended with important advantages . . .'"

The long, pompously worded sentences did not seem comical as she listened to the musical voice. While his eyes were fixed on the book she could study his profile. His voice, his appearance, his manner, everything about him was different from the men of Downieville. She could not remember her father and the other young officers who had gone off to the war in '47 but she fancied that they had had the same careless proud elegance.

"So you see, Miss Louise, Marsh definitely establishes the superiority of the Bactrian camel over the Arabian. And you will notice that

Major Wayne and Lieutenant Porter . . . but perhaps I'm boring you."

"Oh no, Doctor. It's fascinating."

"For instance in the appendix he gives an account extracted from the correspondence of Jefferson Davis and——"

"Well, Doctor." Mrs. Hungerford entered the room. "How are things going at Hungerford & Co.?"

Dr. Bryant jumped to his feet. "Oh, ma'am. Miss Louise and I got so interested in this little book I clean forgot to give my report. But it's a mighty favorable one. I wasn't the first customer after all. Dr. Kibbe got ahead of me. I was impressed, ma'am. The major has a splendid and luxurious establishment. The basin of marble with running water. And the adjustable velvet chair and footstool. You couldn't see anything finer in San Francisco. I heard much comment, ma'am. All favorable."

"Good. You were kind to look in and tell us about it. We are much obliged to you." Mrs. Hungerford stood by the door.

"I must be getting back to the hospital. I'll just leave the book if I may, Miss Louise. I think you'll find it of interest."

"Thank you, Doctor." Louise curtsied as they had taught her at Benicia. The doctor was from the Atlantic states. He would expect such niceties of behavior. She watched her mother accompany him through the door. She held the book against her heart.

"Louise."

"Yes, Mémé." Louise opened the book at random and looked, unseeing, at the page. She did not want to meet her mother's eyes.

"Louise, I——" Still Louise did not look up.

"No matter. Finish your book if you like. You can help me later. I'll leave Ada in here with you."

When her mother was gone Louise picked up her sister.

"Oh, Ada, oh, Ada." She carried the child into their bedroom and sat her on a pillow on the floor.

Ada staggered to her feet. "Lou-ee, Lou-ee!" she cried.

"Here, you may play with this." Louise took a ribbon from the chest of drawers and gave it to Ada.

Louise stared earnestly and hopefully into the small square looking glass that hung on a nail in the wall over the chest. Was she really pretty? She had thought so. But she had thought so lightly, not caring deeply. Her father said she was but he loved her. The neighbors said she was but they were kind and, living in this remote place, they were probably easily pleased. Would she seem pretty to someone from the Atlantic states? In the Atlantic states there were many girls, beautiful girls, fashionable girls. How would she seem, compared to them? She studied her reflection. Her eyes were big and set well apart and they were a good bright blue. Her lashes were long and thick and her brows arched nicely. She unpinned her dark curls and brushed them vigorously. Brushing made the hair shine. She pinned her hair up again. She smoothed it over her ears and massed the curls on the nape of her neck. She must get one of the new nets. That was a fortunate thing about curly hair. It could be dressed in any style that fashion decreed. Her hair, her eyes, they would do. She parted her lips. Her small teeth were white and even. That was a blessing. If only she were taller. She stood on the tips of her small slippers and balanced herself, holding one hand on the wooden chest. Just an inch or two would make such a difference. Five feet was a ridiculous height. She looked disconsolately at her reflection. And her nose, oh dear, her nose. Do what she would, it still turned up. Not very much, but enough to prevent anyone's thinking it classical. She had used the clothespin faithfully, but it had done no good. Besides, it always fell off in the night. She wouldn't be able to use it much longer. A married lady could hardly go to bed with a clothespin on her nose.

"Oh!" she exclaimed aloud. What a thing to think of. Bright color stained her white skin. She turned in hot embarrassment from her blushing reflection. She knelt on the pillow beside her sister.

"Oh, Ada, am I pretty enough? Am I as pretty as those fashionable ladies in the Atlantic states?"

Ada laughed and gurgled unintelligibly.

"Am I, Ada? Am I pretty enough?"

"Lou-ee pretty, Lou-ee pretty," Ada repeated and patted her sister's cheek.

Louise took the small hand and kissed it. "Oh, Ada, such a thing has happened to me. Such an unexpected thing."

After that March morning Louise knew that 1859 would be a good year. For several weeks the snow was still piled high. Outwardly everything was the same, but she no longer looked back. She looked ahead to the summer.

Dr. Bryant came often to the house with her father, but Louise was not alone with him again. They could wait. They could wait for the freedom that summer would bring.

In May the Yuba rose rapidly. Even on the Buttes the snow was melting. The river roared, deep and cold, through the town.

On the thirteenth of May the California and Utah Camel Association was incorporated. Dr. Bryant showed a copy of the charter to Major and Mrs. Hungerford and to Louise. "If such dull legal terminology can interest a young lady."

"It interests me, Doctor."

"I am gratified, Miss Louise."

He had not asked her to return his book. They did not mention it. It lay in the drawer beside her ribbons: she did not try again to read it. When she was alone with Ada she took it out and traced with her fingernail the pyramids and the palm trees and the patient camel stamped on the cover.

It was in May that the piano arrived. Louise stared with unbelieving joy at her father's gift. The golden-oak base bulked large in the small parlor.

Mrs. Hungerford polished the wood until it shone. "Can you really afford it?" she asked. "Is the barbershop doing well enough?"

"I can afford this piano. I got it cheap from a fellow moving to the Northwest. That's a great country, Eveline. They say fortunes will be made overnight."

"Oh, Daniel."

"Don't worry, I'm not ready for a move yet. I still have faith in the California mines. The diggings around here are booming. The Oregon, the Live Yankee, the Monumental—every last one of them. The Uncle Sam boys are getting their main tunnel ahead. No need to move on. A man can still find a fortune here. Any day, with a little luck, a man can strike it rich. Meantime . . ." He pressed a key and listened to the clear tone. "She's sweet and true as a bell. Meantime, I got Louise her piano. No sense in her forgetting everything she learned at Benicia."

Louise touched the keys lightly, soundlessly. When she was alone she would try them. When she was alone she would see if she remembered. Mémé would help her.

Mrs. Hungerford did her best. Louise practiced diligently. Slowly she learned to find her way on the keyboard. Her fingers moved more easily, more supply.

She learned to play "The Last Rose of Summer" and "Annie Laurie" and "Drink to Me Only with Thine Eyes."

It was June. The window was open. She did not mind the open window. Anyone passing would hear a song nicely played. Anyone entering would see a young lady at her piano, a young lady as accomplished as any in the Atlantic states.

"Louise," Mrs. Hungerford called. "Louise, will you take this embroidery for me to Mrs. Genung's in Jersey Flat?"

After she left the package at the dressmaker's Louise walked slowly past the old Fetter Building. It had survived the great fire and was fitted up as the county hospital.

"May I walk a little way with you, Miss Louise?"

"Certainly, Dr. Bryant." He must have been waiting too.

"Your father tells me that he has written to invite Major General Sutter to review the Sierra Battalion at Forest City on the Fourth of July. I'm looking forward eagerly to seeing the old soldier."

"Have you never seen him? When I was a little girl my father took me once to his house near Marysville. They had a beautiful rose garden, so beautiful that visitors, even from the Atlantic states, remarked on it. And the general took Father and me for a drive by the river. He had a very smart turnout."

"You know, Miss Louise, when I first saw you I thought you were still a little girl."

"I know. And goodness knows, I am little."

"But you hold yourself like a young queen. A straight carriage is a rare and lovely thing in a woman."

"General Sutter has a splendid carriage. He's every inch a soldier. It will be a fine sight to see him review the troops on the Fourth."

"Perhaps you'll let me escort you."

"Why, yes, Doctor, if Mémé—and I think we should walk a little faster."

"Let's stand here for a moment. I always like the view from this bridge."

They looked down at the swift river. On its banks the houses were clean and bright in their summer coats of new white and yellow paint. Beyond the forks of the Yuba the mountain green was fresh and brilliant, unscorched by the heat of midsummer.

This was the summer as she would remember it: the river running clear and cool between the brimming banks, the new paint glistening on the stores and dwellings; the deep fresh green of the hills beneath the bright cloudless blue.

"Oh, Doctor." She clasped her hands on the wooden railing.

"Yes, Miss Louise?"

"It's that sometimes I've hated this place. The cold and snow in the winter and the dust in summer. Most of all I've hated the narrowness. Like a prison. But on a day like this"—she looked up at him and again at the valley in wonder—"on a day like this it's beautiful."

In the narrow town it was easy to meet casually, unexpectedly. In the late afternoon Louise took her mother's parcels to Mrs. Kibbe, to Mrs. Purdy, to Mrs. Langton.

"May I carry your parcel, Miss Louise?"

"If it's not out of your way, Doctor. I'm going to Mrs. Kibbe's."

"Not at all. I want to have a word with Dr. Kibbe."

Dr. Kibbe was not at home. Would Dr. Bryant and Mamie like to wait for him in the garden?

"Thank you, ma'am. Do you mind, Miss Louise, just a moment or two on the chance that he may come? Then I'll see you safely home."

"Not at all, Doctor."

In the garden the peaches were ripening.

"The Kibbes have the finest peaches in these parts, Doctor. It's a pity they're not yet ripe."

"They will be, Miss Louise. We must have patience."

They never acknowledged that they met by design.

July came with blazing heat. Dr. Bryant accompanied Louise and her father to the celebration at Forest City.

"You'll want to remain with the general and the others, Major. It will be a pleasure for me to see the young lady safely home."

"But the fun's just beginning. Of course, Louise really ought not to stay longer."

"Indeed she shouldn't. And much as I should like to remain, I'm obliged to look in at the hospital. So you see, it's really no trouble, sir, no trouble at all."

"Very kind of you just the same, my boy. But since it's not taking you out of your way, I'll get back to General Sutter. The administration has been treating him shamefully. One wants to do what one can for the fine old soldier. That fellow Buchanan! For our great

Democratic party to be represented in the White House by that man."

"You're very good at arranging things, Doctor."

"This ride? I arranged that. You knew I didn't have to be at the hospital. You knew I wanted to be with you."

"I'm flattered. The gentlemen will begin to enjoy themselves now that the ladies are leaving."

"The gentlemen will get drunk. Oh, perhaps not your father and General Sutter, but most will. I would if I stayed. That's one of the things——"

"What's one of what things, Doctor?"

"That I get drunk on occasion."

"Goodness. So do most gentlemen, I believe. Not my father, but Mémé has always said he's exceptional that way. Even Grandmother used to praise him for it. And she didn't praise much. So you see——"

"So I see what, Miss Louise?"

"Well, if it's so exceptional not to drink, it can't be too awful if a gentleman indulges once in a while."

"You're such a child. That's the other thing. Oh, I suppose I could join a Dashaway Club. You know what they are. Fellows get together and vow to dash away the bottle for a month or a year or longer. They've just organized one at Marysville. I wouldn't need the club. I believe I could make that vow for you. But you still remain a child and so—and so——"

"And so?"

"And so we talk about camels and politics and the beauties of nature."

"And what would you like to talk about? You look so fierce, Doctor." She laughed. "We can talk about anything you like."

"I don't want to talk at all." The horses were walking quietly close together. He leaned toward her and held her for a moment. He bent and kissed her mouth. "This is what I want. And what I have no right to. You're a child."

She lifted her gloved hand to her mouth. Her fingers and her lips were trembling. She felt the trembling through her whole body. She forced herself to sit erect and steady but she could not speak.

"Oh, my dear," he said, "I didn't mean this to happen."

"Yes, you did, Doctor," she said firmly. "We both did. And I arranged to meet you just as much as you ever arranged to meet me. And I never mentioned our meetings to Mémé. So you see I knew they weren't accidental."

"She'll think you're too young to marry. I think I can manage the major, but your mother will say you're too young and she'll be right. You are too young. You won't be sixteen till the end of the year."

"Sixteen isn't young to marry. Not nowadays it isn't. Why even in Mémé's day—she was only eighteen."

"Sixteen is young to marry a man like me. I'm not good enough. I'd try, God knows I'd try. And I love you enough so that by a miracle I might succeed."

"We'll succeed. I'm old for my age. I'm old enough and you're good enough. You're a graduate and a gentleman. You're everything I dreamed. But there are so many dreams in the diggings, so many hopeless dreams—I never thought mine would come true."

She smiled up at him. "Don't look so solemn, Doctor. We're through with solemn things. Oh, I've enjoyed talking about the California and Utah Camel Association and about politics. I've enjoyed it all. But it's been a little stiff. It's going to be fun talking about us. You'll see, Doctor. It'll be fun."

"My dear, I can't quite believe you. Do you think you could call me Edmund?"

"Well, not all the time. I might forget and say it in front of Mémé and Father. I don't want them to know yet. I want to keep it to ourselves for a little."

"Would you now, in front of me? I'd like to hear you say my name."

"Edmund," she said. "Edmund. It's a beautiful name. It's a beautiful, elegant name, Doctor, and it suits you."

They kept their secret for the rest of July. They met casually. The doctor took Louise's parcels and carried them for her. Sometimes they sat in the cool of Mrs. Kibbe's garden. "Rest yourself, Mamie," Mrs. Kibbe would say. "This is hot weather for running errands. Take a peach, it'll refresh you. And the doctor, too. I know Dr. Kibbe wants to see him. He'll be in any minute."

The flowers were in full bloom: roses, larkspur, mignonette. The doctor said how like it was to an eastern garden, shaded and carefully tended. The peaches were ripe, downy to touch, and sweet and cool to taste.

Once they walked to the bridge where they had stood together for the first time. Captain Bunker was sitting on a stool before an easel.

He greeted them. "Day to you, Doctor. Hello, Mamie. Nearly finished my painting of the town. Dr. Kibbe ordered it of me."

"It's very like." Louise looked from the picture to the scene below them. "Oh, Captain, it's very like the mountain town. Each house is so exact and the hills clothed in bright green as they were in early summer."

"They say the new road will be finished and the stagecoaches in before autumn. I'll not finish the canvas till after that. It'll be a great event. Dr. Kibbe will certainly want the stage in the painting. People like to have everything in a picture."

"It really is like the town," Louise said as they walked up the hill to Mrs. Genung's.

"If it wasn't a commission, I'd buy it for you. It's not finely done, no, but it's exact to the town. Even the flags of our Fourth of July are there."

"I don't need the picture to remember this summer in Downieville. I'll always remember it apart, exactly as it was on the day we stood on the bridge and looked at it together for the first time."

On the last day of July, Mrs. Hungerford spoke to Louise about Dr. Bryant. Mother and daughter were in the kitchen preparing supper.

"Mrs. Kibbe mentioned that she'd seen you and the doctor together. And then Mrs. Purdy. Have you been meeting him when you went on my errands?"

"It was accidental at first, Mémé, and then——" Louise faltered.

"It doesn't seem honorable of Dr. Bryant not to have declared himself to your father, that is if——"

"Oh yes, Mémé. His intentions are honorable and he wanted to speak. It was I who wanted to wait."

"Why, Louise? Why couldn't you come to us?"

"Partly because I knew you'd say I was too young until my birthday. And partly to keep it the way it was."

"Your birthday!" Mrs. Hungerford exclaimed. "But, child, even then you'll be only sixteen. Sixteen is very young."

"Not too young. Not at all too young," Louise said stubbornly.

"But that's almost five months away. We have time to think about it. Tell me what you were saying when I interrupted you."

"We couldn't bear to tell. At least I couldn't. The secret was my idea. I couldn't bear to break the magic spell. The whole summer has been different. The whole town. As if Downieville were an enchanted place. As though it were all like Mrs. Kibbe's garden or the hillside where the Italians' vineyards are, on the way to Goodyear's Bar. I can't explain."

"You're doing very well." Mrs. Hungerford touched Louise's shoulder gently. "Sit here beside me; you're trembling."

"Oh, Mémé, I'm a little frightened."

"I too," Mrs. Hungerford said gravely. "I'm frightened for you. You're too young. I'm a blind old fool to have let a child of fifteen fall in love. I might have remembered that fifteen is too near the end of childhood for safety. It's the age when one is in love with love. One can fall in love with anyone."

"But he isn't anyone. Don't you see, Mémé? That's the lucky part. Edmund is a gentleman and a graduate. You know how highly Father regards him."

"Yes, I know. He's very charming. He's educated. He has a profession. But we know little about him. If it had been a neighbor's son, someone we're long acquainted with——"

"But there's time to get acquainted. As you said, there's more than four months until my birthday."

"Don't get your heart set on your birthday, Louise."

"My heart is already set, and my mind. I'll wait till I'm sixteen but no longer."

"Oh, my darling." Mrs. Hungerford sighed and rose to her feet. "I must be getting supper ready. Your father has invited the doctor." She laid a cloth and set the dishes on the kitchen table. "And, Louise, I'll see you have a moment or two alone with Dr. Bryant. Tell him he is to speak to your father."

"He'll be glad, Mémé. He wants to do everything the proper way. He's very like Father in that, you know. He's very gentlemanly."

"Yes, my dear, we know he's a gentleman, but what we don't know is what sort of a man he is."

By September Louise knew that it was well that the secret summer had ended when it did. She needed time in which to persuade her parents to permit the marriage. They had never denied her anything within their power to give. They would not deny her Edmund Bryant but they must become accustomed to the thought.

On this September day the town was in holiday mood. The bridge was crowded. All were eagerly awaiting the coming of the first stagecoach on the new road.

Old-timers recalled the opening of the wagon road in '54. "That was a great day. There were nine six-mule wagons lined up on the hill this side of Galloway's ranch, waiting for word that the road was through."

Many greeted Louise and Edmund. "Good luck, Mamie. Congratulations, Doc, when's the happy day?"

Someone called, "There she is!"

The dust swirled about the still invisible vehicle. As it came nearer, music was heard. The scarlet stagecoach, drawn by four black horses, swept proudly across the bridge. In the plaza the bandsmen and the invited guests from Marysville stepped from the stage. The music blared and the townspeople cheered.

"Captain Bunker's picture, complete at last," Louise said.

"His picture of our summer."

"This is like a postscript to it. In a crowd like this we're alone again."

"Do you miss the times together, Louise? I suppose they were stolen. I know they were sweet."

"Yes, but I told you how it would be. Once Mémé knew, we couldn't be alone any more."

"But in the end we'll be together. Soon, Louise. Let it be soon that we're together." He clasped her waist and held her against his side.

"Not here, Edmund."

She moved a little apart from him in the crowd. For a moment she was afraid. She clasped her hands to conceal their trembling.

Suppose Mémé was right and she was wrong. Suppose fifteen was too young to decide a lifetime.

"Are you well, Louise?" He touched her hand. "You're cold and your hand is shaking."

"I'm perfectly all right. But I've had enough of the crowd and the noise. A Downieville celebration is always a little frightening. You never know when there'll be trouble."

As they walked home, she placed her hand confidently on his arm. Of course she was all right, she thought, and she must seize her chance. Where again would she find it? She looked proudly at the handsome man beside her. Where would she find anyone like him again?

"I'm lucky, Edmund," she said. "So lucky to have found you."

"My dear, it's I who found you. It's I who am lucky. I came three thousand miles to find my luck."

Louise was sixteen on the twenty-first of December. On the first of January she married Edmund Bryant.

She awoke before daylight on her wedding day. In the trundle bed beside her Ada was still asleep. She would miss Ada. She would miss them all.

She heard her mother moving in the kitchen. She rose and, very quietly not to disturb Ada, very quickly because of the cold, she dressed.

"My darling, you shouldn't be up at this hour, but come and I'll make you a cup of coffee."

"We've been up as early as this before. Remember on the journey west and when I went to Benicia and——"

"I remember, Louise. Don't look sad. Mothers like to remember."

"I can't help being a little sad for you. Of course you'll still have Ada and Father."

"My darling child, you're only moving up the hill to Jersey Flat. That's not the end of the earth."

"And you're pleased? In these last weeks you've grown to like Edmund?"

"I never disliked him, Louise. It's only your youth and his being a stranger to us that worries me."

"Is that all? I thought sometimes——" Louise hesitated. "I thought, only I didn't like to say and you wouldn't on account of Father, I thought you minded his not being a Catholic."

Mrs. Hungerford stirred her coffee and smiled. "My dear, you can't really have thought that. Father Delahunty was disturbed by what he so solemnly calls a mixed marriage. To my way of thinking any marriage is mixed—a man and a woman are quite a mixture. If there's peace and love and faith between them, religion won't divide

" . . . I have a dream too. A key to St. John's Park." The park, photographed by Rockwood in 1867. Courtesy of the New-York Historical Society, New York City.

View of Pearl Street, 1858. From D. T. Valentine's Manual, 1859. Courtesy of Museum of the City of New York.

"You listened when I told you about Irving. And you said you enjoyed Mr. Woollcott's book, where the story was better told. Woollcott was very eloquent about the poverty of the tenement in which Irving lived on Cherry Street. Did you remember Cherry Street? It runs into Pearl, where you were born. Did you remember when you lived nearby on Varick Street and Grand Street in little more comfort than Moses and Leah Baline were to know forty-five years later?"

The Franklin mansion at the corner of Pearl and Cherry Streets. From D. T. Valentine's Manual, 1853. Courtesy of Museum of the City of New York.

Union Square about 1885. The Everett House is on the right corner. Courtesy of Museum of the City of New York.

San Diego
Dec 18th 1914

Dear George,

Yours of Dec 9th received and was pleased to hear from you & you are well — I am not very well but course can not always feel just so humanity is so changeable & all around us change change. Well George you ask me to write you what I can remember about Picture of Downieville. first of all I was about 10 years of age when it was painted. The gentleman that painted it was a self made artist never had a lesson just his witts & talent for sketching his name was Captain S. A. Bunker an inglish gent from England. he came to Downieville to hunt for gold along the Yuba River; which ran through Dow - - - - he was Captain of the Horse Marines in England, and was sent also to join Cap - Dr. Hungerfords U.S.A. guards of Downieville then numbering 100 - Dr. Hungerford was a Barber in Dow - - - - besides, & father of Mrs. John McKey, the mining King of Nevada he shaved Pa & I used to go to barber shop with Pa & sat on Dr. Hungerford's lap many a time as a child he was fond of children. Well to return to my subject. Captain S. A. Bunker failed to make much in river from washing, and was not paid enough for services under; Uncle Sam, so he then come to our house & told Pa he wanted some way to make some outside money; he was giving me Pencil drawing lessons at the time; & Pa asked him why not do some good work in sketching that many of Dow - - - folks would buy of him, well he then said to Pa - suppose I paint this little Town; & Pa laughed & said alright Captain; I will buy it of you when finished; he took a stool & canvas; & stand & went over acrost the Yuba river, onto the wagon road where all travel came in to town & he there had full view of the three forks of the Yuba River that met & the great high beautiful mountains clothed in green; the town had three Bridges spaning the Yuba River and I can tell you, that river some times boomed so terrible, it rose & swept every bridge away well Capt. Bunker finished his picture, every day for three weeks he went back & forth, & from our front door I as a child watched him sitting on his stool day after day, till one day he came to our Home with the picture finished & so correct was it to Downieville that many neighbors bought of him Pa paid him $50 for it & others done the same this is about all that happened at the time. Don't ask me about the hanging of the woman; was not in my time was when there was nothing but a Vigilence Committee to avenge wrong. I knew nothing about it & if I did would not like to write any particulars for tis to horrid to mention . . . hope you will fix the dates right to what I have written remember I was born in 1848 April 3d I guess you can make a little item to put with Downieville picture to prove its merit Bunker was an amature artist self made

Merry Xmas & kind wishes to all

Orrilla

Letter from Dr. Kibbe's daughter Orrilla to her brother George. Orrilla must have been eleven when this picture was painted, because the first stagecoach came into Downieville in 1859.

DOWNIEVILLE, 1856.

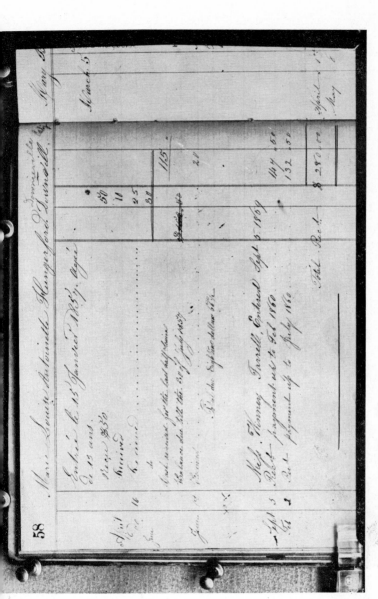

"The Mother Superior took from the safe the red ledger in which are the records which were kept in Mother Goemaere's own hand."

Photograph of the Mackay house at the corner of Howard and Taylor streets in Virginia City. The photograph is incorrectly dated, as the house burned in the fire of 1875.

Mr. J. W. Mackay.   Mr. U. S. Grant, Jr.   GEN. U. S. GRANT   Gov. J. H. Kinkead.
        Mrs. M. G. Gillette.   Mrs. U. S. Grant.   G. Yanada.   Mrs. J. G. Fair.   Col. J. G. Fair.

GEN. GRANT AND PARTY, AFTER COMING OUT OF THE BONANZA MINES.   OCT. 28, 18

them. It's never divided your father and me. The priests and the ministers are men, and men ever love the importance of controversy, but it's my belief that Father Delahunty and Reverend Pond are not as far apart as each of them would like to think."

"Then you're happy for Edmund and me?"

"That I can honestly say. Ever since you obtained your father's consent to the marriage it's been a joy to look at the pair of you."

"And you think now Father was right to say we could be married?"

"Indeed I do for if he hadn't, I think you'd have eloped to Marysville."

"Oh, Mémé, I'd never have dared. Even if I'd wanted to, I'd never have dared."

"You wanted to, that was plain enough, and there's nothing you wouldn't dare——"

"Mémé, what a thing to say of me."

"It's not a bad thing to say of anyone, my dear. Courage and determination can be a little unhandy when one's too young to know how to use them, but they'll stand you in good stead once you're grown."

"I'm grown now." Louise seized her mother's hands and danced her around the kitchen. "In a few hours I'll be a grown lady like you, a married lady." As she twirled she knocked a cup from the table. It broke on the floor.

"Never mind, Mémé, it's good luck. There's a saying that it's good luck to break a cup on your wedding morning."

"I never heard such a saying."

"This is the start of it. Years from now when people ask the origin of it the old wives will say, 'Why, don't you know that? It started because Marie Louise Hungerford broke a cup on the lucky day she married Edmund Bryant.'"

Louise's joy lasted through the morning. Its fierce strength supported her until she stood outside the parlor where Father Delahunty and Edmund were waiting. Her hand trembled as she took her father's arm. She felt a sharp cold fear. Jersey Flat was not far but it was outside the circle of home. Half a mile might as well be half a world away. She looked wonderingly at the stranger whom she had chosen. What had possessed her? Why hadn't Mémé stopped her?

Edmund smiled at her gently, encouragingly. His hand reached toward her as though to help her over the threshold that divided them. The cold fear melted in the warm proud happiness. Her head was high, her hand was light and steady on her father's arm as she walked across the room to her waiting bridegroom.

Chapter VII

Washoe Fever

"THE WASHOE FEVER seems to be the prevailing mania at present."

At present! Louise looked from the article to the masthead: the *Mountain Messenger*, March 28, 1863. Since the first year of her marriage the fever had raged in the mountains. In Downieville, in Marysville, in Yreka, in Forest City, in all the towns, the young men had caught the fever and gone across the Sierras east to Washoe. The miners went first. The young miners deserted California. Now it seemed that only old-timers were left in the played-out diggings. The trades and the professions followed. Tinkers and tailors, doctors, lawyers, and merchants, they, too, went to Washoe where any day now, any day, any hour, a man might strike it rich. For almost four years the Virginia City dispatches had told of the riches that waited. Ophir, Gould and Curry, Gold Hill, Silver City: these were the magic names. These were the places where a few feet of land changed hands for thousands of dollars. A thousand dollars a day. Fifty thousand dollars a week. The figures leaped from the pages of letters and of newspapers. Almost every hill and mountain, they said, from Humboldt to Mono was quartz-capped and metal-bellied.

In spite of the fever, in spite of two wars, the years with Edmund had been happy. A daughter had been born to them. Edmund had become one of the leading doctors of the town. In a serious accident or for an inquest he was the first one called. Louise was proud of him and she was grateful for her pride. To love without pride must, she thought, be a hard thing.

Only the few weeks of the Piute War in the spring of 1860 had been frightening. Louise tried not to remember the May morning when Edmund had gone with the other able-bodied men to defend Virginia City against the Indians. From all over the diggings the men had gone to the assistance of the friends and neighbors in the threatened town. Edmund had come home safe and so had her father. Many had been less lucky. Among the dead had been William Spear, Harry Meredith, Major Ormsby, Captain Storey. "The gentle, the generous, the lionhearted Storey"; so he was remembered.

Colonel Hungerford had brought William Spear's body home to Downieville.

"One of my boys," the colonel had said sadly. He had not spoken of his own part in the victories over the Piutes. It was Creed Haymond who had told Louise of the praise her father had received from Colonel Hays, the famous Indian fighter.

"At our first brush with the redskins near Williams Station, Jack Hays rode clear across the field to Dan to congratulate him on the excellence and promptness of his disposition of the infantry. Your father won't speak of any of this yet. None of us want to. This ugly little war was too close to us. We knew the dead too well."

It would not have been considered much of a war in the Atlantic states, Louise supposed. The dead had been counted in scores, not in thousands, but the dead had been friends and neighbors. Wars should be for the military, she thought, not for ordinary folk.

The present bloody conflict was remote. In the mining towns sympathies were with the Union; generous contributions were made to the Sanitary Fund, but not many felt impelled to go to the war.

Colonel Hungerford had gone. As soon as the War of Rebellion broke out he had announced his intention of offering his services in Washington.

There wasn't much military renown to be won in '61 and '62 in the Army of the Potomac by a lieutenant colonel. At least they had made him a lieutenant colonel. Louise sighed. She remembered his letters from Camp Brightwood. He had succumbed to dysentery.

Then he had been plagued with boils. He had suffered an injury to his leg through a fall from his horse. There was an epidemic of smallpox in camp. He needn't have traveled thousands of miles to meet these enemies. At last in the spring of '62 came the chance he had longed for: Fair Oaks, Malvern Hill. Proudly the colonel had written to his family and friends of his experiences in battle. He had quoted the praise of his superior officer.

The Sierra County *News* had reprinted Colonel Charles H. Innes' official report of the 36th New York Regiment and 3rd Brigade, of the part they took in the battle of Fair Oaks.

"General Devins having been disabled, I assumed command of the Brigade and the command of the Regiment devolved upon Lieut. Col. D. E. Hungerford, who led it off in good order, taking a position in the rifle pits near Battery Couch, by my orders. All of the officers and men of my command behaved with the utmost coolness and bravery. I make particular mention of Lieut. Col. D. E. Hungerford (who exhibited great coolness, bravery and judgment in the skillful handling of the Regiment after having the command), Major J. A. Raney, Surgeon Ed. B. Dalton, Capt. Jas. J. Walsh, Lieutenant D. W. Murphy and Sergeant Major Chas. P. Lindsey."

There it was in print, his name leading all the rest. There it was in print for the neighbors to read, for Mémé to save for him.

"This is what he dreamed," Mémé had said. "Mentioned in dispatches, immortalized in the fine print of the records of the War Department. A brief and easily forgotten glory, but it's what he's always wanted. Long ago in the barbershop on West Broadway, I remember him hankering after the military life. But this new scheme. Poor Daniel, I don't think anything can come of it."

The colonel had come home full of enthusiasm for his scheme. He would raise a California regiment and attack the Confederacy through Texas. He had been promised this command. The authorities in Washington had promised. Any day now, he would hear from the governor of California. Any day.

He had not heard. The orders had not come. Weary of waiting, the colonel had gone to Virginia City. There he would help in the recruiting and organizing of a territorial regiment. All the young men were in Washoe. That was the place to raise troops. He had gone in December and he had not returned. He and Mémé were now settled in Washoe. "Hungerford, Col. D. E. mining claims, res. Cedar Ravine." So read the listing in the new Washoe directory.

Many had gone from Downieville. How did the *Messenger* put it?

"Many of the citizens of Downieville and influential men are taking their departure from us."

Influential men. This would please Edmund. She must save the article for him.

"Some for the purpose of locating permanently, others merely to 'look around,' before taking up residence in silver land. Judge R. H. Taylor and Dr. E. G. Bryant left us last week, and propose sticking up their shingles in Virginia City."

"How could he resist?" Louise spoke aloud. So she had spoken two weeks ago to Dr. Kibbe. "How could he resist, Dr. Kibbe? How can any of the young men resist when day after day they hear it from returning travelers, they read it in the papers? Ore in Washoe assayed at thirty thousand dollars per ton for silver alone. Trade is brisk in Washoe. No unemployment in Washoe. Cities of silver. Hills of gold. How can they resist, Dr. Kibbe?"

"My poor child. It's well named: it is a fever. And none of us is immune. I can rail against it but I may be the next to succumb. And do you know, Mamie, it wouldn't matter as much about me? But Edmund is gifted. He's a brilliant surgeon, that boy."

And Judge Taylor is a brilliant lawyer, Louise thought. They are all brilliant. Mr. De Long, Mr. Mighels, Mr. Langton, Mr. Cossett. All their futures are bright, but the silver is brighter.

She walked restlessly across the narrow room. The dark street beyond the windows was quiet. Downieville was settling into a peaceful town. Stagnant, Edmund had called it. But surely it would never stagnate entirely. After all it was the county seat. It might become a commercial center like Marysville. It would be quieter than in the old days but it need not be less prosperous for those who had a trade or, more proudly, a profession. Downieville was becoming a place in which a child might grow up in peace, unafraid.

She picked up the lamp and shaded the brightness of the flame with her hand. She carried it into the bedroom where Eva slept. She had been christened Eveline Julia, but since she could speak she had called herself Eva.

She was so little. How would it be for her in Virginia City? They said it was like Downieville in the days of '51 and '52. Even in '54 and after that, Downieville had been a frightening place for a child.

"Mémé managed and I'll manage." She touched the dark sleeping head. "I'll manage, Eva." She tightened her hold on the lamp. For her child in her turn there must be a circle of safety. Louise hoped that 10 North A Street, where Edmund had taken rooms, would not be too far from the Hungerford dwelling in Cedar Ravine. But safety must not be a block away. It must not be even a door away. It must be within the walls that enclose a child at night.

"I'll manage, Eva," she whispered. "Your father and I will manage. We'll make the circle for you as once they did for me."

Louise left Downieville in the stage early on a summer morning. She looked back in farewell at the green valley. It was even greener now than it had been when first she had seen it. Many of the wide dust-red scars on the mountainsides were covered with a second growth of young bright-leafed trees. It was a curious feeling to look on a place for the last time. When she had left New York she had felt certain she would someday see it again. But Downieville was disappearing forever. She would never, she thought, see the valley again. Edmund would not return. He had given up his position at the hospital. Their cabin was sold. And yesterday Miles Langley had agreed to purchase their interest in the Pioneer Livery Stable. That investment had brought in a nice little sum, but Edmund insisted that there were investments a thousandfold richer to be made in Washoe.

The road turned sharply in the forest. The last sight of Downieville was gone. She would never see it again. She would see the neighbors and friends. Many were in Virginia and others, no doubt, would come. But she would never see the forks of the Yuba dividing the town. She would never stand on the bridge and look across at the vineyards on the slope beyond the Catholic church. "Never" was a cold and final word. She shivered as if someone were walking on her grave.

On the afternoon of the second day the narrow road curved out on the slope of a mountain. Below them was a wide expanse of blue water. A passenger said it was Lake Bigler.

The landscape began to alter. Yesterday and today they had driven through a green and smiling land. Suddenly, in the swift descent, it seemed, of one mountain, the change came. The pines were less deeply rooted. They clung precariously to the stony earth. The trees were not so tall. They grew less thickly together. It was as though they were dying of a gray blight. And then there were no pines, there were no trees at all. All around there was nothing but the dusty gray of the sagebrush. Beyond the slate-colored valley were hills, bare of vegetation.

Eva exclaimed with pleasure, "Look, Mammy. It's pretty."

The rock shone red as the sunset sky. The barren hills shone bright in unexpected colors. Nowhere was there any green.

"Very pretty," Louise said mechanically. But it wasn't pretty. It was strange and unnatural. Green was the natural color in which the eye could take delight. Here there was no green. There was only the gray brush flowing over the uneven ground like the waves of a mournful sea. Beyond were sand-colored hills, brilliant now in the reflected red and gold of the sunset.

"That's cinnabar, ma'am, that red rock," a passenger told her. "Beautiful, ain't it?"

"Beautiful," Louise said politely. She thought of the gray rocks in the bed of the Yuba. Gray was the proper color for rocks. In the shade of the forest the green moss grew on the gray stone and the gray bark. There would be no forest shade in this barren country. Only in the morning and in the evening there would be the shadows of the mountains. The shadows were falling now. They were vast shadows. Their length and breadth must, she thought, be measured in miles.

Silver City broke the darkness of the journey. Bright lights gleamed and brassy music rang from the bars that lined the steep street. The stage stopped briefly and then rolled quickly through the dark again. Gold Hill blazed around them. Then they drove on. From Mount Davidson the wind howled across the divide. Here were the lights of their destination, Virginia City. Above them in the west and below them in the east the noisy sprawling city clung to the mountainside. Louise looked down at the roofs of the buildings below her on her right. On her left the streets rose steep as attic stairs. This narrow crowded street was C Street, Virginia's main thoroughfare, of which she had read. It seemed narrow as a Sierra trail. From the bars came the singing of the hurdy-gurdy women, heard long ago. Craycroft's Saloon, the Gem, under different names they were here. The Eldorado Saloon. The Delta. The Snug. On the wooden sidewalks and across the muddy street the crowd surged. Here they all were again: the miners in flannel shirts, the women in flaming spangled dresses, the gamblers in black broadcloth. From saloons and gambling houses came the raucous voices she remembered. On the steep, barren ascent of Mount Davidson was the mining camp she had seen nine years before in the valley of the Yuba.

The passengers descended wearily from the coach. Louise carried Eva. A voice welcomed them. The child stretched out her arms.

"Tired, dearie?" Edmund lifted Eva onto his shoulder. He reached his other hand to Louise. "It's not far to our lodging, just two blocks up the hill. I'll call a man to take your luggage."

Louise smiled at the sound of the warm confident voice, at the sight of the strong arm that held their child safe above the crowded street. He was very like her father. She had chosen well. And he had chosen well. She would be to him as Mémé to her Daniel. Mémé had managed in Downieville in the '50s. She would manage in Virginia in the '60s. It was not a harder time nor place. Edmund had been right to come. The present peacefulness of Downieville was the worn-out peacefulness of age falling into sleep and death. Virginia was in the time of its youth. Edmund would make his way here. He would grow with the young city. And she would make for him and Eva a home. She would make for them a safe and peaceful home in the heart of the tumult.

Chapter VIII

···—◆◎◆—···

10 North A Street

FROM THE LODGING house on North A Street, Louise looked out over Virginia City. From the window at night she had seen only the lights that straggled down the mountainside to the dark invisible plain. On the first morning she ran as quickly as her child to the window.

"Look, Mammy. Look at the roofs. It's funny."

"Very funny, darling, to look down on roofs instead of up."

Beyond the steep street, beyond the houses piled against Mount Davidson, the distant plains stretched wide to the distant mountains. She remembered pictures she had seen in Mr. Langton's books and at Benicia: the huge broken pillars, the forgotten idols blinded and defaced by time, the curious shape of a pyramid sinking into the tide of sand. She had imagined the desert, smooth and yellow, the sands moving beneath the wind like water. She had not imagined such colors as these. She stood beside her child and watched the sun rise. She watched, amazed, the brilliance of the sky reflected and altered in the mirror of the plain. Here even darkness had color. The shrinking shadows of the distant hills were purple and blue.

"Look, Mammy." Eva pointed to a church spire. "They have a steeple like at home in Downieville."

"Virginia City is home now." Louise looked down at the shabby unfamiliar houses. She would come to know them. They would seem less ugly. Perhaps they would be replaced by fine buildings of stone and brick. If all the tales told of the Comstock were true, a city of marble could rise on Mount Davidson. Some already had built fine mansions. She had heard of one magnificent dwelling near Washoe Lake. Its stones were imported, they said, and its doorknobs of silver. She would like to see that and she would like to see Maguire's Opera House. They said it was an immense and handsome building, larger even than the opera house in San Francisco. It could accommodate sixteen hundred people. She would see all the city, its ugliness and its grandeur. She would come to know it well from A Street to H Street and from the divide to Cedar Ravine.

On her first day abroad in Virginia she could scarcely see the town for the blinding dust that blew.

"How do you like our Washoe zephyr?" the storekeepers asked. "No wind like it any place on earth." Their voices were proud.

Louise answered politely, "You do everything in a big way in Virginia."

"That's the spirit, ma'am. Take things that way and you'll like Virginia."

Louise sheltered Eva against her body as they climbed the steep street against the wind. Their bonnets were askew, their hair and their clothing disarranged. Their smarting eyes watered.

"Poor Eva, Mammy'll take you home. We'll see the rest of the city another day."

If they could not see the city they could hear it. As they climbed Union Street the noise of the city rose with them. Machinery roared and pounded, louder and more persistent than the wind. The traffic never stopped. The streets were more crowded than Marysville on the busiest day. The hoofs of horses and of mules thudded. The heavy wagon wheels rolled. The teamsters shouted. C Street was choked with wagons, with pack trains, with omnibuses, with horsemen, and even with an elegant carriage or two. In front of their rival firehouses the engine companies waited to add to the confusion with a practice run. Outside the stockbrokers' offices the way was blocked by clamorous customers.

"Is this a city, Mammy? A really city?" Eva asked.

"It's not much bigger than Downieville, is it? It's just called a city but it's not a real city—not like New York or even San Francisco."

Louise smiled at the pride which called this sprawling pile of wooden shacks a city. It had no more right to the appellation than Brandy City where the prize fights were held. She looked back and cupped her face in her hands to protect her eyes. It was the pride that made the difference. Brandy City knew full well it was a little town. Virginia believed it was a city. The opera house on D Street was a handsome edifice, well ventilated and extravagantly lighted with oil. But it also had gas fixtures and a gasolier. Mr. Maguire was prepared for the coming of gas. The recently finished spire of St. Mary's rose tall, and its Angelus bell rang clear above the tumult, but the Catholics weren't satisfied. They meant to build a finer church at Ridge and D streets. That was it: all of Virginia meant to build finer and taller. And while some mocked Mrs. Sandy Bowers for building à la fancy beside Washoe Lake, they would, when their turn came, emulate that luxurious mansion. Even Colonel Hungerford had spoken of it admiringly. "It's not entirely to my taste, dearie. In a few details there is a certain ostentation, but some of their things are very fine. Their bookroom, which also contains rare bronzes and bibelots, is magnificent."

Louise carried Eva up the last block to A Street. "Poor lamb, it's a hard city to walk in. I was wrong before: it is a city. It believes it's a city and it feels like a city."

Times were good for all of them in that year. Colonel Hungerford had been commissioned by Governor Nye as colonel of the 1st Regiment of Infantry and he was in charge of recruiting. He issued orders to the commandants of the military companies, requiring them to make daily reports of their progress in obtaining volunteers.

Edmund was doing well. Several small financial ventures turned out nicely for him. More important, he was rising in his profession. He was called several times in consultation by the city's most prominent physicians.

The Hungerfords and the Bryants prospered with the prospering city. They rejoiced when good news came from the armies in the East. Virginia was now heart and soul for the Union. "We're driving them all out," the colonel said firmly. "I was a Democrat at one time myself, but we're all staunch Union men now. No room here for Copperheads. No room for traitors. Judge Terry discovered that when he tried to sell us out to the Confederacy." The bullion gleamed bright and heavy and abundant. Nevada's silver would win the war. Nevada would next year become a state, an integral part of the Union which her wealth would help to preserve.

Louise drew Eva against her knee. "Someday, Eva, someday in this city of silver, someday you'll see." She laughed. That sounded like her father long ago in Downieville. But this wasn't Downieville. This was a different place, a different time. In this place, in this time, hopes would come true.

Her own dreams were coming true. In their two rented rooms she was making for Edmund and Eva the home she had planned. Eva would never be a beauty like Ada, but she was growing more appealing every day. There was a sweetness in that solemn little face that drew even strangers to the child.

It was good to be twenty years old and happy. It was good to love and be loved by her parents and her sister, by her husband and her daughter. Soon there would be another child. She smiled contentedly. That was good too. A loving home had room for many children.

The new baby was another girl, but even Edmund was not disappointed for long. Little Marie was too pretty a baby to be anything but a delight and a pride. Pink-cheeked and blue-eyed, Marie escaped the unbecoming ailments of early infancy. Mrs. Hungerford and the midwife exclaimed over her rosy perfection.

Eva neglected her doll to watch over her sister. While the baby slept Louise took the older child on her lap and held her close. This one would need her more. The little one's way would be easier. If things were arranged with justice in this world, all women would be beautiful. But charm helped, and goodness. Surely goodness helped too.

"You're my first, Eva," she whispered.

"And she's my first," Eva answered proudly. "My first sister."

For eight months Marie grew in health and beauty. She was patently the pride of her father's heart. Louise watched Edmund indulgently. She supposed gentlemen couldn't help favoring prettiness even in a child and, of course, in every family the new baby came first. Fortunately Eva was too little to mind.

The septic sore throat had raged in Downieville when Eva was an infant. Louise had been frightened. She had wept for her friends, for the heartbroken, comfortless young mothers, and she had hidden her own fierce joy that her first-born was safe. In Virginia, too, there were epidemics of illness among young children, but the grieving parents were not known to Louise, so the danger seemed more distant. And if Eva, a small and delicate child, had come unharmed through the perils of infancy, surely Marie would be safe.

Marie, the strong one, the pretty one, the favored one, was not safe. It was to her that illness came. The others in the lodging house were untouched. The fever seized Marie.

"No one is safe." Louise spoke in terror and anger to her mother as they watched the doctors whispering to each other beside the baby's bed. "No one is safe. I should have known. Little Nito was a fine strong child, too, but he was defenseless against the smallpox. And this sickness—this terrible burning sickness. She's too little, Mémé."

The doctors could not help. They could only watch while Marie choked herself to death.

The illness had been so brief that the baby's face and body were not wasted. She was pale but otherwise she was unchanged. She lay still and peaceful like a healthy sleeping child.

Louise knelt beside the bed. Soon they would take her away. There was hardly any time left for pity and tenderness and love. She heard her mother's step.

"See, Mémé, how pretty she looks. How pretty and happy and safe."

"She is safe now, my darling, and happy. Don't let me interrupt you. Finish your prayers."

"I wasn't praying." Louise sprang to her feet. "I'm not thinking about God just now. It's better I don't. This world of His. This fine world He made."

"Louise darling, hush. I'm sorry, Father Manogue."

Louise stared with blazing eyes at the priest. Let him dare to offer comfort.

"Mrs. Bryant, we must think now of this little one, of doing the last things for her." For a big man his voice was surprisingly gentle. He could speak loudly enough in the pulpit, but in the small room his voice was low and without clerical unction. "You'll want a High Mass. It'll be a comfort to the child that's left. She'll want the best for her sister."

"We can't afford too much, Father. My husband has had rather heavy expenses just of late. It's a new stock about which his brokers have told him, Mémé, and while I'm sure . . ."

"Don't worry about expense, Mrs. Bryant. I'll arrange everything at St. Mary's."

"But we must have a plot and I'd have liked her to have a pretty monument, an angel or . . ."

"It will be all right, Mrs. Bryant. There'll be a place for her on the hillside in our new cemetery. It's a lovely hillside, I promise you. And for a marker, don't you think a little one would be best? Let the earth lie light under grass and flowers. Stone is heavy. And she has no need of a carved angel."

Since the earliest days in Virginia there had been expeditions to the outlying districts. "Ho! for Humboldt!" the prospectors shouted. "Ho! for Austin!" In 1864 as Virginia's prosperity declined, the lure of far places grew stronger. Somewhere in this rich country another lode must await discovery. "Ho! for Austin!" "Ho! for Reese River!"

It was natural, Louise supposed, for Edmund to follow a new trail. It was well for him to go. Grief had made her a poor companion. It was no wonder he grew impatient with her and sought in the bars more cheerful company. He, too, in his own way was sorrowing. It was natural, people said, for gentlemen to drown their sorrows.

Mrs. Hungerford spoke reluctantly of Edmund's drinking. "Several have mentioned to your father seeing him in the saloons night after night."

"They could hardly have seen him had they not been there too."

"My darling, it's not to criticize or to carry tales. But if you could try, on his return, not to forget your sorrow but to put it away a little. Gentlemen don't always understand. They grow impatient with long grieving."

"Edmund is never impatient with me, Mémé. And even in drink, he's always a gentleman." Louise faced her mother proudly. Not even to Mémé would she admit that Edmund could be unkind. It was not he but the devil which, in unhappiness, in disappointment, possessed him.

"Perhaps I shouldn't have spoken. The stories we heard may have been exaggerated. And poor Edmund has had several disappointments. If only this new venture turns out well . . ."

"I hope so, Mémé, but he's been gone longer than I thought and my funds are low, really very low. The broker on C Street cleaned out our small savings. Father Manogue is trying to get me work. He knows some ladies for whom I can sew."

"My darling, if only we could help, but things haven't gone well with your father lately. Indeed, things are not well with Virginia, he says. But I cannot think the reports of San Francisco are much more hopeful. If the output of our mines is low and our stocks fall, they're bound to feel it at the Bay."

"Father Manogue advised me to stay here. He has confidence in the future of Virginia's mines and he should be well informed. He has known many of the superintendents since early days when he was a miner with them in Sierra County. I thought we might escape the gambling fever in San Francisco, but he says no. It's the stock gambling that frightens me. It's a temptation and it's so easy. And the gentlemen can pretend to themselves it's business. Even Edmund."

"I know, Louise, but possibly this present venture will be a success."

"If only it could be enough so he would be satisfied. Then perhaps we could go to some quiet, respectable place, not in the gold and silver country."

"Oh, my dear, it's not the place, it's . . . it's . . ." Mrs. Hungerford hesitated. "It's the man. I must say it to you, Louise. You must understand the problem you face."

"It's not Edmund, Mémé. It's not his fault. It's the fever. The Washoe fever, the Humboldt fever. The Reese River. Dr. Kibbe said it was well named. And the young and the gifted and the clever succumb. Even Dr. Kibbe himself. I hear he's coming out. Not that he's so young, poor Dr. Kibbe." Louise forced herself to smile at her mother. "Don't worry about me. I'll like having work to do, it'll keep me busy."

The work was a comfort to Louise. She sewed late into the night until her eyes were heavy and her back ached. The physical fatigue was welcome; it made her sleep. It was better to fall asleep from exhaustion than to lie awake thinking of the grave on the hillside, to lie awake in a warm bed listening to the cold wind blowing, to lie safely housed listening to the rain beating on the roof.

Edmund returned, penniless and in debt. Against his wishes Louise continued to work. "Just until you settle into your practice again, Edmund, just until your obligations are paid."

"A fine chance there is of any sort of practice in this decaying mining camp. The Comstock's done for. Even your father speaks of moving away. And the colonel is ever optimistic beyond reasonable hope."

"It's different for Father. You have your profession."

"There are too many of my profession here. The doctors are starving. And it doesn't help my position to have you going to work."

"Folks understand that you've had reverses. It's not unusual in these times. I must work. Don't be angry, Edmund."

"Oh, Louise, Louise. I'm not angry. It's not I. A doctor has temptations you can't understand."

For a moment he spoke in the voice she knew. In his pale strained face his eyes were kind.

"Edmund." Her voice was unsteady. Her tears overflowed.

His eyes hardened again. They were the cold bright eyes of a stranger, the eyes of a man sick with a strange fever.

"Crying won't mend matters," he shouted. "You couldn't bring your dead baby back to life with tears."

Eva awakened. She began to cry. Louise lifted her from her bed. "Hush, dearie. She's frightened, Edmund. Comfort her a little."

"She was born frightened, that one. Pity she didn't inherit a little of your spirit. Not that you've shown much lately."

He pushed Louise and the child out of his way and rushed from the room. Louise caught hold of the bedpost and saved herself from falling. Eva landed, unhurt, on the quilt. "Mammy, Mammy."

The street door slammed. "It's the wind, darling. The wind slammed the door."

Through the window she could see the lights of Virginia. If she opened the window she would hear the noise of the brightly lit saloons. On every street, on every nightmare street, the lights shone through the glass windows and the music blared loud. C Street was the brightest and the noisiest. But a man need not go as far as C Street. He need go only a block to 7 North B to the Arbor Saloon, or the Niagara at Number 18, or the Virginia across the way.

She closed the inner wooden shutters. She must get rest. She must not be tired for the next day's work.

When Louise went out to sew in bad weather she left Eva in the care of her landlady.

Up and down the steep streets Louise carried her parcels as once she had carried Mémé's. She dressed as befitted a doctor's wife. Her gloves were neatly mended. Her bonnet strings were clean and carefully pressed. She held herself straight against the wind.

On a late afternoon she came home. As she turned the corner of A Street she hurried. She was long after her usual time. She should not have gone to do that last alteration, but the extra money would be useful. As she approached the lodging house the door opened.

"My dear, I was watching for you."

Louise stared at the pitying face of a neighbor. "The doctor, is the doctor . . ."

"Him? He's all right. It's your little girl. Had a bad fall. They took her in the parlor. It was here in the hall she was. At the foot of the stairs and if you ask me . . ."

"Forgive me." Louise hurried through the parlor door. She stood still for an instant to accept the blow and to gain sufficient strength to receive its impact.

Edmund was sitting with his head in his hands. He did not look up. Another doctor was bending over the sofa. "There now, you should feel better, dearie." He turned and saw Louise. "Glad you're here, Mrs. Bryant. The little girl's been asking . . ."

"Mammy. Mammy. They couldn't find you, Mammy."

"Darling, I'm sorry. I met a new lady at one of my customers' and I went home with her. Are you . . . is she all right, Doctor?"

"She suffered a great deal. But she's a brave girl. And the pain is lessening. Now that you've come we'll take her upstairs."

"How did it happen?"

Eva began to cry.

"It frightens her to speak of it. And Dr. Bryant is, ah, not quite himself. But I gather that she slipped away from your good landlady to follow her father upstairs when he came home and she must have missed her step and fallen."

"She's quick as a flash, Mrs. Bryant. I had my back turned only a minute. I'd never have let her away with him, but . . ."

"Mammy." Eva clung to her mother's hand.

"We'll take you upstairs now, darling. Edmund." Louise raised her voice a little. "Edmund, if you'll help us, my dear."

Edmund lifted his head and looked at her vacantly. He got slowly to his feet and walked unsteadily to the sofa.

"No!" Eva screamed. She buried her face in her mother's dress. "I want her to stay with me. Mammy stay."

"She's afraid of being moved, Mrs. Bryant," the doctor said. "She suffered a good deal before the splint was put on. Let me carry her. It won't hurt, Eva."

Without loosening her grip of her mother's hand, Eva allowed herself to be carried upstairs.

The doctor placed her gently on her bed. "She should sleep now. I've given her something to ease the pain."

Presently Eva's hand relaxed. She lay still.

Louise walked to the door with the doctor. "How grave is the injury? I'd rather know."

"I can't make an exact prognostication, ma'am. It's the hip. That's always slow and uncertain."

"You mean she may not walk?"

"Oh, not as bad as that, ma'am. I can almost promise you not as bad as that. But she may be lame."

"For a long time or all her life?"

"For a long time, certainly. It's a bad break in a bad place."

"But it can be cured? You're not saying it can't ever be cured?"

"No. I'm not saying that. Wonderful progress is being made, but I can promise nothing."

"Thank you, Doctor. I'd rather know."

"I'll come back in the morning. Now I think I can best help you by taking Dr. Bryant along with me for the night. The little girl must have absolute quiet. I'll leave a powder with you in case she's restless. She's had a bad shock."

Louise sat beside the bed and watched the sleeping child. To an adult a fall like that, pain like that, would be a terror and a shock. But the stair was rickety and badly lighted. An adult would understand how an accident could happen. To a child the terror would lie in not understanding that a known and familiar place could hold such danger. That must be the terror. That must be it. That must be . . .

Worn with fatigue, Louise dozed in her chair. Eva's screams awakened her. "Mammy's here, Eva. I'm here." She grasped the hand that sought hers. "You're safe, Eva."

She waited for the hand to grow soft and relaxed with sleep. Poor baby, she thought. And it was my fault. I shouldn't have left her so long. I shouldn't have left her till the stair grew dark and dangerous. "It was my fault." She repeated the words aloud like a prayer. "It was my fault."

By the end of '64 it was clear even to the most optimistic that the great days of Virginia City were over. Stock values steadily decreased. Wages fell and unemployment rose.

"The boom is over, dearie," Colonel Hungerford told Louise.

> "'In wildcat's fall
> We were skinned all.'

"But it's not just the wildcats. They're wiped out, of course. But when Gould and Curry can go down to nine hundred dollars a share it's the beginning of the end."

"But, Father, the papers seem hopeful. The *Enterprise* says . . ."

"I know what the *Enterprise* says: We are at the bottom of the wheel and when the wheel moves we are bound to rise. Louise, dearie, this wheel is stuck for good and I don't intend to be stuck with it. I'm clearing out."

"Back to Downieville?"

"No. Not Downieville. They're worse off than we are. The fire last February almost did for them. I mean to move on to San Francisco. If I'm right there on the spot I can deal better with the government and the military. I still hope to be given command of troops for the eastern front. And if that fails, there is something else in the wind. I'm not at liberty to speak of it just yet, but there is more than one field on which the battle for freedom against tyranny can be fought."

"And Mémé goes too?" Louise asked.

"Yes, but you'll not be away from us for long. Edmund tells me that he, too, has plans. Poor boy, he's had a run of bad luck. Washoe was an unlucky venture for us all. When I think of the rich promise I saw here in '60, when I remember the high hopes, it makes me sad to see the slowly receding tide of Virginia's prosperity. But I don't mean to be caught in the ebb. As Edmund was saying, 'There is a tide in the affairs of men . . .'"

"I know, Father, 'which taken at the flood . . .' Edmund is fond of that quotation."

"He has his little weaknesses, poor lad. But he is a scholar and a gentleman and that means much, dearie. And as for his, ah, his, well, to put it frankly his drinking, I lay that to his present environment. He was never like this before. Why, I remember when I came home to Downieville in the summer of '62 I thought there never was such a happy young couple as you two."

"There never was, Father. I remember that summer and the summers before and after. It's only lately. And even now Edmund is a gentleman and a graduate. He never forgets himself."

"I'm sure not, dearie. But all the same, we must get him away from Virginia. If he can go into practice in San Francisco with that friend of his, it'll be the making of him."

"Yes, Father."

Louise bade farewell to her parents and Ada. She hid from them her ignorance of Edmund's plans and waited for him to tell her.

Soon after the Hungerfords' departure he spoke to her. It was in the morning and he was sober.

"Well, Louise, I've put off telling you but I suppose the colonel's been ahead of me. I mean to go to San Francisco."

"Father said something. Have you an opening? Does it promise well?"

"Better than here at least. Though what promise I have left . . ." He spread out the fingers of his hands. He could not hold them steady. "See that? Ten o'clock in the morning and I shake like an old woman. But perhaps if I can get away from here. This city of unfulfilled promise, of hope deferred. The preacher says hope deferred maketh the heart sick. And the body, he might have added, and the mind and the whole man. I whine like an old woman too. How can even you endure me?"

"I love you, Edmund."

"It's as simple as that, isn't it? You were very young and there had never been anyone else and so you were caught. Poor Louise, because you were once fifteen and it was summertime in the Sierras, you were caught and now you can't escape your unhappy love."

"I don't want to escape. And it's not unhappy. Almost never unhappy."

"Poor child." He walked away from her and stood looking out of the window. "You'd be better off without me, Louise. They grant divorces very readily in the state of Nevada. You could take advantage of it. It would be an escape for you."

"I don't want to escape."

"And you're a Catholic. I forgot. That escape isn't for you."

"That's not why it isn't for me."

He turned back and took her hand. His hand steadied in her firm clasp. "It's because I love you, Louise, that I must set you free. There's no use in our both being destroyed. You've suffered at my hands and you'll suffer more if I let you. You and Eva both. You don't want her to suffer any more through me."

"It was not through you, not through you." Her voice rose.

"Hush, my dear. I think it was. I can't remember anything but I think I must have been clumsy. Perhaps when I went to help her I was clumsy and hurt her. I can't remember but I must have hurt her. If I did, it was just clumsiness. You know that, Louise."

"I know."

"If I could only remember. But she remembers. Ever since that day she's been afraid of me."

"Not of you, Edmund, just afraid. She'll get over it. The doctors say that quite soon now she may be able to walk a little. She'll forget."

"Would you rather stay with your mother in San Francisco, Louise, until I get established and can take care of you?" He looked again at his hands. "Do you suppose that will ever be? The brilliant young Dr. Bryant." He laughed. "My kinsman, old Dr. Bryant, should see his gifted pupil now. Do you suppose I am wrong and that, after all, the clever young doctor can be brought back to life?"

"Soon, Edmund. Soon as ever you can get away from this hateful place. But I won't go to Mémé now. She has too much as it is. With Ada to provide for and Father not settled at anything. I'll stay here. I can manage for Eva and me. I have many customers, Mrs. Cossett and Mrs. Taylor have given me work. And the ladies to whom Father Manogue spoke."

"Ladies! It makes me sick to have you working like a slavey for those jumped-up wives of common miners. You carry yourself like a queen. In your shabby clothes you hold your head high and yet you have to humble yourself before those ex-scullery maids and boarding-house keepers."

"Work isn't humbling. Mémé's worked all her life that I remember. Once the Hungerfords were somebody, I think, but that was before Father's time. And it doesn't matter to anyone but me. The ladies would never believe in Farleigh Castle."

"Farleigh Castle." He smiled. "The colonel has told me."

"You see? Not even you, but I choose to believe it. And it helps. When the ladies are impatient—I'm not as quick or as skillful as Mémé—it helps."

"The ladies! Mrs. Bonner, the wife of a mine superintendent, and . . ."

"They're kind; Mrs. Bonner, Mrs. Jones, Mrs. Taylor. I've known Mrs. Taylor since I was a child. She can't afford to have much done but she always sends for me."

"Yes, Bob Taylor's a fine chap. But he's not had much luck in Virginia. There's been no luck here for any of us. Poor Sam Langton—crushed under the wheels of a lumber wagon and taking two weeks to die of it. This is a murderous city, Louise. You can see it plain now that its luck has left it. You mustn't stay in it. You must go to your mother."

"I can't do that. I'll manage. Until you send for me I'll manage just fine."

"I mean to send for you. I've meant so many other things. All I meant to do for you, remember, Louise? They could pave the Geiger Grade with my good intentions."

Through the hard winter no word came from Edmund. Mrs. Hungerford mentioned him rarely in her letters. She urged Louise to come to her. She was giving French and Spanish lessons and making out nicely.

Perhaps in the spring, Louise thought, she would pay them a visit. In the meantime she would manage. She moved to cheaper lodgings. One room was enough for her and Eva.

The spring brought victory to the Union. At noon on the tenth of April one bell after another began to peal until all the bells of the city were ringing out the glorious news of Lee's surrender. The National Guard and the Emmet Guard paraded. The howitzer of the Provost Guard thundered. Steam whistles and anvils, guns and pistols added to the din. From every flagstaff the colors flew. Banners were strung across the streets. Windows were wreathed with patriotic bunting.

The celebration lasted into the night. Many dwellings were illuminated. Bonfires were lit in the streets. Crowds marched singing through the town.

In her room Louise could hear the noise of celebration. The sky was bright with victory bonfires. She read and reread her mother's letter, trying to grasp its contents. The facts were plainly stated but her mind refused to accept them. Edmund had disappeared. After he had been gone for a week his partner had come to the Hungerfords for news of him. That had been two weeks ago, Mrs. Hungerford wrote, and there was still no news. She urged Louise to come to San Francisco.

Louise determined not to leave Virginia. She must not add to Mémé's responsibilities. And besides, Edmund might return to her. If she were here alone, he might come.

Within a few days the public rejoicing turned to mourning. The church bells tolled for the murdered President. The flags that had flown for victory were lowered to half-mast. Buildings were draped in black. Shops, theaters, and saloons, all were closed. The papers issued extras. Men gathered on street corners to discuss the news. They breathed curses upon the assassin and muttered oaths of vengeance. The low angry talk was helpless. None seemed to know what to do or say. In Gold Hill a man named Absalom Coxey who dared to speak his joy at the murder was flogged almost to death. In Virginia no act of violence was committed, although everyone knew that a start only was needed to produce the wildest kind of violence. If there were southern sympathizers abroad, they wisely held their peace. The tense quiet was unbroken except by the ever-increasing wind that whirled the dust in clouds above the darkening streets. Louise walked through the strangely silent, sober city. She was grateful for the general mourning. She could hide her private sorrow under the mask of public grief.

If she wanted a refuge from Virginia City, there was none. Her father's scheme at which he had hinted was put into action at the end of May. He and several others under the leadership of General A. C. Williams planned to go to Mexico as settlers. Many veterans of the recent war were seeking to continue in the military life by going to Mexico, ostensibly as peaceable settlers. Once there, secretly armed, they would help to overthrow the tyranny of Maximilian. The colonel's company had no luck. They were stopped before their ship was out of harbor. They were arrested and jailed for piracy.

Louise could learn little from Mémé's brave and loyal letters. Mrs. Hungerford wrote that the colonel had been betrayed by some of the very men he trusted. General Williams was a fine man, of course, and absolutely honorable but perhaps a little rash. . . .

In the Nevada papers the San Francisco dispatches were puzzling. The Virginia *Daily Union* quoted the San Francisco *Bulletin:*

"The Brontes Emigration was a piratical scheme. Numerous affidavits have been made by parties connected with it showing a deep-laid plan for seizing the steamer *Colon* and making her a piratical craft to prey on French and other commerce under pretext of aiding Mexico. The principals are admitted to bail in the sum of five thousand dollars each."

Louise sighed. One thing was clear. She and Eva could not add to Mémé's burden. They must remain in Virginia.

The spring burned into summer. In July the colonel and his comrades were acquitted.

"Vindicated, my dear, at last," he wrote to Louise. "In the conclusion of my address to the jury I asked only for simple justice. 'Now, gentlemen,' I said, 'if you can find anything in the evidence to even excite a suspicion of guilt, then I am willing to abide by your judgment. I ask no charity or leniency; will receive none. I ask not in charity, but demand in the most sacred name of justice a free acquittal from your seats without resorting to the jury-room.' All the allurements of French gold and the vile attempts of the shameless conspirators could not hold against the twelve honest men. They acquitted us instantly and unanimously."

Her mother, he wrote, had been a tower of strength and courage. Now she rejoiced in the glorious outcome.

It might be glorious, Louise thought. It was bound to be expensive. She cut from the Virginia *Daily Union* the paragraph headed "The Brontes—*Colon* Pirates." The last sentence was disturbing, but the article would please her father. And if he had further plans, Mémé must already know of them.

"The indictment against Gen. Williams, Col. Hungerford and others, the leaders of the Brontes Expedition, for conspiracy in preparing to seize the little Peruvian steamer, *Colon,* and running her out to sea for piratical purposes, came up in the County Court last week for trial. After hearing all the evidence about which such wise and damaging predictions had been made by our French citizens, and all the arguments of counsel, the jury brought in a verdict of not guilty in less than five minutes' deliberation. Some of the jurors proposed giving it without moving from their seats but the Judge thought

the form of retiring should be observed, so they went out, but returned as above states, about as soon as the verdict could be written.
Strange that men of responsibility and good reputation should be thus
incarcerated in dungeons for months, their bail being fixed at such
high figures that they were unable to obtain it; and all upon charges
to which not one of the impartial jury of twelve men would give a
moment's consideration. It looks rather more like *per*secution than
*pro*secution on the part of the examining tribunals and officers. The
accused are now free, however, and are delighted at the result. Im-
prisonment has not broken their spirit in the least, and they propose
immediately organizing for another start, which will doubtless be
more successful than the first!"

Louise enclosed the newspaper cutting in a cheerful letter to her
parents. She must lessen Mémé's worries, if possible. Certainly she
must not add to them.

The wind blew hot across the divide as though a great furnace
were hidden in the mountain. It was hard for Louise to keep herself
and her child looking clean and respectable. It was hard to hold her
head high, to refuse to see the pity in the eyes of neighbors. She
would not give in to poverty and fatigue. She would not change.
Edmund must not find her altered.

The summer ended. The winter began. She would endure the cold
as she had the heat. She would manage. She had several customers
who could afford the best and paid well: Mrs. Reed, Mrs. Fair, Mrs.
Jones. Eva was almost herself again. Her face was filling out. Soon,
the doctor said, she might be able to discard her crutch. In the
spring, he thought.

Louise pushed her way against the blinding, snow-laden wind.
Beyond the icebound winter spring was waiting. On the sunny street
corners the Washoe Indians would sell their bright bunches of red
and yellow wild flowers. The tooting of the ice-cream men's horns
would be heard and their little red donkey carts would make their
daily rounds again. The winter would pass. "*Tout lasse,*" Grandmother used to say, "*tout casse, tout passe.*" This weary time, in its
turn, would end.

As she approached her customer's house she lifted her head and
fixed a smile on her cold, chapped lips. The door opened.

"Come in out of the cold, Mrs. Bryant, dear. You must be perfectly frozen." The warm Irish voice welcomed her. "We'll just have

a nice cup of tea and a little visit before we get to the trying-on."

"Thank you, Mrs. Fair." Louise smiled at her hostess. Edmund was wrong. They were ladies. Only a lady would remember to make the doctor's wife feel like a guest, not a seamstress. And Mrs. Fair was pretty. Not handsome and imposing in a regal way but warm and laughing and softly pretty as a rose. Her dark wavy hair was fine as silk. Her wide-set gray eyes were clear. Her pink cheeks were dimpled and her laugh, wholeheartedly gay, was like a child's.

The little visit before work was more comforting than the hot tea. It restored Louise's pride. Mr. Fair was very well off. He was superintendent of the Ophir mine. The wife of a newly rich man might have been what Edmund imagined, jumped-up and proud, instead of welcoming and easy. Sudden tears filled Louise's eyes.

"My dear, you're crying."

"Oh no, Mrs. Fair, not at all. It's just the hot tea after the cold." She did not say it was the courteous kindness, warming to her heart as the promise of spring in winter. She did not mind if the other knew. Perhaps someday when Edmund returned and there was not such a desperate need for pride, they would speak of it. Perhaps they would come to be friends and Louise could tell what comfort it had been on that winter day to receive kindness that had in it no chilling touch of patronage.

Chapter IX

······◆◎◆······

Poverty Hill

In the spring of 1866 Louise received news of Edmund from Father Manogue. She returned from work to find the priest standing in the lodging-house parlor.

"Your landlady said I might wait for you here, Mrs. Bryant." His face and his voice were grave.

Except when he was dealing with an evildoer, Father Manogue was usually a cheerful, easy-mannered man. Louise looked at him anxiously.

"If you'll be seated, Father."

She pulled nervously at her glove and waited for him to speak.

"I have news for you, Mrs. Bryant, hard news. Best to say it quickly. Edmund is ill."

"You're not breaking it to me gently, Father? He's not . . . he's not . . ."

"No. He's not dead but he's ill, very ill indeed. I was over to Yuba County and I got news of him in La Porte. He's lying ill near there at a place called Poverty Hill."

"How ill?"

"Pretty bad, I'm afraid."

"But there'll be time for me to get to him?"

"Yes, and with your good nursing, perhaps—no, I shouldn't say that. We Irish always have a way of trying to find hope when there is none."

"None at all, Father?"

"Very little. He's a desperately sick man."

"But of what?"

"You know how things have been with him. Even before he left here. You know of his drinking. The poor fellow, we all knew. And you must have known too . . ." The priest hesitated.

"Have known what, Father?"

"Or perhaps you didn't know, my poor child. You're very young. Even before he left Virginia he'd gone on the drugs."

"I didn't know. He was strange sometimes, but I thought it was the drink. And that wasn't his fault, Father. There are some men who can't stand drink. As for the other, I think he tried to tell me. He said a doctor had temptations. If I hadn't been so stupid, if I'd understood . . ."

"The poor fellow was tempted and him being a doctor the evil stuff was always at hand. He's far gone, the folks in La Porte tell me. In going to him you're not setting yourself an easy task. And I'm thinking you'd be better not to go alone. Your mother now might go with you, or the colonel."

"No, Father." Louise's voice was steady. "I don't want them to see him. They mustn't know. I can go alone. I'm a little acquainted in La Porte. There's Mr. Creed Haymond and—and . . ."

"You'll not want for friends. I've spoken of you to Ellen McMahon. She's a sort of connection of mine by marriage. And Father Delahunty has a brother living in La Porte. No, you'll not want for help and kindness. But have you the strength to face this with none of your own? With only strangers, however kind?"

"Edmund's my own and he wouldn't want my mother and father to know. I'll go to him and I'll nurse him and I'll save him."

"It may be. It may be he can be saved."

"At least I can save his pride for him. He deserves that. He didn't deserve to come to this. Edmund wasn't meant for this. But then he wasn't meant for this country. It's a wicked, destroying country."

"It's a hard country. Many haven't the strength for it, poor souls."

"I'll go out on the morning stage. But Eva. I wouldn't want her to see her father like this."

"She can stay with the Sisters. They'll be glad."

"And will you tell them that I've gone to join Edmund, that I'll make arrangements to bring Eva on presently? The less said, Father."

"I'll say nothing."

"Whatever the folks there know, La Porte's a little pocket off by itself."

"Don't worry, Mrs. Bryant. We won't start any talk. When there's no great buzz of talk people soon forget."

"I'd like the people of Downieville and Virginia not to know. Not ever. Edmund's been well thought of. If he recovers he can start again. And if not—if not . . ." Her throat closed. She could not finish the sentence. She held herself stiff. She clenched her hands hard. She must not let grief and fear get started or they would overwhelm her and make her useless to Edmund. She swallowed the sobs that choked her.

"I know, my child. I'll not say a word. Not ever. Not to anyone. I promise you." Father Manogue stood up. "And now, I'll just walk along with you to the stagecoach office and we'll make the arrangements for your journey. That's right. Hold yourself steady. You've a long hard way before you. To get through it you must hold yourself steady between grief and hope. Give in to neither of them. Just keep in the middle."

"Keep in the middle. That's what Sister Louisa used to say."

"Then she was a wise woman. Come along now. It's a fine evening. The bit of a walk to Wells Fargo will do us good."

"Thank you, Father. And thank you . . ." She hesitated for a moment and then continued in a rush of words, "And thank you for not talking religion and prayers. I just couldn't have stood it."

"No need to talk of religion when you're acting it. You're a good child to go bravely and unquestioningly to your poor husband. And I'll not talk about prayers either. I'll just say a few for you. Come along now. The best way with a hard road is to get started on it."

In the high Sierras the snows were not yet melted. The journey was long and hard, first by stagecoach and then on snowshoes.

Mr. Haymond and Mr. Delahunty accompanied Louise on the last part of the journey from La Porte across the mountains.

In a one-room wooden shack on the outskirts of the mining settlement of Poverty Hill, they found Edmund. The room was cold and dirty and evil-smelling.

"Louise." For a moment his eyes met hers in recognition. Then he sank back on his disordered bed.

She bent to kiss the pale face. Above the unkempt beard his cheeks were hollow. She smoothed his hair. It was lusterless and grown too long but it was still black. The beard was streaked with gray. She would hardly have recognized the gaunt stranger. In the white weary mask, only the eyes, when they had looked on her for an instant, had been Edmund. Behind the mask Edmund was lost in danger and pain. She must reach him. He must not lie alone in that darkness. "Edmund, Edmund. It's Louise, Edmund. It's Louise."

"It's no use, ma'am." An elderly woman stood in the doorway. "I live up the road a piece. I do what I can. But it's no use to call him. Sometimes he comes out of it of his own accord. Mostly he lies like that."

"It would be better," Mr. Haymond said, "to get him into La Porte. We should at least try what medical aid can do."

"There's a place all ready for you," Mr. Delahunty said. "The doctor took it, and when he disappeared into the hills it was left empty. When we thought you might be coming my wife and Mrs. McMahon fixed it up."

"But he's ill. Can't you see how ill he is?" Louise asked. "He's not fit for the journey."

"We can make a litter and get him back. He don't weigh much, the poor fellow."

"Will he stand it?"

"He won't stand much more of this. And it won't be too long a trip. That's one thing to be said for the shoes, they're quick. We travel faster in winter than in summer. We're lucky to have the last of the snow."

To Louise the journey to La Porte seemed long. She had not snowshoed since Downieville days and the long heavy staves were hard to manage.

Edmund lay on the litter like a man dead. They stopped to rest at Brandy City.

As she watched him, his eyes opened. "Remember, Louise. The little bit we had, remember that."

"I'll remember."

"I meant—I meant . . . *Facilis descensus Averno* . . . paved with my intentions." He was quiet. He did not move or speak for the rest of the journey.

Edmund lived until the twentieth of June. Under the care of the doctors he seemed to be mending. He spoke quietly with Louise of the years in Downieville. He reminisced with Creed Haymond of old days at Monte Cristo. He never spoke of the future or of the present, only of time past.

On the afternoon of the nineteenth he dressed and moved about the house. Then quite suddenly he collapsed. Louise waited through the night while the doctors worked over the bed. It was morning when someone summoned Mrs. McMahon.

Louise felt a strong arm supporting her. "You must be brave, Mrs. Bryant. It's best for him that in the end it was quick like this."

Louise rose slowly to her feet. Steady, keep quite steady; it was Father Manogue who had told her she must. She must keep steady. There was still a little more to do for Edmund. She suffered herself to be led away. She stood quietly while the kind women pinned and sewed and fashioned her mourning garments.

She waited for her father. Mr. Haymond had sent for him. He would help her with the last thing. Her father and the doctor must write a death notice that would not reveal the nature of Edmund's illness.

When Colonel Hungerford came she held herself steady in his embrace. "Father, you must see to the obituary. Mr. Haymond has arranged for the funeral. The Reverend Mr. Chivers is to preach the sermon. And many are coming from Downieville and the other towns. Edmund was much loved and respected. It must say so in the paper. You must tell them how to write it. He would want it written right. And for Eva's sake there should be a record. And for the cause of death, the doctor is willing to say that his disease was contracted some years ago while holding a post-mortem, the immediate cause of which was lockjaw. You will remember he was quite ill in the summer of '64."

"My darling, don't worry, I'll arrange everything."

"No, listen." She spoke steadily without inflection. "I told the doctor of his illness that summer and of its cause. I told him he had

repeated attacks. The doctor said his system seemed much pros-
trated and so he was unable to withstand this final attack. You understand, Father? You will have it written as Edmund would want."

"I understand, dearie, and I wish I could do more than arrange
matters with the *Mountain Messenger*. They'll write the article any
way you want it. That's easy enough. But the fact is that for the
time being . . . I understand that Edmund left some debts, poor
lad. I can contribute to their settlement, but not to any large extent."

"It's quite all right, Father. Mr. Haymond has promised to take
up a collection for his debts and for the funeral expenses. It's nothing
to be ashamed of. Edmund did much for the people of Yuba and
Sierra counties. As Mr. Haymond said, many will be glad to repay
Edmund for his past liberality and kindness."

The funeral was as Edmund would wish. Through her heavy veil
Louise could see that the church was well filled. Mr. Chivers' eulogy
was eloquent.

"Louise, dearie," her father whispered, "I'll take you now to see
him for the last time."

The church was empty except for the clergyman and three or four
gentlemen. Edmund lay in the open coffin. Mr. Chivers was waiting.
He was waiting beside the coffin to close it. The composure in which
Louise had encased herself shattered like a shell of glass. She broke
away from her father. She threw back her veil and ran to Edmund.

"No. Edmund, no." She pressed her lips to his. This cold, quiet
flesh was his. This still was he whom she loved. "Edmund, they
shan't." She tried with her hands and her lips to warm the cold life-
lessness. "We two are one," she sobbed, "one flesh. We must still be
one, both living or both dead."

It was with difficulty that Colonel Hungerford and Mr. Delahunty
managed to pull her strong young body upright. They half carried,
half led her out of the church.

Her father drew the thick crepe veil over her face. "Be brave,
dearie," he said, "there's only a little more. Be brave."

Louise did not answer. Her arms, her legs, her whole body trembled. Her head shook like a sick old woman's. She gripped her father's arm and tried to walk with him. The noonday sun beat down.
It was difficult for her to breathe through the heavy black folds. The
weight of her mourning garments was insupportable. The suffocating
heat was merciful. It saved her from enduring the ceremonies to the

end. Her father's sleeve seemed to dissolve in her grasp. Her veil seemed to grow thicker. She could not see through it. Its swirling blackness enveloped her. She fainted.

Mrs. McMahon and Mrs. Delahunty put Louise to bed, and for a day she allowed them to nurse her.

On the second morning she got up and dressed. She looked at her image in the mirror. It was quite unaltered. One would have expected a physical change, but she was young and healthy; her body could stand grief and shock. That was a good thing, she thought wearily. She would have need of all her strength. She must return to Virginia City. She was established there. She could make a living for herself and Eva. In San Francisco she would be a stranger. She and her child would be a burden to her parents. Virginia would be no harder than it had been. Grief would make the summer no hotter, the winter no colder. Grief would be the same anywhere. Without hope—that was the only difference. Now she would be without hope. The difference would not be very great. The hope had been small. She had not really believed in Edmund's return. She had hoped, knowing that hope was false. Any day, she had told herself, any day. But in a clear corner of her mind she had known that that day was as imaginary as the once upon a time of Eva's fairy tales. Now she would have to manage without fairy tales.

She told her father of her decision.

"But, dearie, your mother and I would be glad . . ."

"I know, Father." She smiled at him lovingly. He did not hear the sound of uncertainty in his own voice. "And later, when things are prospering with you and Mémé, I'll come."

"If our Mexican expedition had been successful . . ." He sighed. "It's the times, Louise. Dear knows, I've tried to get settled, but San Francisco seems no better off than Virginia. So many have returned from Washoe. So many are out of work. A man hardly knows."

"You'll think of something, Father. And in the meantime things are quite prosperous for me in Nevada. It's best for me to stay there for the present."

On the next morning she started her journey back to Virginia City. It was like that other journey three years before. The perilous trail clung to the steep edge of the forest. She held herself from looking back. Resolutely she looked ahead. Without hope one saw the future plain. With clear, dry eyes she saw the future she would make for

Eva. It would not be the golden future that first her father and then Edmund had dreamed for her. But she had never entirely believed in the dream. It was not too hard to face the reality that lay before her. Out of that reality she would make a respectable and happy life for Eva. It could be done in Virginia City. Mémé had done it in Downieville.

Chapter X

···———◆◉◆———···

The Bottom of the Wheel

WHILE LOUISE WAS in La Porte a fire had ravaged Virginia City. The wind had swept the flames in a widening path from A Street down to D. The breadth of the fire extended from Mill Street to Union. In the burned district almost nothing was left. Even buildings of stone and brick had not escaped destruction.

On her way to fetch Eva from the Sisters, Louise looked dully at the devastated area. They would build again. The mining towns had ever been built and rebuilt on ashes. Downieville had risen three times from fires worse than this. Virginia would build again. Would build? She smiled. They were rebuilding. On C Street many stores were rebuilt and open for business. The rest would follow. The California Bank Agency had offered a reward of a thousand dollars for the arrest and conviction of the incendiarists responsible for the conflagration. It must be incendiarists. It must not be the wooden buildings so easily set alight by an oil lamp or a defective stovepipe. It must not be the flimsy cloth-covered walls and ceilings. It must not be the strong wind feeding and spreading the flames. It must be incendiarists who, for a thousand dollars, could be caught and locked safely away.

On an afternoon soon after Louise's return her landlady, Mrs. Mock, knocked at her door. "You have visitors, Mrs. Bryant. It's the two Mr. Roseners and another man, a miner by the look of him. They're waiting in my parlor."

Sam Rosener stepped forward as Louise entered the room. "Mrs. Bryant, ma'am, my brother and I and John Mackay here have called to offer our sympathy."

"Thank you, gentlemen."

"We knew Dr. Bryant," Sam Rosener continued. "And we were fellow Masons. Anything we can do for his widow and his little girl . . ."

"There is something . . ." Louise hesitated.

"Anything at all. Don't be shy to ask. No need to feel ashamed." Henry Rosener smiled reassuringly at Louise. "We know your circumstances from Creed Haymond. We'd like to tide you over for as long as is necessary. John here can speak for Escurial Lodge Number Seven. The boys have got together and taken up a collection and . . ."

"No. No. I won't take charity." Louise heard the angry sharpness in her voice. She stopped herself. "Forgive me, gentlemen. I sound like a shrew and you are meaning only to be kind."

"This isn't charity, Mrs. Bryant," Sam Rosener said. "This is our plain duty to a fellow Mason."

"Please, Mr. Rosener," Louise said gently, "it is charity you are offering me. I know it is meant in all kindness but I can't accept it. You see . . . you see . . ." She held up her hand to keep them silent while she found the way to make them see that if she accepted alms from them, it would be a beginning. For her and for Eva it would be the beginning of beggary. She had seen the widows and orphans begging in the streets of Virginia. Alms, however kindly given, would place her and Eva in that lost and pitiful company.

The miner in the gray shirt broke the silence. "You were saying, ma'am, that there was something. You've only to say if there's any way at all we can help."

Louise smiled gratefully at John Mackay. It was odd, she thought, that this plain man wearing a miner's shirt and speaking with a brogue should have the same name as the successful prospector who was said to have made a fortune in the Kentuck and to be one of the coming men of the Comstock.

"Thank you. I am grateful to you for wishing to help. I'm grateful to you for holding my husband in such high esteem. And there is something that the two Mr. Roseners can do for me. Let me sew for your store. I do fine sewing and embroidery. Many ladies will tell you. Mrs. John P. Jones, Mrs. Robert Taylor . . ."

"It's a bargain, Mrs. Bryant." Sam Rosener held out his hand.

"I think you will not find it a bad bargain. Thank you."

"Good-by, ma'am. You'll be hearing from us."

Louise turned to the miner. "Thank you for coming, and will you express my thanks to the members of your lodge? I cannot take the money but I am truly grateful for the kindness which made them offer it."

The California Bank Agency's reward was not paid. The incendiaries were never discovered, but before the Fourth of July they were forgotten. C Street was almost in order again. All over the burned district new buildings were in the process of construction.

This was to be the most splendid Independence Day in Virginia's history. This was to be a glorious Fourth such as had been celebrated in California before the war. Eva pleaded to be taken to watch the parade.

"Could we, Mammy? Could we see it from the beginning to the very end?"

Louise fingered her black veil. She shouldn't be asked so soon to be part of merriment. She might be allowed to absent herself a little while longer. And not only for herself. Out of respect she shouldn't go; it wouldn't be proper for a widow in the first weeks of mourning.

"Please, Mammy. It'll be a wonderful parade with bands and decorated cars. Please."

Louise hesitated. If she refused Eva this, what else could she give her? Lee and Ryland's Circus was coming to town, but there was no money for circus tickets. They could afford the Fourth of July. It was free. Even the toll roads leading to the city were to be opened for the day.

"Of course we'll go, darling."

Early on the Fourth the booming of cannons announced the great day. It was a clear, warm summer morning. It would be a fine day for a child to remember. Small arms sounded and firecrackers exploded as Louise and Eva walked toward C Street.

The parade was a fine sight. The National Guard, the Sweeny Guard and the Emmet Guard marched behind the Metropolitan Brass Band. Then followed the fire companies and their bands. The firemen were in uniform and the engines were trimmed with flags and flowers and ribbons.

Eva exclaimed with pleasure at the blue and crimson Zouave uniforms of Carson City's Euterpe Band which led the Virginia Circle of the Fenian Company down the street. Most of all she admired the car of state. This was a large boat, mounted on wheels, and drawn by six bay horses. In it, sheltered by a canopy, was a crowd of little girls dressed in white. Each child represented a state of the Union and held in her hand a small American flag.

The procession ended with nine carriages in which rode the mayor and the board of aldermen, the invited guests, the officers of the day, the Orator, the Reader.

"There's Judge Bob Taylor, Mammy. He's going to read the Declaration. Could we go to Fort Homestead to hear him? The omnibus goes almost all the way."

"No, darling, we'd never even get inside the hall. We'd have had to go early to get places. It was better to see the parade and tonight you shall see the fireworks."

The fine day clouded over. In the afternoon a heavy rain fell. Louise and Eva escaped the storm but from the windows of the lodging house they watched the downpour anxiously. If this continued, there would be no fireworks.

The landlady returned, drenched, from the celebration. "Were you wise, Mrs. Bryant, not to go to Fort Homestead!" she exclaimed. "Look at me—a sight! But my bonnet you trimmed so nice for me I saved. I wrapped it in newspaper and held it under my cloak. You missed nothing. Poor Mr. Fitch had to stop in the middle of his oration. He couldn't make himself heard above the storm. And the little girls in the car of state—they were soaked to the skin. The men in charge had no more sense than to leave them in the car in the rain—as if that flimsy canopy was any good. Men!"

"And the fireworks, Mrs. Mock?" Eva asked. "Will the rain have soaked the fireworks?"

"No, love. The men will have seen to it that the fireworks are dry. If the rain stops you'll see a fine sight from my parlor window."

In the evening the rain ceased except for an occasional light sprinkle.

Mrs. Mock drew Eva's chair close to the window. "A cloudy sky is good. You'll see the fireworks all the better against the dark. Now you sit here and we'll have a regular little party." She placed a pitcher of lemonade and a plate of cakes on a table between Louise and Eva.

The first rockets streaked the black sky. "You too, Mrs. Bryant." Mrs. Mock pushed Louise's chair nearer the window. "For you a little party is good too. So enjoy, enjoy."

The whole city seemed ablaze with rockets and Roman candles, with Bengolas, with blue and red lights. From public buildings and from private dwellings the lights rushed upward and fell in showers of colored stars. Here and there a bonfire blazed. Guns were fired and crackers, big and little, exploded. Somewhere in the distance a brass band played "Hail Columbia," and "John Brown's Body," and "We'll Go with Grant Again."

The lemonade was cold and sweet. The little cakes were rich and spicy.

Louise put her hand on her landlady's. "You're kind to us, so kind."

"Who's kind? It's a pleasure. You trimmed my bonnet and that was kindness."

"It's so little."

"It's little enough any of us can do in these times. And the little is a pleasure for me as for you. Now we must keep a little quiet. For Eva this is the theater—better than Maguire's. Let the child enjoy."

Mrs. Mock was right. Let the child enjoy. Let her have this bright day and evening complete to enjoy and remember.

After the glorious Fourth there was little pleasure to remember. Louise thought of the *Enterprise's* prophecy that the wheel would turn and rise again. The optimistic editor had been wrong. Her father had been right. The wheel of Virginia's fortune was stuck for good. It seemed as though time stood still.

Louise sewed for the Rosener brothers. She sewed for the ladies. By the time Eva was grown the stitches would be measured in miles. And somehow, someday there would be money to pay a great doctor to cure her lameness. From her wages she saved a little almost every week. It was better for Eva to do without the small pleasures so that someday she might be healed.

Through Father Manogue, Louise was able to earn a little extra money by giving piano lessons at St. Mary's School.

"You'd be doing the little ones a kindness, Mrs. Bryant. The Sisters of Charity can't afford to pay much."

"I'm not worth very much, Father, but I'll try."

Louise knew only a little more than her pupils. She went early in the morning to St. Mary's. Before her first pupil came to her she sat at the piano and practiced for the lesson she was about to give. It took all her meager skill to keep even a step ahead of the children. She rested her aching fingers and looked at the neat little basement room. It was a clean and peaceful place. The quiet reminded her of Benicia. She pressed her lips firmly together and held her hands over the keyboard. "So," Sister used to say, "the wrist arched and each finger strong and steady."

"So," Louise taught the children, "the wrist arched and each finger strong and steady."

On Christmas Eve Louise walked slowly home. The stores were decorated with sweet-smelling evergreens. In every window there was a rich assortment of Christmas goods. Ladies' dresses in one window and in the next a splendid gold watch and chain, earrings, bracelets, necklaces, and finger rings. In the butcher shops were tempting displays of fine fat beef, of venison, of fresh pork. At the Union Market and the National the meats were handsomely trimmed with ribbons and rosettes and Christmas greens.

Louise stopped opposite Wells Fargo on C Street to look into the windows of Dale and Company. They had a beautiful collection of toys of every kind and of musical instruments from penny whistles to a big bass drum. In her purse was the money earned by two weeks of music lessons. In the window was the blue-eyed wax doll of Eva's dreams. Louise held her purse tight shut against temptation.

"Your servant, ma'am. As you see they've let this unreconstructed rebel out of jail for the Yuletide—not much of a Christmas present to turn me out to find my own bed and board."

Old Pike was standing beside her, Old Pike, the half-witted vagrant who preferred jail to freedom. He walked into the station house as gaily as to a wedding. While he worked on the city streets in the chain gang, he sang in a high cracked voice.

Today he carried a small broom made of twigs. "I'm the last of the broom sagers, ma'am, a McClellan man, but not a secesh, not a true secesh. Remember our campaign songs, ma'am?" His sour beery breath blew against her face as he sang:

> *"Huzzah! for brave McClellan!*
> *Huzzah! for Pendleton!*
> *Disunion's hosts lie bleeding,*
> *The glorious field is won.*
> *Beast Butler lies a fugitive*
> *Upon a foreign shore,*
> *Black Stanton hurls his edicts*
> *From his bloodstained throne no more;*
> *Mr. Greeley leaves the Tribune,*
> *'Abe' split rails with a knife,*
> *Fremont seeks 'Mariposa'*
> *And Bill Seward private life."*

As Louise stepped backward, he followed her. "Don't go, ma'am. I'll sing you another: a ballad of my own devising, of how in a duel brave Judge Terry slew blackhearted Irish Broderick."

Louise felt in her purse. A ten-cent piece was the smallest coin she had, but she must give him something. She must escape the vacant face, the ragged, evil-smelling presence. She held out the coin.

Old Pike reached out a dirty hand and paused. "No, ma'am." His hand dropped. "No, I can't take it from a poor widow woman. They didn't call us the chivalry for nothing. We're gentlemen." He lifted his hand to his bare head and swept an invisible hat to his breast and bowed low. Louise turned and ran into the store.

A poor widow woman, the old man had called her. The poor Widow Bryant could become a character known to Virginia and pitied, not filthy like Old Pike and the poor drab, Mrs. Ramsheart, not mad like them, but a pitiable figure thought to be a little touched. "Saves every penny she can," they would say, "on account of the child, you know."

"How much is it?" Louise pointed to the wax doll. It would take everything in her purse to pay the price. She hesitated. Then she slowly held out the money.

It was better that Eva should have a little pleasure now. Eva must be more than the crippled child of a widowed mother. She should have her new doll for Christmas and tonight they would go to midnight Mass. It would be late for a child, but the beauty of the service would make up for the drab months. For Eva's sake Louise must find a way to relieve, with gaiety and color, the gray drudgery.

Louise touched her black cloak protectingly. No one could ask her to put off her weeds so soon, but she knew that her black-clad figure was a mournful sight for a child. Two years would be a long time for a child to live with mourning. Next summer when the first year was up, she should, for Eva's sake, put away her black garments. Even now, at the half year, she should discard the heavy crepe. A pretty, cheerful mother would be better for Eva than the forlorn Widow Bryant. Eva's body might never be entirely healed, but her spirit must be kept whole. It must not be crippled by living with the outward and visible signs of sorrow and anxiety.

St. Mary's bell rang three times to announce the Mass: at half past eleven, at a quarter before twelve, and at midnight. Before the second ringing of the bell Louise and Eva were in their places in Mrs. Fair's pew.

The church was filled to the doors. It was bright almost as noonday with the light of many candles. The statue of the Blessed Virgin at the gospel side of the altar was brilliantly illuminated. Suspended overhead was a huge cross of evergreens. In the warm candlelight the boughs were fragrant and vividly green. A tall row of burning candles was suspended above the choir behind the altar.

At midnight Father Manogue entered with the altar boys dressed in white. The church, quiet until now, was filled with music. To the accompaniment of the Metropolitan Brass Band, the choir sang the *Admiramus Deum.* On the altar the flames of the candles were reflected in the magnificent gold and silver vessels. The incense rose and mingled with the scent of pine.

"'And it came to pass that in those days there went out a decree from Caesar Augustus that the whole world should be enrolled . . .'"

The congregation stood motionless as Father Manogue read from the pulpit the Gospel according to St. Luke.

Louise looked up at the statue of the Blessed Virgin. "Please," she prayed silently, "please ask Our Lord to cure Eva. You know a girl minds lameness more than a boy. It's harder for a girl. And until she's cured or if . . . or if . . . help her not to mind. Make it all right for her somehow."

The voices rose in song again. The brass band blared. In the air the incense was heavier. Louise looked at Eva. The child was not praying at all. She was enjoying the singing and the band and the rich array of lights. Louise glanced at the statue. In the candlelight it seemed alive. Well, if Mary were here herself she wouldn't mind Eva's cheerful enjoyment of the solemn ritual. She wouldn't mind at all. She would be glad to have her church make up to a little girl for the treats she had missed. Louise had not been able to afford the Panorama or the matinees at Maguire's. Our Lady, she thought, would surely be glad for the child to have a good time at St. Mary's.

It was two o'clock in the morning when Mass was over. Eva's eyes were heavy with sleep. Her cheeks were flushed from the warmth of the crowded church. Her lips curved in a contented smile.

"Merry Christmas," Mrs. Fair whispered. "Let me drive you home, Mrs. Bryant dear. It's too far entirely and too cold for the little one to walk."

In the carriage Eva slept. The women smiled down at her.

"It's their day, Christmas," Mrs. Fair said. "Bring her to dinner with us. It'll be only ourselves and a poor lonesome bachelor friend of Mr. Fair's, that's all."

"Why, I . . . thank you, but . . ."

"There's no but about it at all," Mrs. Fair said firmly. "The both of you'll come and make a happier day for all of us. It's no Christmas without a child at table and young Jim's in bed with a heavy cold."

Eva slept late in the morning. Louise did not wake her until it was time to dress for dinner at the Fairs'. When she was ready Eva took her two dolls to Mrs. Mock.

"Will you mind my children for me, Mrs. Mock?" She touched the wax cheek, the golden ringlets. It was hard to surrender so new and beautiful a treasure. Then she caressed the old doll with equal tenderness. "You must be nice to them both, Mrs. Mock, and not let the old one know how much more pretty the new one is."

"I'll take good care of both." Mrs. Mock looked approvingly at her lodger. "You look nice, Mrs. Bryant. I noticed last night, if you'll pardon my mentioning." She touched the brim of Louise's bonnet. "Much better without the veil. For the little one and for you, too, it's much better. And I have a Christmas gift for you."

"But, Mrs. Mock, I didn't expect . . . You shouldn't."

"And who has the better right? Didn't you fix my old dress from the Bay good as new so I could wear it to the Sisterhood's Hanukkah supper? Now for your holiday I have something. Look, you'll like it." Mrs. Mock opened a box and held out a necklace of sparkling jet. "Don't worry, only the box is new. I didn't spend money. I had this already for a long time. And jet you could wear. It would only brighten your mourning a little."

Louise caressed the beads. "You shouldn't. I shouldn't . . ."

"Come put it on. Going to those rich Fairs, better you should look nice and hold your head high."

"Mrs. Fair isn't like that. She's not proud."

"The rich are always proud. And why not? They know they've made the riffle. To wear a little piece jewelry wouldn't hurt you in their eyes."

Louise clasped the jet around her neck. She ran to the mirror. "Oh, it does look nice! Thank you, Mrs. Mock. You are good to me. Come, Eva, we mustn't be late." She took her new gloves from the tissue paper in which she had kept them until the last moment. "See how fashionable I am, Mrs. Mock, with both my Christmas presents, the gloves from Mémé and the necklace from you."

"Wear them in good health, my dear."

Her new necklace gave Louise confidence. She held her head high as she greeted Mr. Fair. Mrs. Fair, she knew, had not meant her invitation in the spirit of charity, but of Mr. Fair's friendliness she was less sure. He was a heavy-set, black-bearded, handsome man. He was dressed with care and moved in an expensive aroma of cigar smoke and pomade. He had, as Mrs. Mock said, as he would say himself, made the riffle. Louise thought he might have little patience with those who were less strong, less lucky.

He held out both hands in welcome. His dark eyes were bold and admiring. "A Merry Christmas to you, Mrs. Bryant. You're looking very well on this festive day. And so is this little lady." He lifted Eva in a bear hug and set her down.

Louise smiled. A woman need not be successful. Mr. Fair required only that she be pretty and agreeable. She touched her necklace. Still, she thought, in gratitude to Mrs. Mock, a little piece of jewelry didn't hurt.

"Glad you're with us, ma'am," Jim Fair continued. "I know your father. A good man, the captain, colonel I should say, but more cut out for soldiering than mining. And that's only to his credit, eh, John? You've met John Mackay? Heard of him anyway, I'll be bound."

"I . . . I have had the pleasure." Louise looked in amazement at the grave, fair-haired man. John Mackay who was known to all Virginia City was the gray-shirted miner who had called on her with Sam and Henry Rosener. He certainly hadn't the appearance of a millionaire.

As she talked to Mrs. Fair, Louise watched John Mackay. He made no attempt to interrupt the ladies' chatter. He did not seem to hear it as he sat silent and withdrawn, untouched by the merriment suitable to the day. He hadn't the quick easy charm of most Irishmen, Louise decided. Jim Fair had it to his finger tips. He was a handsomer, warmer man altogether than Mackay. Theresa Fair was a lucky woman with her rich, good-looking husband and her fine house. Lace curtains hung at the parlor windows and the chairs and sofa were richly upholstered. The Turkey carpet was thick underfoot.

Eva left her mother and limped across the room. Louise watched her. "See how at home the child is, Mrs. Fair. Usually she doesn't leave my side."

"Come to say how-de-do to me, have you, my dear?" John Mackay held out his hand to Eva. He lifted her carefully onto his knee. "Come and sit with me."

As he talked with the child, his gravity relaxed. They laughed together. She reached up her hand and stroked his long blond mustache.

"I like you," she said.

"John's the sly one," Jim Fair said. "To look at him first, you'd be taking him for a dour man, but he always gets off with the prettiest girl in the room."

He offered one arm to his wife and the other to Louise and led them into the dining room. John Mackay and Eva followed hand in hand.

Louise looked admiringly at the table handsomely set with matching china and glass and with an abundance of solid-silver implements. She unfolded her napkin and felt the smooth surface. It was real satin damask.

The food was plentiful and good. This must be, Louise thought, the very cut of beef which she had most admired in the National Market. She looked across the table at Eva. The child was puzzled by the choice of silver before her.

"Let me give you a hand, Eva." John Mackay cut her meat for her and put her knife and fork on her plate. "That was quite a big helping Jim gave you."

Louise enjoyed her food. She enjoyed listening again to hearty masculine voices. They were cheerful voices, warmly Irish in intonation and pronunciation. John Mackay's brogue was the stronger of the two. Louise liked the sound of it. It reminded her of Father Dalton, of Mr. Galloway. Mrs. Fair spoke like Mrs. Galloway, the first lady of Downieville. Her soft intonation, the way she turned a phrase, reflected the accent of her Irish-born parents. So Mémé's speech reflected the French and Spanish of her childhood. They were pretty, Louise thought, these American voices that still held the echo of another time and place.

When the long meal ended the daylight had gone. Mrs. Fair lit the lamps. "I wish they'd bring the gas to us. As you see we're ready for it. The gasolier and the wall brackets are just awaiting the pleasure of the gas company."

The brightly papered room was warm in the soft light. The smoke of Mr. Fair's cigar mingled with the smell of food and wine. Louise breathed deeply. The fragrance of luxury was pleasant in her nostrils. She did not want to leave the comfort and ease of the Fair house but she must not outstay her welcome. She could live the day over as she told every detail to Mrs. Mock.

Mrs. Mock was an eager audience. She listened with rich enjoyment.

"And then they sent us home in their carriage. I was grateful for Eva not to have the long cold walk. And glad for me too." Louise laughed with remembered pleasure. "A private carriage has long been my ideal."

"And was it Mr. Fair himself who brought you? I heard a man's voice."

"No, it was John Mackay. He offered to accompany us."

"That's nice." Mrs. Mock sighed with satisfaction. "He's a coming man in Virginia. He's not married and he's of an age to think of settling down. Well past thirty he must be."

"He's thirty-five, Mrs. Fair said, but he was Eva's conquest, not mine, Mrs. Mock."

"That was clever of him. I heard always he was a clever man."

"No, not clever, kind. With Eva I mean. You could see the kindness in his face and in the way he was with her."

Louise remembered the gentleness and consideration with which the man had assisted the child down the steep steps of the Fairs' porch and into the carriage. He had helped her lameness without emphasizing it.

"He's kind," Louise repeated. "Not so handsome as Mr. Fair, though his features are finer and he's taller. But he hasn't the warm, taking way."

"Taking is right, if all they say of Jim Fair is true."

Louise smiled.

"He was good to Eva and I was grateful. She is ever a little shy."

"And it was smart of him to make friends with her. He's a smart man and a good one. Listen, I'm telling you, you could go further and fare worse."

Louise did not resent the matchmaking gleam in Mrs. Mock's eye. She had seen it often enough in Mémé's. Mémé took credit for several Downieville marriages.

"I fancy many a cap in Virginia is set for Mr. Mackay, Mrs. Mock."

"And why not yours? You're young, you're pretty. And already he likes the little girl."

Louise shook her head. "You have to care to win that sort of a race and I can't care for anyone." She stood up. "I'll put Eva to bed. She's tired and she'll need no supper after that enormous meal."

When Eva was in bed Louise stood before her mirror. She unclasped her necklace. She had done more than lighten her mourning. She had, for a few hours, forgotten it.

She picked up the frame that held Edmund's photograph. She touched the glass that protected it. She set it gently down again and looked in the mirror. Edmund would have been pleased to see her admired, to see her hold her own with the rich and successful. Her young, rosy-cheeked reflection smiled at her. She remembered Jim Fair's flattering voice and eyes. She laughed. She could recognize blarney when she heard it but she had enjoyed it.

She walked quietly to Eva's bed. The child was asleep. Louise blessed Theresa Fair for sharing her Christmas feast. It had been a good day. The memory of it would lighten days to come.

She put her lips softly against Eva's cheek. "Don't you worry," she whispered, "we're going to manage. I've got my courage back and we're going to manage just fine."

Chapter XI

...➤◉◆—...

A Quiet Courtship

THE STORMS IN January of 1867 were the worst Louise had experienced in Virginia. It was dangerous to walk abroad. Windows were blown in, signs and awnings were swept from buildings. Sometimes a roof or even an entire frame structure was blown away. The air was filled with dirty, heavy debris. Pieces of canvas, tin, and wood whirled overhead in the strong wind.

On the twenty-first of the month an icy storm of rain and sleet was raging as Louise climbed from the ankle-deep mud of the street to the porch of the Fair house.

"Come in, Mrs. Bryant." It took all Jim Fair's strength to hold the door open for her entrance. "Not that you'll escape the wind indoors. Look at that, will you?"

On the cloth-covered walls the paper bulged, the ornately framed pictures swayed.

"The womenfolk will cover the cloth with wallpaper à la fancy and all looks solid till a real Washoe zephyr gets to blowing between the wooden boards of the outer wall. Hear how it howls outside and whispers within." As he took Louise's wet cloak, they listened to the rustling of paper against cloth, of cloth against wood. "Eerie sound, isn't it?" he asked. "You'd swear the place is haunted. Trouble with us is we build too fast and too often. Maybe someday we'll get a chance to build properly between fires—even to plaster our walls."

Louise held out her parcel. "I promised Mrs. Fair her dress for today. I hope I'm not too late."

"Let me relieve you of that." He put the package on a chair. "She'll not be needing it till we go to the opera house. Next week sometime. Mayor Piper's doing great things with it since he took over the management. Soon you won't know the place, cushioned seats, new scenery. Gas lighting to be installed. No, this evening we're to be home and you're to stay and have supper with us."

"I can't. Thank you for your kindness, but I can't. Look at me." Louise's boots and her skirt were mudstained.

"Theresa will lend you something. She intends for you to stay. She promised John Mackay you'd be here."

Louise had seen John Mackay twice since Christmas Day. Twice when she had been with Mrs. Fair he had come in.

"You don't seem as eager as he is." Jim Fair laughed. "Oh, he's eager all right, but I'm the only one would ever know it. John has the face to play cards, not to flatter a woman. And you give him no encouragement. You should have stayed when he came calling at an hour of the day when obviously he was looking to find the ladies. A clever woman like you should have lingered a little."

"You're kind, Mr. Fair, and I know you mean to be flattering, but I'm not interested in gentlemen. It wouldn't be fitting." She touched her black dress. "Even if I had the heart for it, which I haven't."

"Never mind your heart now. I'm speaking of your head. And your mourning, that's another thing, my dear. Doff your black. You've worn it long enough. Don't frown at me. It's not becoming and those black brows don't frighten me. You're a smart woman. I'm a smart man and I can recognize brains even behind as pretty a face as yours. You're a clever, determined woman. You'd never have lasted in Virginia else. Washoe's no place for weaklings. If you'd been a man you might have gone far. But you're not and you need a man, a smart man and a strong one, to take you the rest of the way."

"Please, Mr. Fair."

"No, you listen to me. Oh, Theresa'll talk to you. If it isn't tonight it'll be tomorrow. She has the matchmaking bee in her bonnet, like all women. Poor John so lonely and little Mrs. Bryant so pretty and so brave. I see more than that. John is lonely. It's a wonder he hasn't married some fool woman before this. I don't want him to marry a pretty fool. You're no fool. You'd be a help to John. And he to you. He much more to you. He can manage without a woman, and could even manage with a silly one. Plenty of those after him. But you're the silliest of the lot if you don't see this is your chance."

"I thank you." Louise kept her voice low and polite. "I am indeed grateful for your interest because I know you mean it in kindness. But I am not interested."

"Spoken with dignity, my dear. You may even think you mean it. I mean what I'm saying and that's a luxury I don't often indulge myself in. But I'm being straight with you. You've done all a woman can do alone. You've made a nice respectable little living for yourself and your daughter. But come, Mrs. Bryant, that's not living. You want better than that. You want it for your child and you want it for yourself. Well, go and get it. Put off your weeds, set your cap for John Mackay, and get the life you want."

"Even though this is all meant in kindness, Mr. Fair . . ."

"You don't trust my kindness. Not many in Virginia trust Jim Fair. But John can and so can you. On his account, so can you. I've decided you'll do. I'm not often wrong in my judgment. That's how I got where I am from Angels Camp. Now run up to Theresa and borrow something pretty to wear to supper. No black, mind."

"I'd like to stay and I can hardly appear like this." She looked ruefully at her dress.

"That's a sensible woman. And, so you can trust me, understand me. I care about Fair and Mackay. I think you'd add strength to the combination. We're going to own Virginia before we're through and you're going to help us."

"Is that you, Mrs. Bryant?" Mrs. Fair called from the head of the stairs. "Come up to me. You must be drenched entirely."

Mrs. Fair lent Louise a black dress. It was trimmed in deep red.

"You won't mind wearing it because of the little touches of color? It'll only be ourselves and John Mackay."

"Indeed you're kind to lend me the dress and slippers."

"The touch of ruby sets off your coloring." Mrs. Fair straightened the velvet bow at Louise's throat. "You know, Mrs. Bryant, I've been wanting to say this. For Eva's sake you should discard your black."

"I mean to when the year is up."

"But to buy all new in the summer would be an extravagance."

"I don't buy much in any season."

"The more reason why any little thing you get from now on should be in color. And to start you off I have the very thing."

From the wardrobe Mrs. Fair took a bolt of violet satin.

"I've no earthly use for it. Jim hates the color on me. But on you" —Mrs. Fair held the shining folds against Louise—"it's perfect. And you'd be doing me a favor to take the stuff off my hands."

Louise stroked the rich satin. It was a long time since she had had a pretty dress. She had never had one of such handsome material. "You are very kind. Perhaps for Easter. After all, violet is half mourning."

"That's right. It won't be so hard if you do it by easy stages. And do it you must, for Eva's sake if not for your own. You must, for the child's sake, begin to think of making a new life."

When the ladies went downstairs they found John Mackay with Jim Fair.

"Well, John"—Mrs. Fair held out her hand—"you're looking rather sober. Never mind, here are little Mrs. Bryant and me to cheer you up."

"On such a day a man can do with a bit of cheer, eh, John?" Jim Fair asked. "Worst storm we've had in a long time. The zephyr blew the roof clean off Pioneer and Overland's stables. This is no weather for man or beast."

"I'm glad no longer to be out in it." John Mackay took a chair beside Louise.

"Don't tell me you were out gallivanting!" Mrs. Fair exclaimed. "And me telling Mrs. Bryant how you work from dawn to dark. Where were you? With a lovely lady? Tell us, John."

"If you must know I was at Julia Bulette's funeral."

"John!" Mrs. Fair's taffeta sleeves rustled as she gestured indignantly. "Even you cannot take such a liberty. To mention that woman in my house."

"She's d-d-dead now." John Mackay flushed. His words came with a stammer. "Surely the d-dead can be given their d-due."

"John's angry." Jim Fair laughed. "Your stutter always gives you away. But the ladies are the ones to be angry. Theresa's right. Dead or not, the harlot's name shouldn't be mentioned in a respectable house."

"She m-may have been a harlot, Jim, but she was a h-hell of a f-f-fine woman. And well we know it who come out here in the early days."

"John, you shock the ladies. You've shocked them into silence. Spare them your tender reminiscences."

"I'm not t-talking about her t-trade, I'm t-talking about her everlasting kindness to the poor and the sick. The Reverend Martin spoke of it at the funeral. And glad I was to hear him and to see how many turned out for the services. And proud I was of the boys in Virginia Company Number 1 giving their enginehouse for the funeral. L-let her rest in peace in Flowery Hill. Her good or bad traits alike lie buried with her. Not that she'd thank us to remember her dead. She'd like better to be remembered in her sable cape and her scarlet silk dress with stockings to match, and coral drops in her ears and a fine gold pin at her breast."

"You seem to remember the creature very distinctly," Mrs. Fair said severely.

"I remember her well, Theresa. I remember her nursing the m-miners in the epidemics that plagued us in the early days in Washoe. P-P-Pat M-Manogue could tell you. They worked side by side with the sick and the dying."

What sort of man was this, Louise wondered, whose sternness could be melted by a child or a whore? Who could forget his gravity to laugh with Eva and could wax eloquent over Julia Bulette? Pity. That was probably the answer, she thought. If one were strong enough and safe enough one could afford to feel pity instead of fear and disgust for the Julia Bulettes and for such creatures as Old Pike or Mrs. Ramsheart.

"Poor creature," she murmured.

"You're good, ma'am." John Mackay smiled at her. He was truly handsome when he smiled, she decided. "It's good you are to pity her."

"I wasn't thinking of Julia Bulette. I've seen her. She always seemed bold and handsome and well content with her lot to me. And her hideous murder was too awful for pity. Strangled in her bed for the jewels and the furs she wore so brazenly. One feels horror."

"But your kind heart still spoke pityingly."

"My heart's not as kind as all that, Mr. Mackay. No hard-working woman can ever feel much kindness for the Julia Bulettes. I was thinking of Mrs. Ramsheart. Her madness excuses her sins. Her mind and her spirit were broken by misfortune. One can pity her."

"Mrs. Bryant, I think you and John Mackay have both gone daft," Mrs. Fair said. "Mrs. Ramsheart was a poor drab and Julia Bulette a rich one. Wicked women the both of them, mad or sane."

"And both dead," John Mackay said gently. "One can afford to pity both, don't you think, Theresa?"

"I suppose so, but not at my table. The girl's ready for us in the dining room and I want no more of this talk. Let them rest in peace at Flowery Hill and at Lone Mountain but not at my dinner table."

Louise did not wish to give Mrs. Mock an account of her evening. She tiptoed past her landlady's door. She had had enough of dear Mrs. Bryant and poor Mrs. Bryant. She had had enough of kindness.

She moved quietly in her room not to waken Eva. She took off Mrs. Fair's dress and hung it up with care. She was sick of depending on kindness. Such kindness was dangerously close to charity, to pity. If John Mackay could be caught by pity, she would have none of him, though he were her only chance to escape from a lifetime of drudgery.

She smoothed the dress. She touched the soft ruby-red velvet bowknots. She was sick of shabby, made-over dresses. She was sick of poverty, sick of its airless ugly rooms and its greasy ill-cooked food. She was sick of the respectable edge of failure. She was sick of the poor Widow Bryant who for all her pride was only a small cut above the penniless miners' widows who begged their way through the streets of Virginia City.

She looked down at Eva. "For your little girl's sake," they said, "and for your own, poor Mrs. Bryant dear. You're young, you're pretty."

Louise studied her reflection. They had spoken true. She was young and pretty. There was no sin in ambition. In a man it was counted a virtue and a woman could achieve only through a man. How odd, she thought, if John Mackay should be the one to take her the rest of the way on the road that first her father and then Edmund had promised her, the long road that had led from Grand Street to Downieville and from Downieville to Virginia.

She remembered Jim Fair's words. "That's not living. You want

better than that. You want it for your child and you want it for
yourself."

He had seen the truth and spoken it. She wanted an easier life
for herself as well as for Eva.

She picked up her brush and began vigorously to brush her hair.
A cap, she thought, would set better on well-kept, shining curls.

That winter in Virginia the snow lay thick. The icy winds blew
from Mount Davidson. Louise worked long and hard but when she
went out to sew she forgot her drudgery in listening to the ladies
talk.

Not since the first prosperous year had Louise interested herself
in the finances of the Comstock. The fortunes made and lost, the
stocks rising and falling, were no concern of hers. She had clung to
her rung at the bottom of the ladder, desperately intent on main-
taining her precarious hold. Now she raised her head and looked
and listened. The ladies quoted their husbands. They spoke knowl-
edgeably of the hierarchy of Virginia City. When they mentioned
William Sharon their voices changed. In every community there is
a royal name that cannot be pronounced with a natural inflection.
In Virginia City in 1867 that name was William Sharon. Sharon was
the agent for the Bank of California. The bank controlled most of the
leading stocks. It was buying up the mills on which the mineowners depended. The bank pretty well controlled the Comstock,
the husbands told the ladies. In the end it would own the lode and
the city entirely. In Virginia, Sharon was the bank. Sharon, the soft-
spoken little man, was king. He had been a merchant and a real-
estate operator. He had made a fortune and lost it all in San
Francisco in Comstock mining stocks. The Comstock had ruined him
in '64. Now he ruled the city which had so nearly destroyed him. He
ruled a kingdom for which they said he had little love, but he did
not mean to abdicate nor to share his throne.

Could Mackay and Fair become the equals of Sharon? Louise listened and wondered.

Mr. Sharon laughed at the Irishmen, the ladies said. If Mackay
got too big for his boots, Mr. Sharon vowed he would make him
pack his blankets out of Virginia City back across the mountains.
Mackay had made a nice little fortune out of the Kentuck; let him
be satisfied with that. He and Fair were competent mine superintendents; let them be satisfied with the job for which they were fit-

ted. The stocks of the Comstock could and would be managed and manipulated and owned by bankers, not by ignorant miners.

Louise listened to the light feminine voices as they repeated Sharon's judgment of the Irishmen. Mackay and Fair were not, she thought, men easily satisfied. Nor easily tired and discouraged. John Mackay had come from California in the first rush to Washoe. Many of the firstcomers, after an early dazzling success, had been ruined. Now they were forgotten. Only their names were left: Comstock and Gould and Curry and James Finney, called Old Virginny. John Mackay had risen slowly through the hard years. Now that he had joined forces with Jim Fair he meant to rise more swiftly. Could Sharon prevent it?

"Pack his blankets back across the mountains." The light voice laughed. "My dear, they say poor Mackay was furious. But of course he can't afford to quarrel with Mr. Sharon. Not that anyone would wish to. He's such a splendid, high type of man. A gentleman, too, and that means much. My husband says the Bank of California will be the saving of Nevada."

Louise, with her mouth full of pins, knelt as she shortened the hem of the talkative lady's dress. Drive John Mackay back across the mountains? Louise thought not. She shook her head as she pinned the silk slowly and carefully. John Mackay had learned strength and patience from those very mountains. For over seven years he had labored as a miner on the Yuba. He had gained experience that was not to be had in a countinghouse; and in Virginia he had earned as a miner a knowledge of the lode that was not to be learned from the stockbrokers' boards. He would not be an easy man to defeat or to discourage. California and Nevada had schooled him well in patience and endurance.

As she walked home Louise remembered the Downieville days. There, too, the winter darkness fell early on the town. She remembered the miners coming in from the diggings. She wondered if she had ever seen John Mackay in California. She could not remember. All the bearded, flannel-shirted miners had looked alike to her.

The Reverend Mr. Pond remembered John Mackay. The minister called on Louise when he visited Virginia City. "I promised the colonel I'd see how things were with you, Mamie."

"Things are fine, thank you, Reverend. I'm making out nicely. Many of our old Downieville friends are here. I have met with much kindness and consideration. Father Manogue has helped me to find work. Did you ever know him in the old days?"

"Yes. Yes, I knew Pat Manogue on the Yuba. Met up with him just before he went back to St. Sulpice to finish his education for the priesthood. The diggings gave him a better training than any seminary could offer. The miners swear by him. One of their own, he is."

"Father Manogue has been most kind to me," Louise said. "Through him, many ladies have given me work. Mrs. Jones, Mrs. Fair—did you ever know Jim Fair in the old days?"

"No, but I knew John Mackay. One of Father Delahunty's flock, he was by rights. But he was something of a freethinker. We were friendly. I used to see him at the Forest City Masonic Lodge."

"All the same Mr. Mackay is a good Catholic, Reverend Pond. He has contributed generously to St. Mary's. Father Manogue told me . . ."

"I don't doubt that he would give Manogue anything he asked for. And Mackay's an Irishman. He'd fight any man who had a word to say against the Roman Church. Still he's a freer thinker than most. He's a member of Escurial Lodge Number 7 in Virginia."

"But in the diggings, Reverend, many Catholics have joined the Masons."

"Sure they have, Mamie. And I don't believe Pat Manogue would hold it too great a sin. The miners are lonely men. In the California diggings and in Washoe the lodges have been a comfort to them."

"It's strange to think that many of our leading men in Virginia were but four-dollar-a-day miners in Sierra County. You must have known many, Reverend."

"Quite a few, but not many like John Mackay. He was a quiet man. Not one of your rowdies."

"And he's a strong man, Reverend."

"You're right there, Mamie. Lucky, some say, when they speak of Jones and Hearst and Fair and Mackay and the rest, but I say they earned their luck by enduring the hard times. It's in the hard times they've risen. And mark my words they'll rise higher. When Jack O'Brien and John Mackay came to Washoe they hadn't a dollar between them. All the wealth either had was his miner's tools and a blanket packed on his back. I mind too they tell a story of George Hearst." He paused and smiled. "But I think you would rather hear more about John Mackay."

Louise felt her cheeks burn. "He has shown me a little courtesy when we have met at the Fairs', but that's really all, Reverend, except that he's taken quite a fancy to Eva. He has a miner's heart in that. They were ever kind to us when we were children. I remember that Louise Althea and I never needed to be afraid of the roughest of them."

"Have you heard the news about Louise Althea?" the minister asked. "They say she'll likely marry Bob Howland, him that was warden of the state prison. It's a romantic story as they tell it. He was injured in a shooting accident at Emanuel's ranch at Carson. He lay near death for weeks. Louise and her mother nursed him back to life and health."

"I'm happy for her luck."

"As all would be happy for yours, my dear child. You deserve a little luck."

In that winter Louise came to know John Mackay. He spoke sometimes of his boyhood in Dublin and of his mother.

"It was a hard life. I know now how hard it must have been. We were poor as the poorest in this country are not, but I don't remember it as hard, she made it all seem so easy. So natural-like. I was little use to her, though she didn't let me know that either at the time. I was near fourteen before I did a proper man's work. In New York we were by then and my father dead. And at that I didn't bring in much, but she made me feel proud, never ashamed. Never ashamed at all."

His brogue grew deeper when he spoke of his mother as though he were back with her in his Irish childhood. He spoke with affectionate admiration of Theresa Fair. "Jim's the lucky man to have such a fine woman. But then he's a lucky man altogether. And so am I. Me and Fair have both done well. And I think we'll likely do better now that we've teamed up. Me and Fair." His voice was warm as he spoke of the partnership. A partnership with John Mackay, Louise thought, would be long enduring. A woman could depend on such a partnership. A woman would be lucky. . . .

Very few were aware that John Mackay was courting Louise Bryant. It was a quiet courtship. Slow and quiet as the Irishman's speech. Louise was not entirely sure of him but by the springtime she thought it probable that if he were what she wanted, he could, with a little judicious encouragement, be hers.

On a mild sunny afternoon in May John Mackay called for Louise and Eva. The child exclaimed with delight when she spied the hired carriage.

"Thought I'd do my best girl proud." He lifted Eva into the hack. "Mooney's lightest, handsomest rig. Like it, Eva?"

"Oh, I love it." She reached out to touch the gleaming paint. "I never saw such a dressy carriage or such big horses."

C Street was crowded. It seemed as though the whole town was out to enjoy the fine weather. Near Currie & Co.'s door, the carriage was halted by a camel train crossing the street. The horses neighed and tossed their heads.

"Those brutes aren't supposed to be on the streets by day. There's an ordinance against it," John Mackay said. "They frighten both horses and mules."

"Like ghosts," Louise said. "Poor ghosts, only allowed to walk at night."

"You look as though you'd seen a ghost, ma'am. No need to be frightened. Our driver has his horses under control. But come, we'll walk a little till they're entirely quiet. The carriage can wait outside Currie's for us."

"Oh, Mammy, look. There's a little baby one." Eva ran limping after the camels. Louise and John Mackay pursued her. He lifted the child in his arms.

"Let me pet it, Mr. Mackay, please. It's so dear and little."

"It's quite safe, Mrs. Bryant." He stroked the small beast's soft silky humps. "Gently, Eva, pat it gently. It won't hurt her, ma'am. It's tame as a kitten." He looked at Louise. "They did frighten you, didn't they? You're quite pale. The bravest women are afraid of the strangest things. Take my arm." He set Eva down. "Come along, Eva, my dear, and let this little one go with its mother."

Louise's hand trembled as she held his arm. She could not control the shaking. "It's not fright, Mr. Mackay, just the suddenness of seeing them so unexpectedly startled me. I didn't realize there were any camels in Virginia City, that there was any need for them."

"They use them for hauling coal and salt. That sort of thing. A lot of them were brought West before the war. The army was experimenting with their use. Some folks got the idea of making a go of them commercially."

"But it wasn't practical?"

"Not very. They're difficult to transport. Difficult to rear. And the rocky trails cut their feet to pieces. Poor brutes, they're a pitiful sight out of their element."

Louise did not look back at the camel train. The poor beasts belonged to another time and place. Ghosts should not walk by day, and if they did a sensible woman should refuse to recognize them. She held her hand steady on John Mackay's arm as he led her into J. C. Currie's.

"Now here," he said, "is something that's a pleasure to see."

The auction room was filled with flowering plants. The geraniums and the honeysuckle were the finest.

"Which do you prefer, Mrs. Bryant?"

"It's hard to say. The geraniums make a handsomer show but the honeysuckle have a sweeter perfume."

"What do you want for these?" John Mackay asked.

"They go high at auction," Mr. Currie said. "Eight dollars I get for a fine geranium and six for a honeysuckle."

"I'll take a dozen of each for the lady. Put them in my hack, will you, Currie?"

"Mr. Mackay, you shouldn't!" Louise exclaimed. "The plants are beautiful but they're much too dear."

"Not if they please you. I'd give considerably more than that to please you."

"You're very kind."

"Eva, my dear, I've an idea. We'll go to Dale's. You shall go in all alone like a grown lady while your mother and I wait in the carriage. When you've found the toy you like the very best, come and tell me. But be sure you see everything so you can pick the best."

In the carriage the geraniums were bright in the sun. The honeysuckle smelled sweet. Louise took off her gloves. She picked a leaf from a geranium. She rubbed the fragrant leaf between her fingers.

"I'd like to give you a great deal more than this," John Mackay said quietly. "You know that, don't you?"

She nodded.

"I'd like to give you everything I have, Louise. Do you mind if I call you Louise? That's how I think of you."

"I don't mind."

"I'd like to give you everything. And Eva too. But I don't wish to be accepted for the child's sake. She accepts me as her friend. And her friend I'll everlastingly be, whatever you come to decide. Or have you decided?"

"No, not yet." The leaf crumbled to dust between her fingers. "I didn't expect you to speak so soon—if you are speaking."

"I am speaking."

"I'm not a young girl. A young girl decides so quickly, so easily, but at my age, at my age . . ."

"And what is your age, Louise?"

"I'll be twenty-four in December and when one has reached twenty-three and past, one considers, one must consider . . ."

"What must one consider at the great age of twenty-three?" He laughed.

"Don't you laugh at me, John Mackay! I've been a woman since I was sixteen. I was married just after my sixteenth birthday. And during my poor husband's illness and since his death I have supported myself and Eva. And I'm entitled to consider the—well, the circumstances."

"Forgive me laughing. And I know you must consider the circumstances—my circumstances to be exact. I'm a sound man. What I have I keep. You'll not find me studying the stock boards at Bonynge and Hawkshurst or at any other broker's office here or at the Bay."

"But you deal in stocks. You've control of the Kentuck. You must have dealt in stocks for that."

"Sure, you might say I've gambled. But I've bet on my own knowledge of the lode. Not like those poor fools crowding the sidewalks outside the brokers' and knowing nothing at all about mines except the price of the stocks. The only way you can stake a claim in Virginia these days is to buy stock. I'll stake a claim on the Comstock any way I can. The Comstock's not done for, not by a damn sight. Prices don't tell the story. I know the lode. Damn fool if I didn't. I've been working in it since '6o. I'm pretty well fixed. I've got a bit put by. And I've my job at the Bullion. I'll never want for a job as a mine superintendent. I'll have to be going back and forth to San Francisco a good deal in the next months. I'll make it my business to see your parents. They shall know my circumstances in detail." He smiled. "Though at that I think you'd grasp it all as quick as the colonel."

"Still it's more fitting that you should speak to them."

"You're a stickler for form, aren't you? Though where you picked it up, be damned if I know. Not in Downieville, that's a sure thing."

"I lived in New York till I was almost eleven and even after Mémé and I came West I didn't stay all the time in Sierra County. My father sent me to a private academy, to St. Catherine's at Benicia, to be educated. He wasn't able to manage it for very long. Not quite a year. But it's no lie to say I was educated at Benicia. I learned much from the Sisters and from my companions."

"You were born knowing most of it. Still, my hat's off to the colonel for giving you the bit extra he could ill afford. It'll be a pleasure to pay my respects to him and your mother when I'm down at the Bay."

"Perhaps she'll come to visit me. I don't like to press it in case she can't manage. I'll just write and tell her that Mrs. Mock has a room vacant."

"You'd like to have her with you, wouldn't you?"

"It would be more suitable if I were living with my mother at this time. And for Ada, the change of air . . ."

"And you miss them. It's not only that it would be more suitable. You love them and you miss them."

"I haven't let myself miss them. There's been no way for us to be together. We've had to get used to being apart."

"You're a brave woman, Louise. They gave you the frills at the academy. Very becoming they are too. It suits a woman to be a lady. But the Sisters couldn't teach you courage. You're brave and you're sensible. It's only because I have the luck of the Irish that you're pretty too."

"And you've an Irishman's flattering tongue when you want to use it."

"It's no blarney I'm giving you, Louise, but honest praise. In you I'm choosing the kind of woman I want and need. And you must consider the kind of man you want. You know my circumstances. I don't doubt that Theresa's told you a good deal. Marriage is a woman's business. And she has a right to be practical about it. But there's more to a partnership than dollars and cents. You ought to take a long look at the man you're choosing for a partner. He's the man you'll be having to live with. Circumstances can change. They can change almighty fast in the mining country. A man don't change. So think about the man. Forget the Kentuck and the rest for a bit and think about John Mackay."

"I have thought about you."

"And come to what conclusion?"

"I admire you and I trust you."

"That'll do for a start."

"You're strong. I'd feel safe."

"Strong I am and you can feel safe, I can protect you. As long as I have these two hands you can feel safe with me in every way. If I lost every dollar I have in the world I could dig you a living from the rocks."

"And you're handsome, John Mackay." She laughed. "When I was young I'd have put that first."

"Mr. Mackay. Mr. Mackay. Please may I have her?" As Eva approached the carriage she was almost hidden by the enormous doll she carried in her arms.

"Eva!" Louise exclaimed. "You shouldn't take advantage of Mr. Mackay's kindness."

"Do you mean I can't have her? Is she too big, Mr. Mackay, for me to have? Mr. Dale said it would be all right if it was for Mr. Mackay. He said you would pick this one."

"And right he was. Now you take the doll to him and have her well wrapped up so she won't get dusty on the drive home."

"You're too good to her, John."

"John," he repeated and smiled at her. He touched her ungloved hand gently. "Thank you for that, my dear. And think about John, will you, Louise?"

Chapter XII

Mrs. Mackay

"Married

"In Virginia, November 25, by the Rev. Father Manogue, J. W. Mackay to Louisa Bryant. (No Cards.)

"(It is seldom that as brief an announcement affords us so much gratification, or that a case of Krug honors the chronicling of as happy an event. The union of so estimable a couple and the devotion of a thousand worthier friends make every wish of joy and prosperity which we could utter superfluous; and so we simply offer the congratulations which all who know them must extend to two so worthily mated that none can say which made the better choice.)"

The cutting from the *Territorial Enterprise* of November 27, 1867, was pasted on the first page of the plush-bound album. Louise reread the paragraph, though she knew the words by heart. It did not seem possible that the November day was almost a year ago. Time slipped quickly by when one was not afraid, not tired. She had almost forgotten the pleasure of easy remembering. The cuttings she had saved told part of the story.

"The Sisters of Charity return their most sincere thanks for donations received at St. Mary's School to the following: Rev. J. Nulty, a large cake; Mr. John Mackay, two hundred pounds of flour, one chest tea, one gallon brandy, one case wine, half barrel loaf sugar, half firkin butter, piece of muslin, piece of flannel, piece of linen, one hundred and fifteen pounds beef, fifty-one pounds mutton, sixteen pounds sausage meat, two sacks potatoes; Messrs. Kelly & Lowenstein, one box wax candles, one case oysters, four cans chickens, six cans jellies, half dozen boxes sardines; Mr. M. Lynch, three turkeys; Mrs. Fair, two turkeys, one ham, cakes, pies; Miss McGee, a dress pattern of merino, calicoes, gingham, five dozen pairs woollen hose; Mrs. Sharon, three turkeys; Mr. Kavanaugh, a large cake; Mrs. Gardiner, two heavy cloaks; Mrs. Bonnafous, a large cake; Mrs. Derks, a little pig; Mrs. Rhodam, $10; Mr. Barnett, ten gallons cider. In vain might they endeavor to offer thanks proportioned to the gifts received; suffice them to say that they can only offer their prayers, and those of the destitute little ones whom they have befriended, for their temporal and spiritual welfare."

John enjoyed giving. Ada had declared that their first Christmas with him came straight from *The Arabian Nights*. "Like 'Ali Baba,' Louise. Do you know that story? It's very interesting. In it there was a cave of riches and treasure. Well, that's what our parlor is exactly like—Ali Baba's cave."

Our parlor, Ada had said. That was John's best gift. The furs, the jewelry, the richly furnished parlor itself: none of these was as good as being allowed to share the whole with Mémé and Ada.

"No use having a big place unless you've a family to match," John had said. Mrs. Hungerford and Ada had moved with the Mackays to the house on the corner of Howard and Taylor streets. Colonel Hungerford came to visit but for the most part he was away, engaged in a business enterprise in Mexico. That enterprise, Louise suspected, was financed by John, though he would not admit it. He could not deny that the change for the better in Colonel Hungerford's affairs had coincided with John Mackay's visit to San Francisco in June of 1867.

John had piled the parlor with presents for them all. Louise smiled as she remembered the lavish display. The best had not been on display. The best had been promises come true.

For Ada the promises were easy to fulfill. Ada would have all that Louise had dreamed for her. She would grow up to be a lady. She would be educated by the Sisters here and later at Benicia, or even at a convent in the Atlantic states. For Eva it was more difficult, but John had promised that she should be helped. "We'll have the best surgeons for her, Louise. If there's a man anywhere on earth who can cure her lameness, you shall take her to him."

John enjoyed choosing finery for his wife and his mother-in-law, and toys for the children. He even gave willingly what he would not himself have chosen. John had agreed with Father Manogue about Marie's grave. He had seen the small gray stone in the hillside cemetery.

"Plant flowers, Louise, all the flowers you want, but don't you think a little stone is right for a baby?"

"No, John, no. I want the best for her. The living children have so much. This is all we can do for her." She could not explain to him. A man could not understand. Marie would have been so pretty in lace and fine embroidered lawn. She should be remembered with a fine white monument of marble. There should be lambs at each corner and a low, columned wall to guard the plot. The monument must be pretty so that the passer-by would know that here was the grave of a beloved and beautiful child.

John had not asked for an explanation. He had looked in silence at the small stone before he spoke.

"Have what you like, Louise. Sure, the poor little thing is entitled to anything her mother wants for her."

The parlor was quiet. The children had gone to the matinee with Mrs. Hungerford. Louise lit the lamps. She turned on the gasolier. It gave a cheerful light. She closed the shutters against the bleak twilight. She put the album on the table beside her. She drew up a footstool. The buckles on her slippers reflected the bright gaslight. She admired them. She leaned her head against the white, hand-embroidered antimacassar. John would be home soon. In the meantime it was pleasant to sit still with folded hands.

John came home earlier than usual. "Louise, I'm glad to find you alone, but what are you doing sitting so quiet by yourself?"

"I was counting my blessings."

"Have you so many?"

"Oh, John, you should know. You've given me everything I want. It doesn't seem possible that I have nothing left to wish for."

"Nothing at all? That's not possible for anyone. There must be something."

"Nothing possible."

"Then tell me the impossible wish."

"It's not a wish really. I don't let myself think of it."

"Let me think of it for you."

"Oh, John, I sound ungrateful—but if I could—if we ever could get away from Virginia."

"Do you hate it so? Even here safe and high on the corner of Taylor and Howard?"

"I'm not ungrateful for this house. There are few any handsomer in Virginia. But Virginia itself. It's a wicked, cruel city. You don't see it as it is because you've beaten it."

"Not yet. Not yet. But if I should, then what? Is it California you'd be thinking of, Louise? Are you hankering after a fine house in San Francisco?"

"It would be better than here, but if I had my wish, my impossible wish, I'd go home."

"Back to the Yuba? Now that surprises me, though I suppose it's natural enough."

"I mean New York, where I was born. That's truly a city, with its fine residences and its old established families. But you know New York, John."

"I never got inside the fine dwellings nor met the fine families."

"I wouldn't have either except for Mémé going out to sew. But I remember. I remember the very sound of their voices. Theirs is an old and elegant society. I'd like to be part of it. It's just a wish." She smiled up at him. "It's nice to be happy enough to enjoy impossible wishes. And you, John, is there nothing you wish for beyond this mining camp?"

"I don't know as I can tell you that. Once I knew fine what I wanted. Twenty-five thousand dollars to buy a farm in the green country outside Dublin. My mother's people were farmers. A farm in Ireland. That's what I had in mind when I first come out. It was a boy's dream but it kept me going in hard times on the Yuba. A dream like that puts heart into you. So you're loath to give it up even though you've outgrown the wish for it. It wasn't Ireland itself I wished for, but the land where I was a boy. The green fields beyond the city were fine to remember in the early days in New York. But Ireland's no country for a man. Leastways not for an Irishman. A man needs to be free."

"Then what do you want, John? You've money enough for Virginia City. We've everything we could wish for. And you've no dislike for Virginia."

"No, I like it fine. I like the country itself."

"It's so barren, John. There's no beauty in this desert landscape. It isn't even like the desert as one imagines it, as artists have painted it."

"No, it's not what you see in pictures, but it's quite a sight at sunrise. I like it fine. But there are some, I know, can't abide it—the wideness, the absence of green."

"It's not that I can't abide it. It's that I have a dream too. A key to St. John's Park."

"And if, when you can have it, you don't want it?"

"Oh, I'll want it. A woman's dream is less sentimental than a man's. Or maybe she has more time to perfect it. Anyway we're the practical sex. At least in my family we always were, and even you, John, I think it's glory you're after. You want to be master of the Comstock but you don't know why. I think I do. It's the power and the glory you want."

"And you, my dear? It isn't only the money you're hankering for. If I'm right we'll have big money. But you want more than that. You want it for Ada and Eva and you want it for yourself."

"And is there any harm in that? Is ambition a sin in a woman?"

"You're angry, Louise. Why?" He looked at her closely. "Don't be ashamed of your ambition," he said gently. "I've always admired it in you. I'd have no use for a scared little mouse of a woman. It'll be worth it to make you queen of the Comstock."

"Aren't you going too fast, John? Sharon's still king."

"What the books call a strictly constitutional monarch, responsible to Ralston and Mills, responsible to the whole Bank of California crowd, and they are what I don't have to go to a book to learn about. I knew their like as a boy. They're what we call absentee landlords. Me and Fair will lick them. We'll lick them because we know the Comstock. B-b-believe me w-w-we will. We'll make the riffle together."

"I believe in you, John. Have you a plan?"

"Still the same plan. To get control of the Hale and Norcross mine. We failed last winter. We won't fail this time. At the next stockholders' meeting Mr. Sharon and his friends will find that the Irishmen have control of the mine. And furthermore, me and Fair, we have our eye on a couple of mills."

"But you can't. No one can break the Union Mill and Mining Company monopoly. They'll break you. Even if you are right about the lower levels of the Hale and Norcross. Even if you should find a rich vein of ore, the bank will break you through their Mill and Mining Company."

"There's a risk. But I think you're a woman willing to take a risk if the stake is big enough."

"It's not because you're angry at the things Sharon has said of you? Anger clouds the judgment."

"Anger hasn't clouded my judgment of the Comstock. The Hale and Norcross is a beginning. Jim and I haven't been miners over fifteen years for nothing. It'll be a miner, not a banker, who'll be master of the Comstock. A gray-shirted miner."

"And then, John? When you're master? Then what?"

"Master and manager of the richest mines on earth, for that's what we'll find if we go deep enough. With wealth, Louise, with real, great wealth, I think a man might attain any end worth prizing. Wealth is a lever that can move the world. In our time wealth is the only power."

"You see, John, I was right about you. The power and the glory."

"The power and the glory, old lady. We'll enjoy them together. Control of the Hale and Norcross is the first step. Jim Fair will be getting in from the Bay about now. He's been down with Jim Flood and his partner O'Brien. They came in with us again."

"But they're only saloonkeepers, John. What can they know of mines?"

"Careful, my dear. You sound like old Sharon. You know better than that. A man does what he can in the West. Flood and O'Brien are good fighting Irishmen, the both of them. They stayed right with us last winter. Backed us to the end. Never lost their nerve. And they're no fools, Louise. Sharon can sneer at the Auction Lunch, but out of it those two fellows made and saved more than sixty thousand dollars. Flood did the investing for the pair. He may not be much on mines but he has a good business head. He'll be an asset to the firm."

"I think of Fair and Mackay as the firm."

"There'll be Flood and O'Brien too from here in. Jim Fair and I can't swing it alone. Don't worry, there'll be plenty for all. Jim Walker still has his share. He's putting up for the Hale and Norcross along with the rest of us. It's to be share and share alike for the five of us. I'm anxious to see Fair. I'll enjoy the look on his face when I tell him I got part of the money we need on loan from the Bank of California. Sharon thinks he's licked us for good on this thing. He has no idea we mean to have another try for control. He'd never have let the Hale and Norcross stock fall like he did if he knew we were still after it.

"About the loan, it don't matter what his intentions were in making it. We need it."

"And it was wise of you not to let your personal feelings stand in the way of your accepting."

"I let no man stand in my way. Not even John Mackay. I lost my temper once at Sharon. I don't regret it but I'll not do it again. It was two years ago when he s-s-said to my face that he'd m-m-make me pack my bl-blankets down the G-Geiger Grade." John flushed red. His hands opened and shut as though he still heard the smooth, contemptuous voice. "I t-t-told him I'd one day have a m-m-mighty sight of the b-b-best of him. And I will. I'll tell you something, Louise." He spoke thoughtfully. The anger ebbed from his voice. His hands relaxed. "The very words he spoke mark a difference between Sharon and me. It's a difference that can defeat him. If I had to I could pack my blankets on my back and start over with a pick in my hand as I began. Poor old Sharon couldn't pack a pair of blankets two hundred yards without stopping to rest."

"He's a wily man. Wily as a spider, sitting in his bank parlor."

"And Jim Fair's no fool. Nor Flood for that matter, nor I. You wait, Louise. You'll see. This fight is just beginning and we're going to win it. The Hale and Norcross is the first round."

When John had gone Louise returned to her recollections. As she turned the pages of the album she savored the small triumphs.

The orphans' fair in October was agreeable to remember. The *Enterprise* had described it in detail:

"At the table of Mrs. John Mackay, Miss Delaney, and Mrs. Fair we noticed some beautiful bonnets and other articles of dress for children all the way from Paris. These ladies also have a very fine display of fancy articles of all kinds, pictures, jewelry, and much else that is attractive."

It was not so small a triumph to be one of the ladies of Virginia. Mrs. Jones, Mrs. Bonner, Mrs. Sharon herself; all now acknowledged that Mrs. Mackay was one of them by right, not by courtesy.

There were events less agreeable to remember. In May there had been an earthquake. Louise had been with her mother and John at Piper's. The opera house had been crowded for Billy Robinson's benefit performance of *The Soldier's Bride*.

Miss Sue Robinson was seated on stage, writing a letter. "Dear Father," she said. "I sit down—to write—you that—I wish to—to leave this—this horrible place!" Her speech was interrupted by the first violent shock.

Louise smiled as she remembered the appositeness of the scene. John had laughed even then as the building trembled and the people cried out in terror.

"We'd better follow Miss Sue's example and get out of this—horrible place," he said to Louise and her mother. His arms were strong between them and the frightened pushing crowd.

The first shock of the earthquake was the most violent Louise had ever experienced. She felt the sick fear rise in her throat. She held herself steady as she walked from the swaying building with her mother and John. He led them up the steep street toward home.

"That crowd in C Street is more dangerous than the quake. Women fainting. Men shouting the day of judgment. And all running here and there like souls demented. I'm proud of my ladies. There now, steady." He held them as a second tremor shook the earth. "Good girls both, not a peep out of either of you."

They reached home before the last two shocks. The children and Mary, the cook, were huddled in terror in the street. Ada and Eva ran to John. They grew calm as he held them in his arms and spoke gently to them.

It had been the worst quake Louise had ever known. Its threat had been prolonged far beyond the hour of its duration. One could not be certain that the fourth and last shock marked the end. They had waited in the street for an hour more, to be sure that all was over. Now, almost six months later, Louise shivered as she remembered the earth trembling beneath her feet. It had been the worst quake, but other less violent upheavals had frightened her more deeply. It was absurd to trust to any man's strength against the violence of nature, yet Louise knew she had done so. John's presence had held terror at arm's length. Nor, she thought, was this entirely absurd. John did not alter in the hour of danger. His strength did not fail, nor, she was sure, did his judgment falter.

All his household felt the same about him. In October burglars had broken into the house. Louise and John and Mrs. Hungerford had come home to find the house ablaze with light and Mary weeping quietly in the parlor.

"Oh, sir, I never heard them at all till they opened my door, then I let out one scream. Only one, not to wake the children, and when all was quiet I crept out to look and they'd gone. Oh, sir, if only you'd been here."

"You seem to have frightened them away all by yourself." John patted Mary's shoulder.

"Nothing's taken, sir. They never got beyond this room. The cheek of them lighting all the gas to work by at their leisure. But I didn't dare to turn it off for fear they'd come back sneaking in the dark. They're a dangerous gang."

"Not so dangerous if they could be routed by one scream."

"If you'd been home they'd never have dared come at all, sir. There's plenty of robbers in Virginia, but not one of them would dare trifle with you. Now that you're home I feel safe."

"Come, Mary, that's pure blarney, but I'll forgive you for you've been a brave girl. Now off to bed with you. We'll report the burglary in the morning."

They had all gone peacefully to bed, Louise remembered. They had not feared that the thieves would return. John's wife and his mother-in-law had slept as trustfully as his servant.

Louise smoothed the silk folds of her skirt. Here she sat, Mrs. John William Mackay of Virginia City. Little Mamie Hungerford had never imagined being a lady more fashionable than Mrs. Mackay. She had never thought to own a finer mansion than the one on the corner of Howard and Taylor streets. Mamie Hungerford had come a long way, to a high place.

The wind was rising outside. On the walls the paper bulged and rustled. For a moment Louise saw the room clearly. Brocade and velour, polished oak and Turkey carpet, all were new, all were the best that money could buy. It was a handsome room, but she remembered handsomer ones, she remembered a paler and more spacious elegance. She remembered the pictures in Mr. Langton's books. She remembered the houses on Washington Square and on St. John's Park. This was a high place, but she could go higher.

John meant to gamble all they had. He meant to uncover the riches of the Comstock if it took every dollar he had accumulated. Louise knew she should be frightened. She realized she was scarcely afraid at all. She would not try to stop him. She believed in him. She was as willing as he to gamble on his knowledge and on his strength. Hers was a bigger gamble than his. She was more newly come to security, she prized it more dearly. But, like him, she wanted more than mediocrity, however comfortable, however safe. She wanted him to be master of the Comstock. She wanted, for both of them, the power and the glory.

Chapter XIII

Partnership

AT THE MEETING of the stockholders in March of 1869 John Mackay and his partners gained control of the Hale and Norcross. The trustees of their choice were elected. Jim Fair was appointed superintendent of the mine.

Louise rejoiced over John's account of the meeting.

"Sharon must have been angry, John. I'd like to have seen his face."

"It showed nothing. Old Sharon never turned a hair. He walked over to me as polite as you please and congratulated me and said, 'Of course, Mackay, all you care about is the glory of winning the fight. You don't know anything about managing a big mine and you have no facilities for working the ore. We are willing to take all the trouble off your hands and keep right on with the management.' I thanked him and said we'd try and learn what we didn't know about running a mine and that I thought the new management could get along without help."

"He must be shaken all the same. He must see his power slipping away."

"Not yet, it isn't. The bank crowd still have plenty. They can spare the Hale and Norcross. Sharon's still top dog. He was reminding me of that fact when he said we have no facilities for working the ore."

"The Union Mill and Mining Company. He's right, John. They still hold the monopoly."

"They still do, and, holding it, they hold Virginia by the throat. But me and Fair, we mean to break that strangle hold. We're aiming to buy Trench's Mill at Silver City and enlarge it. The firm's on its way, old lady. You watch."

Louise watched with proud satisfaction the firm's successful reorganization of the Hale and Norcross. Instead of assessments on the stock as there had been in the past, this year dividends would be paid to the shareholders.

She appraised the San Francisco partners. The two men were not alike. James Flood was a reserved, short-spoken man. It was hard to imagine him tending bar. When he owned the Auction Lunch he could not, Louise thought, have been a very genial host. Billy O'Brien must have been the one who brought in the customers. Flood was a harsh-mannered man, not given to small talk. When he came to Virginia he listened and watched. He was silently attentive when John and Jim Fair discussed the workings of the mine. He became articulate only when figures were mentioned. He spoke fluently of assessments, of dividends, of all the intricacies of stock trading. He gave so lucid an account of the world of finance that a child, Louise thought, could understand. The stock boards became as easy to read as a blackboard in a schoolroom. The firm needed such a man. In the countinghouse he was Sharon's equal. The battle of the Comstock would not be fought only in the depths of the lode. James Flood would hold the line in the markets of San Francisco.

Billy O'Brien—Louise smiled when she thought of him. No one could help smiling at his broad cheerful Irish face. He was a partner because Flood was loyal to him as John to Jim Walker. And O'Brien's courage and his honesty were, John said, assets to any firm. Louise had not seen him often, yet she felt she knew and understood him. He was an easy, friendly man. Louise was touched by his open admiration and affection for his partners, by his confidence in their judgment and integrity. She smiled with John at Billy's bland unshakable confidence in the luck of the Irish.

"He's right at that," John said. "Endurance, judgment, experience, knowledge of the mines, you have to have all those and then you have to have luck besides."

Louise talked with John about Jim Fair. "I've known him the longest. He's ever been kind to me. I can't mistrust him since you have confidence in him, and yet he puzzles me. At first meeting he's an easy friendly man to know, but it stops there. I feel no better acquainted with him now than I did two years ago."

"A queer cuss, Jim. You think you know him but something evades you. For all his genial open manner, he's a secret man. There's no secret about his cleverness though. Clever as hell, Jim is, and he has a nose for ore. No one like him for that. And brave—that he is too. I've seen him when the going was rough and he never wavered. Never once. You've got to admire him."

"You admire him and you've affection for him, John."

"Sure. We're partners. That means a lot in the diggings. Jack O'Brien and I were partners in the old days. We came to Washoe together. Then we went separate ways. Jack is an easygoing fellow. Placer mining suited him. This hard-rock mining wasn't to his liking. But we were partners once and he'll not want as long as I live. He can have anything I've got. He'd do the same by me if things had gone the other way. Jim Walker. There's another easygoing fellow. I doubt Jim will go to the end of the road with us. His heart's set on retiring and setting up as a farmer in the state of Virginia. But Jim and I were partners in the Kentuck deal. I needed him then worse than he needed me."

"So you keep him as a partner even though he's off in the Atlantic states helping elect his brother governor of Virginia."

"Jim was ever set on politics. He's a pretty big man in the Union party. And that won't do the firm any harm."

"Still he's no real use to you."

"He was of use to us in the Hale and Norcross deal. And he can stay with us as long as he has a mind to. He trusted us and I'll see he's not frozen out."

"You and Flood are alike in more than your quiet ways. You're alike in loyalty. I believe you'll always be able to count on him. But Jim Fair. Can any man entirely trust him?"

"I can. Jim's always played square with me. Jim's a tough customer. And he likes to appear a crafty fellow. There are plenty of yarns going the rounds to prove the folks are right who name him Slippery Jim. They'll have influenced your opinion of him. But remember, Louise, that the best stories on Jim are of his own telling. It was all over town a while back that he gave Theresa a tip that Gould and Curry was due for a rise, cautioning her to secrecy but knowing she'd tell her relatives and they'd tell others and the stock would skyrocket, giving him a chance to unload at a high figure. Jim loves that story. 'And then,' he always says with huge satisfaction, 'and then after the bottom fell out of the stock, but with me in the clear, you undersand, I ask her if she still has her bit of money in the bank. And she tells me I know very well she lost the whole seven thousand dollars in Gould and Curry. So I give her a check for the full amount and I caution her against stock gambling. The poor girl, I tell her it's plain she has no head at all for business.'"

"It's a horrid story, John, and it's true. I didn't like to ask Theresa but I've heard it on all sides."

"Is it a likely story, my dear? Oh, Jim's not above a bit of sharp trading. Who is in Virginia? Or down at the Bay? It's not a bunch of Galahads who'll get the best of the bank crowd. But do you think Jim would play a silly trick like that on Theresa? There are plenty of ways to bear and bull a stock. Jim knows them all. We all know them. He had no need to use Theresa. It would have been a damnfool thing to do. After all, a man likes a little peace and quiet at home."

"Perhaps you're right about that story, but there are so many. Mary was telling me of a poor cousin of hers. I meant to speak to you for him. He was discharged from the Hale and Norcross for smoking. The way it happened was that Jim Fair took out his pipe in the mine one day and asked, in ever so friendly a fashion, for tobacco and a match, and several, Mary's poor cousin among them, were glad to oblige. Now they're all out of work."

"I've no pity for them nor wish to see them back. Nor would you, Louise, if you'd ever seen a fire in a mine."

"But it sounds such an underhand thing. Spying like that on the men."

"Spying, watching. Use any word you like. But if they're not watched the men get careless. A story like that, true or not, is good for them. Shows them Uncle Jimmie has his eyes open."

"You'll listen to nothing against him."

"There's not much that can be said against Jim. He's a hard man. But so are we all, Louise, we've had to be. And under that affable manner of his, Jim's secretive. I want no blabbermouth for a partner.

And he is my partner. That's the important thing. Hard for a woman to understand what that means in the mining country. Like I told you long ago, a partnership is more than dollars and cents. It's more even than respect for the other fellow's business judgment. It's hard times together. Real hard times and seeing them through. It's gambling, not just on the other fellow's judgment—though anyone would gamble on Jim's opinion of a mine. It's gambling on his nerve, on his staying power, on the strength of his guts. Above and beyond everything else Jim Fair's got strong guts. He don't cave in when the going is rough. I've placed my bet on him and I'm staying with it."

The partners intended to be the masters of the Comstock. They meant to destroy the Bank of California's monopoly and to end Sharon's power. Louise wondered if any man would master the lode. It seemed more likely that the Comstock would destroy them all. Danger as well as riches lurked in the depths of the mountain. In the deep hot shafts death waited.

In the early morning of the seventh of April the calamity came. This time it was not a single death by accident. A fatal or a serious accident in the mines was reported almost every day. This time it was not one man who died but more than forty.

During the night a fire had been secretly smoldering among the timbers at the eight-hundred-foot level of the Yellow Jacket mine near the Kentuck line. The men on the night shift were lifted to the surface. The first of the day shift descended. The raising and lowering of the cages created a draft which filled the chambers of the mine with flame and smoke. With an explosive roar the fire spread to the Kentuck and on into the Crown Point. In the suffocating darkness a rush was made for the cages. Only a few could be raised at once. After the cages were lifted to the surface forty-one men remained below. The smoke seemed to turn into a poisonous gas which poured up the shafts. When the empty cages were lowered again, no hand reached out to them. The vast smoke-filled chambers were silent.

No one in Virginia or Gold Hill stayed willingly within doors. Only the firemen and miners could hope to be of help in the disaster, but there was a compulsion, even on those who could do nothing, not to stay at home, unknowing, unseeing. Men and women streamed across the divide from Virginia to Gold Hill.

This hidden fire was more terrible to witness than one that spread openly across the surface of a city. These flames could not be seen. Only the black poisonous smoke was visible. One could hear the noise of explosions and the silence at the hoisting shafts where men listened vainly for the sound of voices below.

Louise and Theresa Fair stood together near the Crown Point shaft. The crowd was quiet. Even the wives and mothers waiting for news made scarcely a sound. They rocked back and forth, silently clasping and unclasping their hands. Only the small children wept aloud. Many of the women were Father Manogue's parishioners. He moved among them slowly, quietly.

In the Crown Point a number of men were known to be at the thousand-foot level, far below the fire. They could not be reached. A cage was sent down with a lighted lantern and a small box of candles upon it and a large piece of cardboard on which was written a message from Superintendent John P. Jones: "We are fast subduing the fire. It is death to attempt to come from where you are. We will get to you soon. The gas in the shaft is terrible and produces sure and speedy death. Write a word to us and send it up on the cage, and let us know how you are."

No answer came. The men for whom the message was intended were dead. Later their bodies, contorted with agony, would be found.

The crowd moved restlessly from place to place. Louise and Theresa, their hands joined, moved with the crowd. Near each shaft women and children waited. The watching crowd kept a little apart from the waiting women.

At the Yellow Jacket all but one man of those known to be below were brought up dead. The smoke no longer issued from the shaft. The dead had not yet been brought from the Kentuck and Crown Point. From those shafts there still rose thick stifling columns of black, evil-smelling smoke.

The slowly moving crowds parted to let the firemen pass to the shaft of the Yellow Jacket. The firemen and miners were lowered into the shaft. For short, barely endurable periods of time the men took their turns below. After hours of slow, painful toil they penetrated into parts of the adjoining mines. Some of the dead from the Kentuck and the Crown Point were brought up to the surface.

In the fierce heat the bodies had begun to disintegrate. The flesh was soft, as with long decay. To keep the dead bodies from falling into a shapeless mass it was necessary to wrap each one in a canvas sheet coated with tar.

The crowd parted where Louise and Theresa were standing. Three of the tar-coated bundles, lashed to boards, were carried past them. The stench was overpowering.

"We shouldn't have come, Louise. No one should who can't be helpful like those fire laddies."

"No worse to stand here than to stay home and imagine it. But you're right. We'll go. We're no use."

They walked slowly towards the omnibus that would take them to Virginia from Gold Hill.

"Those children crying beside the shafts. I think I'll hear them crying forever." The tears poured down Theresa's cheeks.

"It's not being able to help. I remember Mrs. Kibbe saying: 'Desolation is easier to bear when you can help.'"

"Father Manogue will tell us what to do. There'll be funds raised for the widows and orphans."

"They'll still be widows and orphans, hideously widowed, hideously orphaned. Always they'll live remembering the black day, imagining the dark, burning, suffocating death. We can't comfort them. We can't give them a decent bearable memory of their husbands and fathers. But we'll do what we can. We can give them food and clothing and shelter. That much we can do."

The eighth of April was a day of funerals. At eleven in the morning, at noon, at one o'clock, hour after hour the services continued. Every mine was closed that the men might walk behind their dead comrades. The Emmet Guard and the Sweeny Guard paraded in slow solemn step. As the funeral processions moved through the streets, a light snow fell and melted in the dust. In the clear cold air the church bells tolled for the long list of the dead.

Thomas McCoy, born in Galway, Ireland; aged thirty-four years; leaves a wife and five children in Gold Hill.

Jeremony Chenette, born at St. Hyacinthe, Canada; single; aged twenty-two years.

Michael McCormick, born in Massachusetts; aged thirty-two years; leaves a wife and one child in Virginia City.

Anthony Toy, born at Redruth, County of Cornwall, England; aged twenty-four years. He was married two weeks ago today. . . .

John read the names over and over. Many of them he knew. Many had been his friends.

"Come, John," Louise urged him. "Come and get some rest."

He sat beside her on the edge of the bed. His shoulders slumped wearily. "It's not easy to sleep, remembering those poor fellows. Pat Quinn. I got him his job at the Kentuck. Got it for him as a favor."

"Poor fellows. Yes, they are. And so may all of you be. Every day you take the risk of just such a catastrophe trapping you in the rich depths you're so bent on exploring. Is it worth it, John? Are all the riches in the world worth the risk? Sometimes I think no one will beat the Comstock."

"It's not the Comstock. It's human carelessness somewhere. And all of us share guilt for that. All of us. If it happens in any mine it can happen in all."

"It would take superhuman carefulness to be safe at the deep levels."

"Don't be frightened, Louise. We'll find means to lick the heat at the lower levels. And we'll watch for carelessness. It's ever been our enemy in the diggings." He stroked her hair. "Virginia nearly had you beaten once. So you're frightened of it. Though it never did lick you entirely, remember? Don't be frightened, Louise. This is a man's town. You've no need to fear it now. You're not alone any more."

"Many learned to fear it today."

"The miners aren't a fearful lot. And these are still the richest mines on earth. The men came a long way to work in them; Cornwall, Ireland, Canada, the Atlantic states. They'll not be driven out." His hand touched her hair gently. "You've pretty hair, Louise. My mother when she was young had smooth, shining dark hair like yours." He drew her close to him. "Don't be afraid. You've got me to look after you now."

His strength comforted her. She fell asleep in his arms.

The black memory of disaster lay dark across the months of spring and summer. Work was gradually resumed in the Gold Hill mines but the fire was not entirely subdued. For six months it smoldered stubbornly. Some of the galleries were never reopened. Some of the dead were never found.

In spite of the tragedy that shadowed its beginning, the summer promised prosperity for Virginia. Though stock prices were low, many mines were yielding well, many mills were running at full capacity.

That summer the railroads had spanned the continent; in May the last spike was driven, the last rail laid.

Virginia was to be linked with the transcontinental lines. Sharon's Virginia and Truckee Railroad was nearing completion. Sixteen hundred white and Chinese laborers were working on the road. Adolph Sutro was about to begin work on his tunnel. John Mackay and Jim Fair did not look with approval on this grandiose project to build a great tunnel to drain and ventilate all the lower levels of the Comstock. John Mackay, as superintendent of the Bullion, had joined with the superintendents of other mines and with Sharon in urging the Nevada senators, Stewart and Nye, to oppose any government aid to Sutro.

"But, John," Louise asked, "may his idea not be a good one? A great tunnel might benefit all the mines."

"It might. Sutro thinks so and many agree, but he demands, upon the tunnel's completion, a royalty on every ton of ore. He wants to skim the cream off the mineowners' profit. He wants in the end to own Virginia City, or to put Sutro Town in its place. The mines are to pay tribute and the ore is to be refined at mills that he will build at his tunnel's mouth. It will be the Union Mill and Mining Company all over. He's smart. No denying that. He took the congressmen up on the roof of the International Hotel and showed them where the tunnel would begin, how it would work to benefit the Comstock. But he talked, I'm told, like the future proprietor of the lode and of the town. He's ambitious, I tell you, too ambitious to let the rest of us live if he has his way."

"Too ambitious?" Louise asked, laughing. "Too ambitious. Oh, John! This from you."

"Are you reproaching me? I don't reproach Sutro. I don't reproach Sharon for that matter. I just don't mean to let either of them run the Comstock. We'll find means of our own to dry out the lower levels and ventilate them properly. Make no mistake, Louise, ambition opened up this western country. Ambitious men explored the gold fields and built the railroads. It's not for love of Virginia that Sharon's building the Virginia and Truckee Railroad, but Virginia will benefit. Ambition's not to be despised in a man. You can't despise

Sharon or Sutro. Even though I fight them, I've got to admire the both of them."

"And they you. I think even Sharon's learning to respect the Irishmen."

"A little, maybe. We're invited to the reception at his house next week. You can judge his opinion of us then for yourself."

The reception was in honor of Vice-President Schuyler Colfax and his party, who were touring the West in a private railroad car. Virginia gave the visitors a gala welcome. John Mackay and Jim Fair were members of the welcoming committee. With their wives, they were invited to the evening reception that was the climax of the festivities.

Sharon's mansion was filled with flowers brought from San Francisco. The exterior of the house and the grounds were decorated with Chinese lanterns.

It was a triumphant evening for Louise. Mr. Sharon himself presented her to the Vice-President and his lady. Mrs. Colfax complimented Louise on her gown. "Charming, really charming. You ladies in Virginia City are so dressy, Mrs. Mackay. I am quite astonished. And this house, delightful. Not at all what one would expect to find in a mining town. You even have a theater, I believe."

"We even have performances of Shakespeare in our theater. And here is one of our finest amateur actors, Judge Robert Taylor. May I present Judge Taylor, Mrs. Colfax, Miss Calhoun?"

Bob Taylor gave his arm to Louise. "Well, Mamie," he said, "you're queen of them all tonight. Do you mind me still calling you Mamie?"

"I don't mind it from you, Judge. You and Mrs. Taylor have ever been kind to me. I don't forget."

They walked to the end of the room where John was standing alone.

"She's the prettiest girl in the room, John." Bob Taylor bowed over Louise's hand. "Queen of them all, my dear."

Louise placed her hand on John's arm. "Oh, John, I was presented to them all. Mr. Sharon has been most attentive to me. It was he who took me up to Mrs. Colfax. So you see, he does admire you."

"Or could it be your Paris gown from the Bay? Or the girl who can make any gown look as if it came from Paris. I remember you in one you made yourself of violet satin."

"You saw that dress with the eyes of a man in love. I never was much of a dressmaker, I fear."

The cheering voices of the crowd outside came through the open windows.

"We can be getting home now, Louise. Colfax has gone out to speak to them again. This'll be about the end."

Louise detained John for a moment in the garden. "It looks so pretty in the light of the lanterns. Quite different."

"The firehouse looks quite different too." John laughed. "The Eagle boys have sure trimmed her up."

The enginehouse across the way was hung with flags and transparencies and patriotic mottoes. The wide door was framed in an arch of colored lanterns.

The street was filled with people. At the Vice-President's request they gave a final three cheers for the state of Nevada. As the cheering died down, the crowd dispersed. Louise and John walked slowly toward the corner of the street.

"It was a really fashionable affair," Louise said. "So distinguished. I've never mingled with any of the real elite before. Mrs. Schuyler Colfax and that pretty Miss Bross. Her father was lieutenant governor of Illinois."

The band was still playing beyond the open windows of Mr. Sharon's parlor. Louise turned her head to listen to the music, to look at the lanterns swaying in the cottonwood tree. The music and the colored lanterns gave a foreign elegance to the mansion. Mr. Sharon's residence and the softly lighted garden seemed for a moment to be part, not of a mining town, but of some remote and fashionable city.

The end of summer was turbulent. The miners of Gold Hill and Virginia drove the Chinese laborers off the Virginia and Truckee Railroad. With fife and drum playing, the white men marched down the road, herding the Chinese before them. Upon their return march the whites leveled every Chinese shanty in their course. Work on the railroad was halted for more than a week.

Sharon addressed the miners at union meetings in Gold Hill and Virginia. He urged them to allow the Chinese to work on the road.

John told Louise about the Virginia City meeting. "As mad a lot of men as I ever saw. But in the end Sharon talked them round.

You've got to hand it to him. He addressed that rough angry crowd as calmly as if he was speaking to a ladies' sewing circle."

"I wouldn't have expected Mr. Sharon to come to the defense of the Chinese. He never impressed me as a warmhearted man."

"He's not acting out of love for the Celestials. He wants to get his railroad finished. He assured the union he had no intention of putting Chinese labor in the mills or mines."

"Poor souls. They've ever been harshly treated in the diggings. Even the children. The white children, I mean, throwing stones at them. And older folk laughing at their cruelty, encouraging it."

"John Chinaman can live too cheap, Louise. That's the real trouble. He don't care what wages he works for. The miners are afraid he'll steal their livelihood. Fear for his livelihood will make pretty near any man turn cruel."

"Still, it's sickening to see. Only today Eva and I saw a poor Chinaman lying hurt on C Street. His leg had been broken in a fall from a horse. A few loafers were standing laughing at his predicament. He'd been lying there some time, one of them said, probably waiting for the miners' union to come and drum him out of town. Passers-by on the street went their way, scarcely glancing at him. They'd have done more for an injured dog. I stood there like a fool, not knowing what to do. Luckily some of his own people came along and they carried him off. Eva was crying by then."

"She's a good little soul. They'd never teach her cruelty. Never in a million years."

"She oughtn't even to witness it."

"There's cruelty everywhere, Louise. And violence."

"But not so close to a child as in the mining towns. I know. I was raised in one."

"It didn't hurt you. Maybe it's part of what makes you more of a woman than most of the frozen-faced eastern ladies who come out our way. But still you don't want it for your daughter. That's natural enough. I wouldn't want a son of mine to have it as hard as I did."

"I'm not asking, John. Ada and Eva are all right. They're always with Mémé and me or with the Sisters. The Sisters are educating them. Eva and Ada are growing up to be ladies. I shouldn't have said anything. I just couldn't get that Chinaman out of my mind, lying so quiet—like an animal in the dust of the street."

"Sure you couldn't. And ask for anything you want, Louise. I'll do my damnedest to give it to you."

Her eyes filled with tears.

"Why, Louise, what's this for? Not the poor Chinaman still."

"No. It's that you've given me so much. And the one thing you want I've not given you."

"The boy, you mean? He'll be along. Never doubt it. And meanwhile it's a fine family you've brought me. Eva is like my own. And Ada too."

On a morning late in December, Louise told John she was expecting a child.

She heard him moving in the dark of the winter morning.

"I'm awake, you can light the gas." She sat up in bed.

"Go back to sleep, Louise, it's cold and black as night. No sunrise to watch this time of day any more."

"I've better than a sunrise for you. I've news for you. At last I've news of the boy."

He walked to the bed. He put his hand on her shoulder. "You're cold." He wrapped a quilt around her. "Is it true what you're trying to tell me?"

"I'm not trying. I'm telling you. Our baby will be born in August and he'll be a boy."

"Louise, are you sure?" He held the quilt tight against her.

"I'm sure we're having a baby. Of course I can't be entirely sure it'll be a boy, not having joined the ranks of the Washoe Seeresses, but I hope. Oh, John, I hope."

"I'd like fine for it to be the boy. I'd like that fine. But a daughter would do to begin with. And if it should be a girl, don't worry about Eva. No little girl, not even my own, could dislodge her from her place in my heart." He stood up. "Now you get back under the covers and keep warm. I'll light the stove and send Mary up with your breakfast."

"I'm not an invalid. I never felt better in my life."

"And you're damn well going to stay that way. I'll get accommodations for you and Mémé and the children at the Bay. You'll have the baby in San Francisco. You'll be safer that way."

"There are midwives and doctors here."

"Not good enough. And Eva, too, should see the San Francisco doctors. This will be a good time for that."

"Do you think they can help? No one here has given us much hope. Only the other day when I took her to Dr. Kibbe, he wasn't encouraging. I knew him back in Downieville. He'd tell me the truth. And so would Dr. Wixon. I spoke with him when he was last in town from Austin."

"They may not know. They may not know in San Francisco, but we'll give them a try before we go further." He pulled the blanket close to her chin. With a gentle hand he pushed the curls back from her forehead. "I've never been much on pretty speeches so you'll have to do without one on this occasion, but you know. You must know, Louise."

"I know."

"All I've said about partners. That goes double for you and me. We're partners. I can't put words together as for once I'd like to, so try to understand my meaning."

"I understand. Partnership is as good a word as any for what can't be described. None has ever rightly described what marriage is, what a man and wife can come to be to each other. Partnership will do."

When she was alone she lay quiet. John's kiss was still warm on her lips. She watched the black arch of the window fade to gray. Long ago she had known that a partnership with John Mackay would be steadfast and long enduring. She had known a woman would be lucky. She hadn't known how lucky. She smiled. If a woman was lucky enough, partnership was the word for marriage.

Chapter XIV

···━━▷◎◁━━···

Willie

ON AUGUST 12, 1870, John William Mackay, Jr., was born in the Grand Hotel in San Francisco.

The big bedroom was cooled by the breeze from the Bay. With her week-old son in her arms Louise lay quiet, wrapped in happiness and luxury. "It's different for you, Willie," she whispered. "So different and you'll never know. If our luck holds, you'll never know."

She remembered the cabin where Eva was born and the lodging house where Marie was born and died. She looked across the richly furnished room to the tall windows curtained in brocade. She had scolded John for his extravagance in engaging so handsome a parlor suite. "My dear," he had said, "from here on we can afford the best or nothing at all. So enjoy the best while you may. Besides, nothing's too good for the boy's arrival."

John had been confident that the baby would be a boy. Louise had hoped for a boy for his sake, but her fierce, proud delight in her son astonished her. She had never understood the triumphant conceit of the mothers of boys. She had smiled at the smugness with which they had patronized her and her daughter. "Little girls are so sweet," they said, "daughters are such a comfort." It was quite clear that no one need offer compliments to the mother of a boy. Why? Louise had wondered in exasperation. Why should a boy baby make a woman so proud? Men, of course, were different. But to a woman surely any baby was welcome and beloved. Now she knew. It was a curiously primitive emotion, she thought, it must be older than love. Certainly it was quite separate from love. Her father and mother had not loved Nito better than they loved her and Ada, but when Nito died his parents had died in part, never entirely to recover. A son conferred a new kind of immortality, an immortality that was here and now. She looked down at the child. It was absurd that anything so small and helpless should make his parents stronger, more secure. It was absurd but it was so.

She looked up to see John standing in the door.

"He's fast asleep and I'm admiring him and myself for having him. You know, John, I always laughed at women for thinking themselves so clever to have a boy and now I'm simply bursting with pride. I'm no better than a heathen Chinee or a Turk."

"And I admire the pair of you. It's a fine thing to have a boy. All the same, he'll never take Eva's place. You know that."

"I know, but we must make her know. Before Ada was born I was so frightened she'd be a boy. I was a big girl of thirteen and I was frightened. Poor Eva's not yet ten. The younger you are, the more secret you keep your fear. I was afraid a boy would take my place with Father. I didn't know then that a son's place is different from a daughter's and one can't dispossess the other. It's a strange thing all the same." She frowned. "It's a very strange thing, this unreasonable pride."

"It's the most natural thing in the world. Why wouldn't a man be proud to have a son to carry on his name? It gives him a stake in the future, a stake worth fighting for."

"You were ever a fighter, John."

"The boy gives the fight more meaning. But Eva now. I wouldn't want her to worry about her place with us. There's something I've been thinking of . . ." He hesitated.

"Yes, John?"

"It's only her I'm thinking of, mind. Suppose I was to adopt her, make her my daughter in fact as she is in my heart."

Louise was silent. She grasped the hem of the sheet to hide the trembling of her hand.

"It would mean no disrespect to the doctor's memory." John took Louise's hand in his. "She could be known as Eva Bryant Mackay. She would have his picture in her room as she has now. She would remember him as she does now. She'd not cease to be his daughter by becoming mine. If she's any fear of the boy at all, it might comfort her to share my name as he does. It would be a way to let her know that Willie has made no difference between us, that she's still my girl."

"Eva Bryant Mackay." Louise pronounced the names slowly. "It has a nice sound. And you're right, of course. It will make her happy."

"It's me that'll be happy, to have her bear my name along with her father's."

"You're her real father, John." It was difficult to speak the truthful words, but they were John's due. "She was so little when Edmund died and before that he had to be away so much, first on account of business and later because of illness. She scarcely remembers him. It's you she loves."

"But you do well to keep her from forgetting him entirely, the poor fellow, to keep his photograph by her and all. You've great loyalty, Louise, and it's a quality I admire."

He lifted her hand and kissed it. "Thank you for letting me give my daughter my name. Now if you'll let me hold my son a minute before I go down to Montgomery Street." He picked up the sleeping child.

"Must you go?"

"I must, and back to Virginia tomorrow."

"Are things not going well? I know the Bullion proved a disappointment, but the Hale and Norcross . . ."

"The Hale and Norcross will serve its purpose but it's not the way to the heart of the lode."

"And will you find the way? They say even Sharon is getting disgusted with the Comstock."

"We'll find the way. Did I tell you Jim Walker's pulling out?"

"You're buying him out, I suppose you mean. At a high price and with no help from the others."

"It's up to me to see that Jim gets a fair shake. And I've not asked the others to help. I'm well content to own Jim's share of the firm. That'll give me two fifths instead of one."

"And will this new venture take the rest of your capital?"

"Who spoke of a new venture?"

"You did. When you say you'll find a way to the heart of the Comstock I know it's not talk, I know you have a definite way in mind."

"Right you are. I'd have told you before if I had thought you were well enough to listen to business. You know the claims between the Ophir mine and Gould and Curry?"

"You mean California and Dick Sides and White and Murphy? All that lot?"

"That's right. Consolidated Virginia Mining Company, it is now."

"But those mines never amounted to much and they've been idle for years."

"True. And the titles aren't entirely clear. After the consolidation the bank crowd worked the ground for a while. They poured over a hundred and fifty thousand dollars into it. Now they've lost interest. Me and Fair, we have an idea about the lower levels of those mines and we've a mind to get hold of them. Flood and O'Brien are in agreement. It'll take time and it'll take money. Maybe more in the end than we can afford. Are you game, old lady?"

"I'm game, John. I like a parlor suite at the Grand. I like to dress my baby in fine clothes imported from Paris. I like to plan for his education and for Eva's. I've no wish to stand still, no wish to stay in Virginia forever."

John placed the baby carefully in her arms. "Your mother means to make a gentleman of you, my boy, and that costs money. I better be getting along."

"Do you mind, John? You say gentleman as if it weren't a serious word, as if it weren't the thing to be."

"And you're so sure it is." He kissed her. "Well, I guess a gentleman's not a bad thing to be if you're a man as well. And that no one can make you, Willie." He touched the baby's cheek. "That's one thing you'll have to do for yourself."

After John left, the nurse brought in a vase of flowers with a card. "The lady's waiting downstairs, ma'am. I told the boy I wasn't sure you could see her, not having had any visitors outside the family yet."

Mrs. Robert Howland, the card said. Louise Althea. Little Louise Althea, a married lady with her name on a visiting card.

"Bring her up. Go and bring her up right away."

How would she look? Louise wondered. The years rolled back to the deck of a steamer where two little girls stood looking at one another for the first time, two little girls bound on a journey together.

A lady stood in the doorway. She was slim and pretty and fashionably dressed. A feathered hat was perched on her light brown hair.

Louise Mackay held out her arms. "Louise Althea, it's never you."

Louise Howland ran across the room. "Marie Louise, after all this time."

They clung to each other. Willie awoke and began to cry. The women petted him and soothed him.

"He's beautiful, Marie Louise. What do you call him?"

"John William, Jr., is his name, but we call him Willie."

"And your little girl. Is she Marie Louise Antoinette for you?"

"No. She's Eveline for Mémé. Eveline Julia, but we call her Eva. I lost my little Marie."

"I heard about the poor baby dying and about the accident to the other little one and I grieved so for you. When I went to Virginia City from the ranch with my father I tried to find you, but you had moved and there was no address. We wanted to help. Were you all right?"

"I wouldn't have minded your help, Louise Althea. Your father always helped us in the old days. You can accept help from some. Theresa Fair is one and Mrs. Robert Taylor is another. You remember Bob Taylor."

"He that was a judge in Downieville? My Bob knows him but folks use his military title now and call him Colonel Taylor."

"I don't. I call him Judge and he calls me Mamie."

"Do you remember the night he made the speech and gave your father the sword?"

"Louise Althea, you can't remember that."

"I don't really, but I remember you telling it."

They talked until they made the far-off days seem close at hand, as long ago they had made summer days shine again in the dark of winter.

Marie Louise nursed her baby and the nurse took him away and still they talked. They talked of the old days and of the new.

"Were you all right alone in Virginia?" Louise Althea asked again. "Did you manage?"

"I managed and that was about all. But it's done with now. No need to talk of it, though with you I wouldn't mind. We're all all right now, Eva and Ada and Mémé and Father."

"Do you remember, Marie Louise, when Ada was born and your poor father . . ."

"And I was so glad, so wickedly glad. Did I tell you that?"

"I think you must have. Anyway I knew." Louise Althea touched her carved gold earrings. "Do you remember these, Marie Louise? I wore them on purpose."

"Your treasure-trove. Now aren't you pleased that I didn't let you have a plain thing made of your gold?"

"Mrs. Mackay, I'm sorry." The nurse came in. "I'm sorry to disturb you and Mrs. Howland, but Mr. Mackay will take my head off if you tire yourself."

The names were the names of strangers. The women looked at each other. For a moment each seemed to the other a child in fancy dress.

"We were a long way back, Louise Althea. The old days are fine to revisit, but I wouldn't want to live in them again, would you?"

"No, I'm happier now. People say childhood is the best, but I don't believe that, not if you have luck later. And I've had luck. You've not met my Bob?"

"I never met him, but he was pointed out to me once. He's a handsome, distinguished man."

"I guess we're both lucky, Marie Louise."

"That's why we can be comfortable together. I won't be long in San Francisco, so come soon again and bring Mr. Howland."

After the Renaissance splendor of the Grand Hotel the wooden house on Howard and Taylor streets seemed poor and mean. In the small rooms the handsome furniture looked pretentiously out of place. Virginia City was a dusty mining camp huddled untidily on the perilous slope of a mountain that darkened the autumn days. Louise had never intended that San Francisco be the end of her journey, but it was better than this.

Her joy in her son was still strong and complete, but outside that warm happiness, darkly beside it, was the shadow of disappointment. The doctors of San Francisco had been able to do nothing for Eva. The shadow was on John too. Even while he was holding his healthy little son the expression of his face altered. His eyes were sad as he watched Eva limp awkwardly across the room.

At Christmas he said to Eva, "Nothing here or at the Bay is good enough for you, my little dear. How would you like a trip someday to Gay Paree? There we could find you a real first-class doll with a wardrobe fit for a princess."

When they were alone he said to Louise, "If the French and Germans make peace by spring, we'll take Mémé and the children and all go abroad. They say the French doctors are the best. One of them may be able to do something for her."

She felt her heart beat fast with joy and hope for Eva and with joy at release for herself. It would be like release from prison to escape, if only for a few months, from Virginia, to see, even in passing, the city of her birth, to see France and perhaps Italy too. *Know'st thou the land?* She had seen a reflection of it in Panama. Now she might see the land itself; she might visit the warm Mediterranean shore. There she would see the citron-apples bloom and dark-leafed myrtle and laurel growing high.

"You'd like that, old lady. Paris. Maybe London and Rome."

"You've the second sight of the Irish to read my mind—but truly it's mostly for Eva."

"Sure, I know. But I'd like it to be for you too. And for her it's better that we be tourists and let the doctors seem incidental. We can stop a bit in New York going or coming if you like."

"Not this time. I wouldn't want to be a tourist there and I'm not ready to be anything else yet."

"That's my smart girl. But someday, if what you want is New York, I'll make you a present of it on a silver platter."

Her eyes darkened. In her breast the quick beat of anticipation slowed to a dull pain. "We've tried American doctors. The surgeons out here are graduates of the best eastern schools. If in Europe there's a doctor who can help Eva we should get her to him fast. Maybe the delay is harmful."

"Soon as it's safe over there we'll go."

"But by then something may come up here to prevent."

"Nothing will prevent. There's nothing I'd not give up to make Eva whole again. You're the same. You'd give it all up: the safety you prize and the ambition for which you're willing to risk safety. All we've got or might have, you'd give up for her."

"In a minute, John. In a minute, if they'd let you make that kind of bargain."

"You're a pious woman, Louise, but for Eva I believe you'd make a bargain with God or the devil."

Chapter XV

—◦◉◦—

Journey for Eva

THE JOURNEY FOR Eva was like a dream. New York, their first brief stop, was altered as in a dream the familiar place is distorted. St. John's Park was gone. The tall trees had been destroyed, the fountain broken and carted away. The Hudson River Depot had replaced the pleasure ground. Where once there had been the graceful railing and proudly locked gate, the bleak façade of the depot narrowed and darkened the shabby street. Far uptown beside the Fifth Avenue there was the new Central Park. The avenue itself had changed. Between Twelfth and Twenty-third streets there were shops. Beyond the shops were new imposing edifices: hotels and clubs, churches and residences. Granite and marble were replacing brownstone. The new mansions were splendid as palaces. The remembered city was transformed into a dream of the future.

Only Washington Square, wide and tranquil, was unchanged. On the doors and window frames of the stately houses the white paint was spotless; the glass was polished clear as crystal; the brass shone. In the April sunlight the brick walls glowed soft and deep as velvet.

On this journey there was time only to see the surface of the city, time to show Ada and Eva and the baby only a little of what she

MRS. JOHN WM. MACKAY.

The frontispiece of the special edition of *The Queens of American Society* by Mrs. Ellet.

John, about 1890.

"Eva and Ada are growing up to [
ladies."

The Meissonier portrait.

"... she preferred Cabanel; he always made a lady look so pretty."

Willie, Clarie, and the nurse's son, Jean. Paris, 1878.

Mrs. Hungerford with her granddaughter, Edna Telfener.

Clarie, Louise, and Willie, 1886.

Clarie, Louise, and Willie at Cowes, 1886.

remembered. "Here on Broadway I drove in a hired carriage with Father. Here on the square I walked with Mémé. Even then the Fifth Avenue was a fine thoroughfare." She remembered the avenue stretching north, a brown vista stretching straight as a satin ribbon held taut on a table under a lamp. The white stone and the mansard roofs made a handsomer display.

If they came again, Louise thought, not as travelers passing through a seaport but as residents returning to their home, they would stay in one of the new hotels on the fashionable avenue. The hotel would be a beginning. After that there would be a house, an elegant house on the square or a white stone palace near the vast new park. Someday they would surely come again. They would come for good. John would give her the key. St. John's Park and its gold keys had vanished. She supposed the keys hadn't been made of gold but that was how she had imagined them. Louise smiled. It would take a key of gold to open the door to New York society. John would provide the key and once the door was unlocked the ladies would realize that she was not one more unwelcome rich intruder but an exile coming home. Mémé had taught her well, so had the Sisters at Benicia.

Someday a journey would end in homecoming. This journey was for Eva.

Louise was awed by London. She had never imagined such an immensity of stone. She had not expected so vast a metropolis. At first she felt lost within its confines. Slowly she learned to find her way in the cities within the city, cities of finance, of government, and of fashion. She recognized the landmarks she had long admired: the Tower of London, St. James' Palace, the Houses of Parliament, Westminster Bridge. It was all just as she had seen it in the bookstore in Downieville, in the library at Benicia. For the first weeks the weather was chilly, the skies were overcast. In the gloom the famous buildings were exactly as Louise remembered them, gray as the engravings in Mr. Langton's books.

In May the sun shone. In the parks and in the squares the trees and shrubs were bright with leaf and flower. Most of all Louise admired the squares set about with private mansions—Berkeley Square, Belgrave Square.

"This is how St. John's Park was," she told John. "Only in London there are so many."

"Want a key to one of these?" he asked.

"No, but I'd like to come here as a visitor. I'd like to see inside some of the grand houses and even perhaps be presented to the Queen. They say Mrs. Sandy Bowers was."

"And she sure was proud of it."

"I'd be proud to be presented and visit the mansions of Belgravia and become acquainted with lords and ladies but I could never feel at home here as I could in New York."

In June it was at last safe for tourists to go to Paris. The Commune was over. The defeated city was at peace. Paris was more beautiful than Louise had expected. The pictures she had seen, the books she had read, the French dispatches in American newspapers and magazines: none of those had prepared her for the reality. In spite of war and siege and revolution Paris was a city of light by night as well as by day. In the day the wide vistas of the new boulevards and flowering parks were open to the sun. At night the gaslight shone on fountains and monuments. In the Place Vendôme the tall column was broken, but the smooth, curved façade of the circle was unspoiled. The palace of the Tuileries was in ruins and in the Place de la Concorde one of the fountains was shattered, but beyond the horses of Marly, beyond the burned and broken buildings, at the end of the broad Champs Élysées the triumphal arch stood proud and tall as though no invading soldiers had lately marched beneath it.

The young surgeon whom John had been advised to consult was not in Paris. He would not return until September.

"We'll see the sights here," John said. "And then we'll make a bit of a Grand Tour."

To be a tourist in Paris was, Louise decided, more agreeable than to be one in London. The English capital was for those who had penetrated its fastness. Paris seemed more welcoming to a stranger. Perhaps it was the air and the light. Whatever his sins, Napoleon III had certainly opened his city to the light and warmth of the sun.

French society had returned to the capital. In the afternoon the Champs Élysées and the drive beside the lake in the Bois de Boulogne were crowded with fashionable vehicles.

Louise and John watched them pass.

"Enjoying it?" he asked. "I am. It's good as a show. Good as one of Piper's extravaganzas."

"And the cast is better dressed than any we ever saw." Louise gazed admiringly at the ladies in their elegant, pale summer dresses.

"They sure are. With their parasols and their little dogs, the ladies are sure dressed à la fancy. I never saw anything to beat it."

"Nor I." Louise frowned at the dress which had looked so fine when she had tried it on in San Francisco. The skirt was cut wrong, there was too much embroidery, too much lace. She touched the brim of her hat. She was wearing far too many colored ribbons and feathers. "Compared to those ladies, John, I feel as loud as the Fourth of July and as gaudy as a hurdy-gurdy woman."

"There's not one of them can touch you for looks. But if you want to fix yourself up like them you go ahead."

"But with all the clothes I brought——"

"Coals to Newcastle, I guess, and inferior coals at that. You go buy yourself a trousseau and fix Mémé and the girls up too."

"But what will you do with yourself if we're at the dressmakers' all day?"

"I have it in mind to make a trip to Ireland."

"But I'd love——"

"You wouldn't love Ireland if that's what you were meaning to say. Dublin's a fine city right enough, but it's not so fine as this. And anyway it's not the high and mighty neighborhoods I'm wishing to see. Nor the high and mighty people, the English at the castle and the Protestant landlords. It's the streets I knew I'm hankering after, and perhaps a little of the green country beyond."

"But you'll be lonely. You've no friends or relations there."

"No relations. There was only the two of us, me and my sister that became a nun. And my parents had no folks left. Still I'd like to be sure, now that I'm in luck, that there's no one at all I owe a kindness to from the old days."

When John returned he spoke little of his trip. "There was no one left at all, though that I was expecting. It was all as I expected, it's me that's different. The land hasn't changed, the soft green land."

"Then why are you disappointed? Because you are disappointed."

"No, I'm not. I did what I meant to do. Made sure there was no friend left and I saw the green fields again. There's no green like it anywhere on earth. But I've lived too long in America to be at my ease in a country that's not free."

"Maybe it's that, John. But I think you're sad from trying to go back across too many years. That's never a cheerful journey and it certainly isn't one to make alone."

"Right you are, Louise. So let's go forward. And for a start let's see a little more of this Europe we came so far to visit. We've time for Rome before the doctor'll be back in Paris."

"And the Italian lakes?"

"Sure, if you want to, though I bet there's not a one of them is a patch on Tahoe, but we'll take them in. We'll take in every last thing we've time for between now and September."

In September the doctor advised against an immediate operation. The winter was not a good season for convalescence and for weeks, perhaps months, he would not be able to let Eva leave Paris. The best thing for the child, he said, would be to take her south for the winter. In the Mediterranean sunshine she would grow strong. She would then be more fit to undergo the operation and treatment in the following summer.

John decided that Louise and the children should remain in France with Mémé. "The doctor's right, Louise. A winter in the South will do Eva good. And it'll be nice for Ada too. She's getting a big girl, near fourteen. It's time you were giving her those educational frills you've had your heart set on."

This was not the way in which Louise had hoped to visit the southern shore. She had not thought that she would first see it veiled in apprehension. "If you think I ought, John."

"I think you ought. It may make all the difference to Eva. And it'll do you good. You'll like a winter under blue skies and with warm breezes instead of our eternal Washoe zephyr. I'll come back in June and we'll see Eva through her ordeal together. Meanwhile you look on this time as a holiday."

The winter was a happy one. Nice and its environs were all Louise had dreamed. Ada and Eva attended an academy that was the equal of Benicia. It was not winter unless one looked at the calendar and read the names of the months. Winter had no reality in the Riviera's summer. The year stood still. The coming of the real summer was almost forgotten. The winter turning imperceptibly to spring was motionless as time in a fairy tale.

John was not able to return in June. He wrote to Louise, urging her not to wait for him. For Eva's sake it was best that the operation be performed as soon as possible.

Louise returned with her mother and the children to Paris. During the long weeks that preceded and followed the operation she hid her fear. She forced herself not to feel afraid. It was difficult to hide fear from a child.

She remembered what John had said when they had decided to allow the French doctor to operate. "He's supposed to be the best man in Europe on this sort of thing. If, in a bad situation, in the mines or anywhere else, you call in an expert you've got to trust him or he's no use to you. Eva's in a bad situation. It may be this fellow can get her out of it. I doubt he can make it any worse for her."

The doctor made Eva's situation no worse. Indeed he improved it, but only a little. Louise listened to his explanation.

"The operation has been a partial success, madame. A complete success was, as I told you, to be hoped for only, not to be expected. Still we have accomplished something, all that was possible. The child will be a little less lame."

"A partial success! A little less lame! What use is that to her?"

"It is something that there is an improvement. In this type of operation, even an improvement is rare. You see, madame . . ."

Louise did not listen. The man had failed. Why must he go on talking? He had failed, but somewhere there must be someone else.

"Forgive me," she said, "but perhaps there is someone else. You are, after all, rather young."

"No, madame, there is no one. Has anyone else offered you even hope?"

"No." Louise remembered Dr. Kibbe's kind, pitying voice and all the voices before and after his. No one had had anything but kindness and pity to offer.

"There is no further hope, madame. It will be best if you will accept that. It is best if one can recognize that one is at the end of a road that leads nowhere. The stretching process has lengthened the leg a little, but only a little. More is not possible."

"You are quite sure that there is no possibility?"

"Quite sure, madame. Anyone with any knowledge of surgery will

tell you the same. Further operations, further treatment can cause
only useless suffering."

Louise walked slowly away from the nursing home. It was hard
to relinquish hope. Somewhere there must be another cleverer doctor. She stopped herself. They had tried so many. For Eva's sake
they had tried. Now for her sake they must stop trying. Their hope,
their self-deceiving hope, could not forever deceive her. In the
child's heart the vain hope, too long prolonged, would turn to
despair.

Louise found herself walking on the Champs Élysées. Children
rolled their hoops or watched the puppet shows. In August the fashionable thoroughfare was almost empty, but here and there Louise
saw an elegant figure. They were extraordinary, these French
women. They were not as pretty as American women, they were
not as well made. Yet they gave the impression of beauty of face and
figure. They knew how to dress, they knew how to move. They knew
how to make the most of every scrap of prettiness, they knew how
to conceal a defect or to turn it into an asset.

Louise stood still. That was it. Lameness could not become an asset
but it could be concealed. The end of the road, the doctor had said.
So be it. Now she would find another road for Eva. Eva was lame.
She would always be lame, but much could be done. There were
dancing masters who could teach her to move with grace. There
were dressmakers who could hide the slight crookedness. Eva had a
pretty voice. She should be taught to sing and to play the piano.
She must be helped. She must not be destroyed. And she would be
destroyed unless those who surrounded her ceased to think of her
as a cripple.

They must begin now. A trip to Gay Paree, that was what John
had promised. That was what, from this day on, Eva must have.
Tomorrow she would come home. Tomorrow she must begin to forget the weeks of pain.

Louise turned back toward the hotel. She must prepare Mémé
and Ada for disappointment. She must tell them that this slight
change was all the improvement that could ever be expected. She
must tell them to pretend, for Eva's sake, that they were not disappointed.

She frowned. She did not see the children playing beneath the
chestnut trees. She saw Eva's hopeful eager face as she limped across

the room in the nursing home. Pretense would not deceive the child for long; she must see in the faces about her real pleasure in her improvement. Louise determined to tell the truth only to John. To Mémé and Ada she would speak of Eva's improvement. She would speak briskly and cheerfully and they would believe her. "With the years," she would say, "with the years as Eva grows stronger there will be an even greater difference. Her lameness will become almost imperceptible." And her words would have a sort of truth. She would believe as she spoke. For she, Louise, would make the difference.

In the two months before John came Louise watched Eva grow in confidence.

The child seemed not to listen as Mrs. Hungerford softly exclaimed, "Oh, she is improved, Louise, quite a marked improvement! And you say that by the time she is grown no trace will be left?"

"Or so little as to be imperceptible. So little that it will not matter at all."

Eva seemed not to listen as she held her doll. She sat quite still holding the doll. Louise remembered and recognized the stillness of a child trying to be invisible as she listened.

"I am happy for you and for our little darling." Mrs. Hungerford gathered Eva into her arms. "After all the years of worry and not being able to speak of it."

Her elders' tactful silence, Louise realized, must have been hard for Eva to bear. How could they all have forgotten the patient understanding with which a child pieces together and interprets the silences as well as the conversations of adults?

Eva pressed her cheek against her grandmother's. "Do you know, Mémé, Mammy says that soon I am to have a dancing master."

"Think of that, my darling!"

The happiness on Mrs. Hungerford's face was reflected on Eva's. The anxious hopeful look which Louise had seen so often in her daughter's eyes was gone. The dark eyes were serene and untroubled.

The first night he was in Paris, John remarked to Louise on the change in Eva. "I didn't want to speak of it in front of her for fear I'd embarrass her, but there's something different about her. She has a new look altogether, a happier look."

"It's been partly the trip to Gay Paree, I think. These last weeks it's been the trip you promised her. We've seen the palace of the Louvre and we've been to the opera and to the theater. Poor Mr. Piper, I fear he'll never really dazzle the children again. I promised that you would take us all in the train to Versailles."

"What's wrong, Louise? You're talking too much and too fast. You're not a babbler."

"Nothing. Nothing new at least."

"So long as it's not Eva. That's the important thing. I could tell by the look on all your faces that she's coming along grand. She still limps quite a bit, though. How long will that last?"

"Always. She'll always be lame. Always."

"Oh, my dear." He took her cold hands in his. He clasped them gently. "And the poor little dear. But we'll not give up. We'll find another doctor. They say that in Germany . . ."

"No, John. No. We've done with that. It's no use." She told him the doctor's verdict.

John frowned. The lines deepened beside his mouth. "He probably has the right of it. He's the only man who's ever helped us at all. And Lord knows we've been to plenty. What's Mémé's opinion?"

"I've told the truth only to you. To Ada, even to Mémé, I've said there is a real improvement, that as Eva grows older the limp will be less and less perceptible. I've spoken of dancing masters. They can help, John, and dressmakers too, but I've made it sound frivolous and worldly, never serious, never important. I've smiled and said, I've said . . ." Her voice cracked with weariness. "I'm so tired of smiling."

"Poor girl. My poor girl." They sat silent on the gilt-framed sofa. Only their hands touched. The heavy brocade curtains shut out the lights of Paris and muffled the sounds of the city. The lamplit room was quiet.

Louise broke the silence. "It's been Gay Paree for her these last weeks. That much she's had."

"Good. That's how it has to be for her everywhere. That's how we have to make every place for her. She must grow up as every girl desires, gay and happy."

"And pretty, John. A girl wants to be pretty."

"She shall be. She has a dear little face. She has Mémé's eyes. They're lovely eyes. She'll grow up pretty and accomplished. We'll have the best teachers for her in music and in art."

"You think it will work?"

"Sure it will. You've made a fine start. We'll give her a little more of Gay Paree and then we'll go to Nice. I can stay till after Christmas. Then you and Mémé and the children can finish out the winter."

"Are you sure, John? Can you afford the time away from Nevada? I haven't even asked about the Consolidated Virginia."

"Nothing to tell yet. We got control last January. That was cheap enough even with searching and securing the titles. The shares dropped to less than two dollars. Since then, though, we sure spent plenty. We've put into the Con Virginia pretty near everything we took out of the Hale and Norcross."

"And nothing to show?"

"Not so far. Sharon calls us the joke of the Comstock. He was none too pleased when Hayward and Jones struck their bonanza in Crown Point. He'll be still more displeased if the Irishmen are right about the Consolidated Virginia."

"And are you?"

"We believe we are. Now if we can only hang on."

"I think we should go home."

"What for? Either the vein will open up as we think, or it won't. Me spending Christmas over here won't change anything. Jim Fair's on the spot and no one has a better nose for ore."

"And you trust him enough to stay away so long?"

"I trust Jim Fair entirely."

"And the expense, John? If the profits from the Hale and Norcross are gone."

"If we're on the last of the money we may as well spend a bit on ourselves and the children."

"Do you and Fair really mean to put every dollar of the firm's capital into those mines? If Sharon failed . . ."

"Sharon's no miner. Never was. Me and Fair have been miners for more than twenty years. We found the vein in the Best and Belcher. A seam is all it is, but we're tracing it north. It's a mighty narrow road, narrow as a string sometimes, but we believe it will lead us to the heart of the lode."

"And if not?"

"If not, we'll go broke and start over. Meantime you'll at least have had your European tour and Eva will have had her chance. Soon as we reach Nice you get started with the dancing masters and the dressmakers and the rest. But remember the hard job is ours. The real difference is up to us. We have to create it in Eva's mind and in everybody else's."

"Can we, John?"

"Sure we can. Together we'll make the riffle for her."

"It won't be easy."

"That it won't, but we'll manage. Together, Louise, we'll manage just fine for our daughter."

Chapter XVI

············•◉•············

Bonanza

IN THE EARLY summer of 1873 John returned to Paris. Louise had known from the tone of his letters that things were going well in Virginia City. She had not known how well until they were alone on the night of his arrival.

"I wouldn't put it on paper even to you, Louise. Letters can go astray," he said. "But we've struck it. Finally, my girl, we've struck it. In March the vein began to open up. The ore is there. From here in it's only a question of time and digging. It's been a long pull, old lady. We were pretty near the end of our rope."

"Is the town in an uproar?"

"Virginia, you mean? No. Folks know we have a big body of ore but they have no idea how big it is. This isn't just another strike. There's a mountain of silver in the depths of the Con Virginia. This is bigger than Crown Point. This is the real bonanza. This is the heart of the lode."

"After twenty-two years. That was the long pull, not just these last months. Twenty-two years in the mining country. So many hadn't the strength for it, but you had. First in Sierra County and then in Washoe."

"You've known the long hard pull too, Louise. That's why it's worth it to make you queen of the Comstock and any other damn place you've got your heart set on. You've known it all, same as me, the whole twenty-two years of it."

"Almost. It was nineteen years ago this summer."

"I was a little ahead of you when the steamers put in at Chagres."

Louise stared at the luxuriously furnished bedroom as though she saw it for the first time. She had never grown completely used to such rooms. She had never come to take them for granted.

"I haven't quite believed in any of it," she said. "It always felt a little as if I were living in a play on which the curtain would come down at any minute and then they'd put away the scenery and the costumes."

"You can believe it now. It's all yours for good. Everything you've had up to now and anything more you want."

"Nineteen years." Louise looked from the wide, deep-carpeted, silk-curtained room to the small remembered rooms in Grand Street, on the summit of the isthmus, in Downieville, in Virginia City. "You've brought us all home safe, John."

"It's you, Louise, who have brought the girls home safe. You and Mémé between you. I thought today when I saw them they were like little princesses, the both of them. Ada was always lovely but now she has style, not just her clothes but the way she speaks and holds herself. She's a real little lady."

"That's what I promised her. Long ago I promised . . ."

"Did you now? Well, you sure kept your word. And Eva is grown pretty and she has a confidence she never had."

"And Willie?"

"He's a fine boy. And thank the Lord you haven't got him rigged out à la fancy. Sure I can see he's going to grow up a good tough Irishman like his father."

"He won't need to be tough."

"It never hurts."

"I suppose not. But he's my baby and I don't want to think of him growing up and having to fight his way as you did."

"Maybe he won't have to—but we want to make certain sure he can. You leave that part of his education to me. The girls I'll be leaving to you entirely. What do you plan now for them?"

"I want to bring Eva home with us. But Ada ought really to stay here with Mémé and finish her education. Perhaps Father would be willing to leave La Paz. He's done well there, but . . ."

"The colonel is leaving La Paz. He's meaning to settle in San Francisco or Virginia."

"Oh, John, no. He's never been lucky in mines. And if another boom is on the way . . . It ever seemed to me that the boom times were the most dangerous."

"You're right there. But don't worry, I'll persuade the colonel to let me do the investing for the both of us."

"And if he would come abroad to be with Mémé and Ada. He's long hankered to make the Grand Tour."

"He shall have his Grand Tour and Ada her education. And what do you want for yourself?"

"I don't know. San Francisco perhaps to begin. I hate to take Eva back to live in Virginia. The Sisters do their best, but . . ." Louise hesitated. "And not just for Eva, for me. I hate Virginia."

"I know you do. I understand. And I'll have to be at the Bay near as much as in Virginia. San Francisco will suit me fine." He smiled and added, "To begin with. For it's to be New York in the end, isn't it? That's your heart's desire. It'll have to wait, but in the end you shall have it. You shall have what I promised—the whole damn world on a silver platter."

"And you, John? Is there nothing you desire?"

"You are my heart's desire, you and the boy—but there's more to any man than his heart. There's his will and his strength. They can make him master of his world. The Comstock's my world."

"The power and the glory. I told you once that you wanted them and now they're yours."

"And I told you that you wanted them, too, and that we'd have them and enjoy them together."

"So enjoy, Mrs. Mock would tell me, enjoy. And I shall, oh, John, I shall so enjoy."

Louise had never known such a summer. She could take pleasure in each hour and let it slip away. Other days as fair were waiting.

She was not part of the European world of fashion but she felt at her ease as she watched that world. Someday, if she chose, she might enter it as a visitor. Already she looked as if she belonged to it. No lady of title was more simply and elegantly dressed than she.

She drove with John in the Bois on one of their last afternoons in Paris. "John," she asked, "do you remember what a frump I looked that first summer? No one would take me for a tourist now." She laughed with pleasure. "Though I like being a tourist," she continued thoughtfully. "I like not bothering to please anyone but ourselves. A child's holiday must be like this. A rich child, of course. Almost thirty and I behave like a girl on her first outing. Do you think me very spoiled, very extravagant? I love it all so: the clothes and the jewels and the beautiful, expensive hotel rooms. Most of all I like knowing it will last. Do I sound very foolish, babbling like this?"

"No, you sound young, younger than I've ever heard you. I like the sound of it. And I like you to enjoy your holiday. You deserve it. You've been game from the day I first spoke to you about the Hale and Norcross. But you were never a willing gambler."

"I was willing, John. But I was frightened sometimes."

"Sure you were. So was I, many a time. So was Jim Fair, though he'd never say so. Only a fool would be otherwise. But the point is we never lost our nerve. And here we are on top."

"With our private carriage and pair. A private carriage has been a symbol to me as long as I can remember. You must have thought me absurd to buy a carriage and pair for so short a time."

"They'll come in handy for Mémé after we've gone. Besides I understand how some little small thing can stand for all the things you haven't got. Take this walking stick." He held out the stick and the sunlight shone on the wide ring of engraved silver that bound the handle. "When I was a boy a silver-mounted walking stick was my idea of the most fine and costly object a man could possess. Jim Walker couldn't have given me anything in parting to please me more."

"But you'd never have bought it for yourself, nor would you carry it in Virginia."

"A fine sight I'd look on C Street, rigged out like a dude in a frock coat and carrying a walking stick. It's different on holiday."

"I wish our holiday could last longer."

"You could stay on a bit, but I must be getting home. We've planned to do a bit of reorganizing. We're putting certain mines into the California Company—keeping control of course."

"This isn't another gamble?" she asked anxiously.

"No, my dear, we're safeguarding what was a gamble and is now an investment. You've no more need to worry. I'll buy stocks as I need them for control of the lode but I'll not gamble in them. My business is mining, not stocks. I'll stick to the mines."

"The richest mines on earth! I want to see your mines. I want to go to Nevada for a little while, though I never thought I should say it. I want to visit the Consolidated Virginia. And I want to see you the acknowledged boss of the Comstock."

"You'll have to wait a bit for that. Like I told you, folks don't realize what we've got. Virginia has other things on its mind. Mining stocks in general are in bad shape. But by October the Con Virginia ought to really open up. I've a mind to take Dan de Quille down before the rumors get to flying."

"But he'll start the rumors with an account in the *Enterprise*."

"You'll not be able to stop them by then. And Dan will write an honest account. Besides he's entitled to the story. Back in '67 as mining editor of the *Enterprise* he saw the future in White and Murphy and the rest. Urged them to consolidate and to sink new shafts to the east. I figure that Dan has a right to be the first outsider to know what we've got."

"I'd like to be in Virginia then. I'd like to watch a lot of faces when it dawns on the city that the Irishmen are masters of the lode."

"Whatever your reason, I'll be glad to have you home."

"I've another reason for going home. A better reason. For over a fortnight I've been sure. We're to have another baby next April."

"Then you'll certainly not be coming to Virginia nor going down any shaft. We'll get a house in San Francisco. We'll do nothing to endanger you or the boy."

"Maybe it won't be a boy this time."

"Sure it will. And I'll tell you, Louise, I've been hoping for this and I've been thinking. I'd like to give this one a biblical name. Abraham maybe, or Samuel. They're very American, those Old Testament names. Abe Lincoln. Sam Adams. I'd like a name like that for the boy."

Louise looked at him in dismay. "But those names are so old-fashioned and ugly. Even Daniel. I know Father would never have chosen such a plain name for himself. Oh, no, John, please. I had something quite different in mind."

"And what would that be?"

"There was the dearest little boy on the beach at Nice. Very like Willie, but with long, long curls. I knew you'd not want Willie's hair so long. He was a little English boy and his name was just as pretty as he was; Clarence."

"Clarence!"

"Many boys nowadays are called Clarence. It's a very fashionable name. Not just English boys. American boys, too, in the eastern states. There's even your friend, Mr. King."

"In spite of Clarence King the name's a mite too fashionable for the Comstock."

"Our boy won't live on the Comstock all his life. I thought we would call him Clarence Hungerford, Clarie for short. That goes nicely with Willie. Please, John. And anyway maybe we'll have a girl."

"We'll have a boy, all right. And you can call him anything you like. It's little enough for a mother to ask to name her child."

"Thank you, John. Lots of men promise hearts' desires ever so grandly and then refuse all the little favors." She put her gloved hand on his. "You keep all the promises, big and little."

Louise did not see the bonanza mines for many months. Her second son was born in San Francisco in April of 1874. In the fall of the year, she visited Nevada.

Virginia City looked much the same. Boom times had returned. C Street was crowded. The saloons and the brokers' offices were overflowing with customers. The noise of machinery roared day and night.

Theresa Fair was waiting to welcome Louise. "Have you come back for good?" she asked. "Though this house can't seem much after your nice place in O'Farrell Street. Or likely you're thinking of building a real mansion at the Bay. I've missed you."

"And I you."

"And you must stay for a bit now. You won't know the place. Such prosperity. It's like old times."

"I know the place. I know it too well to wish to stay."

"Oh, my dear, don't get to remembering the bad days. You must forget them."

"I don't forget any of it. I don't forget your kindness, Theresa. I can speak of it now because if I cry I'm not ashamed. And I don't forget Mrs. Taylor and Mrs. Jones and the Rosener brothers who gave me work when I needed it, and Mrs. Mock. Many a week she carried me when I couldn't pay. And Father Manogue. They are the kind friends I can count on less than my ten fingers." She held out her hands. "I owe them much and I shan't forget, but to Virginia I owe nothing. It's a cruel, destroying place, as dangerous in good times as in bad. It's no longer dangerous to me but I have no love for it."

"Then you're not staying?"

"Not for long. I want to go down in the mine. And after that I'll be glad to shake the dust of Virginia City from my feet." She sipped her tea and smiled at Theresa. "And don't look so disapproving, Theresa, my dear. You won't stay here the rest of your life either. Don't you realize that with wealth like this we can queen it anywhere we've a mind to?"

"You're like Jim. You're not afraid of great wealth. I am. I like being rich, but within reason. This is too big."

"Not for me. I knew poverty too well to be afraid of riches."

"It's not afraid I am exactly, or maybe it is. I don't know. I only know I've been happy here with Jim and the children."

"It's the children you must think of. For their sakes, Theresa, you'll have to move on. You don't want them stuck on this mountainside forever."

"I suppose you're right, Louise. But I've friends here. Other places the people might be too grand for me."

"Many people here used to seem too grand for us. Remember? Senator Stewart and Mr. Sharon. And now we're quite used to them. You can get used to people anywhere. And besides, Theresa, we're grand people ourselves now." Louise laughed. "Sometimes I still can't believe it—Mamie Hungerford from Downieville come all this way. That's why I want to go down into the Consolidated Virginia, though I dread the trip down the shaft. I've a deep desire to see this bonanza of ours. To see it and to touch it till I really believe in it."

Louise was outwardly calm as she prepared for the descent into the mine. Her hands did not shake as she fastened the clumsy garments that were provided for visitors.

At the mouth of the shaft she hesitated as she saw clouds of steam rising from the opening. She closed her nostrils, remembering the evil-smelling smoke that had poured out of the Yellow Jacket in '69.

"Don't be nervous," John whispered. "It's only a vapor that forms when the warm air meets the cold. It'll be gone after a few feet."

"I'm very nervous, but it's worth it." She stepped resolutely onto the wooden floor of the cage. She could see nothing at first. Then her eyes grew accustomed to darkness. She watched the timbers of the shaft rushing upward. Lights flashed and voices were heard as they passed a station. Then there was darkness again, then another station. The smooth motion changed. The cage seemed to swing unevenly. Louise held fast to John.

"It's just the spring in the cable," he said. "It's almost over. We're at about thirteen hundred feet now."

Fifteen hundred feet beneath the surface the cage came to rest. John led Louise along a timbered corridor. The air was hot and heavy. Sweat poured down her face and blinded her.

"Well, Louise, here we are. The richest spot on earth."

Louise wiped the sweat from her eyes and stared around the wide space in which they stood. Miners were hacking and hammering the walls of blue-black rock. Looking up, Louise saw far above her the lights of candles where other miners worked. In places the rock glittered as though it were set with diamonds.

"Pyrites," John said. "Iron and copper pyrites."

"They're pretty to see. Prettier than the dark rock."

"That dark rock is almost pure silver. We can send it to the mills without assorting it. We get a fair amount of gold too."

"How queer, John, that silver should look so plain. I knew it but I didn't expect it. The pyrites sparkle like diamonds, and those crystals! This big pale blue one is like a giant jewel."

"Quartz crystals," John said. "We like to find them, they show there's life in the vein. But silver can be pretty too. I'll show you."

He led her to a chamber about ten feet square. Its walls were flecked with silver. The ceiling was covered with silver in the form of crystals.

"Silver sometimes shines in its natural state," John said. "Wait here a moment."

He left her and presently returned with what looked like a coil of polished silver wire. "I was lucky. One of the men just found a bright bit. Usually this crystallized silver is black. It's only once in a while that it shines like this. Keep it as a souvenir."

"I'll make some fine and memorable thing of it."

"There's not enough there to make much of anything."

"Can I have enough, John? Can I have enough silver from our

own mine to make a memorable thing? A dinner service, I think, made by the finest silversmith in the country."

"You shall have it. I like the notion of eating off silver brought straight from the Comstock. Be damned if I won't bring it up for you myself."

As she walked beside John, Louise twisted the bright silver in her hand. She stared at the dark walls streaked with green. Corridors cut across corridors. Chamber after chamber was floored and walled and roofed with precious metal. Here was a city of silver thrusting ever deeper, ever wider into the earth. She wiped the sweat from her forehead and shielded her eyes with her hand.

"The heat'll be too much for you," John said. "I'll take you up again."

"No, let me look a little more. I've imagined it so long." But she knew she had not imagined it as it was. In the old days in Downieville and in later days in Virginia she had listened to stories of gold and silver mines that had made men rich; she had listened to dreams of the gold and silver that still awaited discovery. Compared to the reality, the dreams were pale as the candles that flickered high above her head. Now as she looked at the reality that surrounded her she understood the fever, the fever of '49, the Washoe fever. Poor souls, she thought. Poor sick souls.

John touched her shoulder. "Come, my dear, don't stand dreaming. This place is really too hot for anyone who's not used to it."

"I wasn't dreaming, John, I was pitying the dreamers who caught the fever. Many of them died, you know, of the Washoe fever. Whatever the final cause, it was really the fever they died of."

"I know, Louise." He urged her gently toward the shaft. "I shouldn't have let you come down. It's been too much for you."

"No, it hasn't. Or maybe it has. Maybe the contrast between this rich reality and the sad remembered days was too much, for a minute. Never think I'm not grateful."

He led her into the cage. As it rose in darkness she moved close to him. He put his arm around her.

"I understand, my girl," he said. "And I love you the better for having a heart that remembers. But now you must look forward again. There's a mighty fine future ahead of us."

"I'm looking at it, John. I see it plain and I like what I see."

Chapter XVII

···➤■◉■◄···

825 O'Farrell Street

THE FIRST YEAR in O'Farrell Street ended and the second year began. These were quiet years. After the long uphill pull Louise was content to rest and look about her. The pattern of western society was not unlike that of the East. The Spanish families were the equivalent of the descendants of New York's colonial families. In San Francisco there were the rich newcomers: the Crockers, the Millses, the Ralstons, as in New York the Astors, the Vanderbilts, the Belmonts. There were differences among the American newcomers. Those settlers who had come from the Atlantic states before the Gold Rush had a higher standing in the contemporary scene than the descendants of Spanish grandees. Twenty-five years seemed to be equal to about a hundred in the East and, Louise supposed, to three hundred according to English reckoning. Perhaps more, she thought, since the English aristocracy looked back to the Conqueror and American society to the landing of the *Mayflower*. In California the ships that counted rounded the Horn before '49. Of course, to count today the pioneers must have prospered in the years since the Gold Rush. To count anywhere one must be prosperous as well as gently born. Everywhere the elegant societies had been kept alive by newcomers, by their strength and their wealth. The wealth of the Comstock would, Louise knew, be more important than Farleigh Castle. Still, the legend of lost grandeur had kept her going in hard times. She owed it something now. She would prove it true and refurbish it. It would be useful. Even in a republic aristocratic descent was much admired. She remembered the crests she had seen shining on polished silver in New York houses long ago. There had to be silver for the crest to be seen, for the legend it represented to be accepted. Well, when the time came there would be plenty of silver. Millions of dollars' worth of silver was pouring out of the Con Virginia and the California.

When John came from Nevada, Louise went with him to dinners and balls. She watched the elite and studied their ways. Her time would come.

Most elegant of all the San Francisco hosts was William Ralston, the president of the Bank of California. In his mansion in San Francisco and at Belmont, his country estate, he entertained as lavishly as a European monarch. No king or emperor had done more for a favored capital than Ralston for San Francisco. He had built the Grand Hotel. He had surpassed it with the Palace that stood even more proudly, surrounding its vast courtyard. The California Theater, the massive Bank of California, and the broad highway of Montgomery Street were all monuments to Ralston's faith and pride in his adopted city. Louise remembered the small seaport she had seen in '54. Even then it had seemed to the traveler a city; it had dreamed that it was a city destined by gold to be a metropolis. Ralston, more than any one man, had helped to build the dream into elaborate reality.

Louise was pleased that the bonanza firm was to have its monument. On Montgomery and Pine streets they were building the Nevada Block. The ground floor would house the Nevada Bank. The completed structure would be as majestic as any in San Francisco.

John smiled at her pleasure. "You like the outward signs, don't you, old lady? Though I'd have thought you'd have wanted to make a bit more of a splash in the town yourself."

"Not yet, not here. I'm still on holiday—the lovely holiday that began when you brought the news to Paris. Do you think me very idle?"

"No woman with three children can be very idle."

"They don't keep me busy. Not with a nursemaid. They just give me joy."

"Enjoy your holiday, as you call it, Louise. You've a right to it."

"If you could only share it. Must you work so hard? The silver can't run away."

"Adolph Sutro's inching along with his tunnel. I don't mean for him to beat us."

"But won't his tunnel make it easier and safer to mine the ore?"

"Maybe so. But if he succeeds with it he'll be boss of the Comstock. I hope his day is long in coming but, by God, if it ever dawns he'll have earned it. We've all tried to stop him, the bank crowd and ourselves. That's one thing every mineowner was agreed on, not to pay tribute to Sutro, but he got going in spite of us. It's a race against time now, and I mean to win, but you've got to admire courage and endurance in any man. Though, mind you, it don't stop you fighting him and licking him if you can."

"You admire even Sharon and Jones and every last one of them whether they've worked with you or against you."

"Jones is my friend. But, friend or foe, Louise, you don't despise the men of the Comstock."

"If you had your way, John Mackay, I think you'd live your whole life in that dreadful Virginia City."

"Not dreadful for a man to work in, only for a woman to live in. I understand that fine. But for a man Virginia's quite a place. We came from a lot of towns and states and countries to meet at the foot of old Mount Davidson. Like them all or not, work with them or fight with them, they're men, hard brave men who came from the ends of the earth to the Comstock and stuck it out."

"You see. You're in love with the place."

"In a way, maybe. Still I like to come home from it. Being in this quiet house with you and the children is a respite for me. But I'm thinking I wouldn't want a holiday all the time. Nor will you, Louise. You'll be wanting to take your place in the world."

"Soon, John, when you can go East. But not yet. For the moment I'm content."

The summer of 1875 was a pleasant one. There were disturbances in the stock market, but Louise had learned from John to pay little attention to the rise and fall of prices. The Nevada Block was nearing completion. Silver flowed in a never-decreasing stream from the mines of the Comstock.

Everything seemed to be going well when, on the twenty-sixth of August, San Francisco was stunned by the news that the Bank of California had closed its doors.

John returned to O'Farrell Street long after midnight.

"Hell of a day," he said and ate in silence the meal that Louise prepared for him.

The next night when he came home he was still tired but his face was less strained.

"It's been a hell of a bad two days, Louise. But Mills has taken over. He'll pull the bank out of this."

"I still can't believe that the California Bank could fail—some folks are blaming the firm."

"We're not to blame."

"Even if you were responsible, I'd not blame you. The bank has been no friend to the Irishmen. Sorry as I felt for Mr. Ralston, I had to smile at the picture of Billy O'Brien starting to serve liquor on the counter of the California Bank. They say it was only a day or two ago that . . ." She hesitated. "You look angry, John. I . . ."

"G-g-go on, Louise. T-t-tell me the story as you heard it."

"Why only that some days ago Mr. Ralston, being, I suppose, quite beside himself with anxiety, threatened to drive Flood and O'Brien back to tending bar and they answered that if they ever served whisky again it would be over the counter of the California Bank. And folks say that yesterday O'Brien actually produced a demijohn and would have placed it on the counter of the bank only for you stopping him. Isn't it true?"

"It's a g-g-goddamn l-l-lie. I don't mind folks thinking we're fools enough to want the bank to go under, as much as I m-mind them believing such a tale of Billy. Billy O'Brien may have his faults, but cruelty isn't one of them."

"I'm sorry, John. I thought it was funny. The only bit of fun in a horrible day."

"It's not you I'm angry with, Louise. You just didn't think. But someone who can think invented the story. Someone who has it in for the firm. Poor Billy, as though with hundreds, probably thousands, of folks ruined he'd have the heartlessness to make a cruel joke of their misfortune. And besides, Louise, a failure like this is bad for all of us. It could wreck the whole financial structure of the city. Never think the firm had any part in it. Once we knew how bad the situation was, we did what we could to prevent disaster. There were assets we could have withdrawn. Poor Ralston cleared us. He told the newspaper fellows we had done what we could. We're standing beside Mills and Sharon. I've no personal love for them but I respect them. I fought them. I'd fight them again but that's of no importance now. Men like Mills and Sharon built this city."

"And Ralston. Most of all Mr. Ralston."

"In his way. The poor fellow. But a fellow like that is dangerous. Oh, I know he had courage and imagination. Too much of both and not enough judgment. Still, like you say, he loved the city."

"Even though he's ruined, don't speak of him in the past as if he was dead."

"He is. I hate to tell you. But he's dead all right. The poor fellow."

Louise's eyes widened. For a moment she could not speak. William Ralston had seemed as immortal as a character in a novel or a play.

"I don't believe it," she said slowly.

"It's true all the same. And maybe he's better off. This was the way of it. There was a directors' meeting and Mills asked for Ralston's resignation. He wrote it out calmly enough. Don't frown, Louise. It was necessary."

"It was cruel, cruel. Mr. Ralston made the bank. There'd have been no bank without him. They needn't have so humiliated him."

"They had to. Their duty is to save the bank if they can. Anyway Ralston took it quietly. Then he walked down to the Bay and went for a swim like he always did in the afternoon. Swam way out. There was a boy saw him. They found the body an hour ago. Poor Ralston."

"Poor Ralston indeed. Driven to suicide by his coldhearted friends."

"We don't know for sure that it was suicide. The man was tired to death, broken by anxiety. It may be his strength just failed. Anyway, may his soul rest in peace. But listen to me, Louise. Though it seems cruel to you, Mills did what was right."

"And Sharon? Sharon whom Ralston saved in 1864 when the Comstock ruined him."

"Not the Comstock, brokers dealing crookedly in Comstock shares."

"Anyway, he was wiped out when he went to Ralston. Ralston put Sharon on his feet again. The man was penniless. Ralston gave him his second chance."

"Even so, my dear, Sharon could act no differently today. Mills made the right decision and Sharon had to go along."

"And never mind Mr. Ralston, who put him where he is."

"There's more than one way of looking at it. Sharon owes loyalty to the bank and to the depositors too. You're like most in San Francisco, Louise. Mourning the death of a king. Ralston was very like a king at that, a king played by a talented actor. 'Let us sit upon the ground'—how does it go?"

"'And tell sad stories of the death of kings.'" She finished the quotation. "You're right, John. It's like that. Poor Ralston. Poor Richard."

In October, Virginia City was ravaged by the worst fire in its history. Louise shuddered at John's account of the devastation. Dwellings, their own included, and places of business, churches and theaters whether of brick or wood, had gone up in flames like so many cracker boxes.

"But we kept the fire away from the mines. That's the important thing. Pat Manogue saw it, God love him, though it must have near killed him to see St. Mary's burn. But since the mines are safe, we can build him a new church. We can build the whole damn city again."

"I know you'll take care of all you can."

"Poor Mrs. Mock was widowed in the fire. Her boardinghouse burned to the ground. Everything she owned in the world is gone with it."

"I must help."

"I'll see to it. There's a committee attending to the needs of the homeless, but when I go back I'll find out how much Mrs. Mock needs to get back on her feet and I'll see she gets every dollar of it and more."

"I'd rather the check came from me, John. She'd rather. I owe her much. She used to say it was little enough. Now it's my turn and it's little enough. And coming from me she can take it, not as charity but as just payment of a debt long owed."

After the fire there was peace from anxiety again. The Nevada Bank opened and the California Bank reopened its doors.

The Centennial Year began. This would be the year, Louise decided. It should be a lucky year in which to change the pattern of her life. It was time to leave San Francisco. Eva would soon be sixteen. She should complete her education in the East. Ada, at eighteen, was ready to come home and make her bow to American society. The easy holiday years were over. It was time to move to New York and to make a place there for her family.

On an evening in February she said to John, "I think it's time for the move to New York."

"You're right. In the spring. It'll seem natural for us to go East then to see the Centennial Exposition. Nevada will have a fine exhibit."

"But, John, the exposition is in Philadelphia."

"Philadelphia and New York are near enough on the cars. Many will be staying in New York during the exposition. I know you're meaning to settle us in New York, but there's no need to tell the world about your plans until you've succeeded."

"You've no need to be afraid of New York for me."

"It's a mighty big camp, Louise."

"New York's not just big, it's different. It's not like Virginia or even San Francisco. It's a city long established, rooted in tradition. I'd like to have Eva finish her education there. I'd like Willie and Clarie to have the advantage of growing up in a cultured, aristocratic society."

"And you'd like to be queen of the biggest camp of all."

"I suppose you're right. It's the finest, proudest city in America and I'd like to be part of it."

"And so you shall. I'll do what I can. There are several men of importance there with whom I've done business. I'll let them know we're proposing to visit their city. And Dick Dey will be useful."

"Dick Dey!" Louise exclaimed. She smiled at John's notion that his confidential secretary could be helpful in opening the door to New York society. "Mr. Dey is useful to you in business but . . ."

"I was thinking of Dick's connections. He comes from one of their old families. He tells me there's even a street named for some ancestor of his. But, mark you, Louise, this is in its way a business deal. And there'll be the equivalent of the California Bank crowd among the society ladies. They may not like the Irish any better than Sharon did."

"John, dear John, you've no need to be afraid for me. I'm a born

New Yorker. The ladies will soon see that I belong among them. And it will make it all the easier for me that many of the husbands already know and admire you."

"They do business with me. Many have done well. Mighty well."

"You see"—Louise laughed delightedly—"not only needn't you worry but you can be happy knowing you've made this possible for me too. This last, once impossible wish. I'm going home. When can we start?"

"Give me a month."

"And then will you come and will you stay?"

"I'll stay. As long as I ever stay anywhere. Now I'm between Virginia and the Bay. But New York's the financial capital of the country and in the end I'll have to be there as much as in the West. You may as well get us settled there."

"John." She moved from her chair to sit on the arm of his. "John, it's been a good holiday." She spoke slowly. "It's been more than that, it's been a good life. Maybe we shouldn't change anything. Maybe we should stay forever in this little quiet house on this quiet street."

"My darling, it was a good life in the old place on Taylor and Howard before even the Hale and Norcross, but I wasn't satisfied and neither were you. We both wanted real big success and by God now that we've made the riffle you're entitled to your share, old lady."

"Please, John"—she frowned—"don't call me old lady. I'm getting too old."

He laughed and drew her onto his lap.

"My poor old lady who's thirty-two."

"Soon enough your calling me that won't seem a joke, and besides . . ."

"And besides, in this grand and elegant society we'll shortly be moving in such expressions aren't used. Don't worry, old lady." He kissed her brow until it was smooth. "I'll only call you that when we're alone."

In April, John was still detained in San Francisco. Louise was impatient to be gone.

"It's as though I weren't anyplace," she explained to Theresa. "I'm not there except in my imagination and I'm not here any longer in my heart."

"Louise, I don't think you mean to come back. It's more than a visit you're planning. Your heart has ever been set on living in New York." Theresa's eyes filled with tears. "I'll be lost without you, Louise. You're my only friend from the old days."

"And you are mine. Louise Althea Howland was my childhood friend and there is still a warmth and a remembrance between us. But you are my only grown-up friend. And ever will be. From now on, Theresa, we'll make acquaintances, grand acquaintances and kind acquaintances. Some might even be both. We won't make friends any more, we won't need to. We'll have each other."

"With me here and you in New York?"

"That won't be forever. Jim won't be satisfied to be a great man in San Francisco. He'll want to shine in a larger place. New York or perhaps Washington. You'll want a larger world for the children, especially the girls."

"For Tessie particularly." Theresa dried her eyes. "She's so beautiful, that child. If only you weren't moving away. I always hoped for Tessie and Willie."

"That can happen too. But, you know, I'm not sure it would be Tessie. Willie has a real fondness for the baby. He quite often leaves the older children to play with Clarie and Birdie."

"She'll be clever, my Birdie. None of the others talked so early, but she'll never be as pretty as her sister, I'm afraid. Tessie has such wonderful high color and that beautiful wavy hair."

"Birdie will have a style of her own. Even now you can see the beginning of it. That jet-black hair and those bright dark eyes. And the quick way she moves her hands and cocks her head to one side. She's like a doll on a French music box."

"You see, Louise, you will miss us. All of us, even the children. You'll never love those strangers, those grand new acquaintances, half as well."

"I'll never love them at all in the true meaning of the word. But I'll like them and admire them and choose among them. You're right about me, Theresa, I have to get to the top."

The two women embraced. Louise went with Theresa to her carriage. She ran up the wooden steps and waved to her friend as the carriage drove off.

When the carriage was out of sight Louise still stood motionless. She stared unseeing at the street, at the house opposite. In her mind she saw a broader street, a finer house. The New York house not yet chosen, perhaps not yet built, was more real to her than 825 O'Farrell Street. This was only a stopping place. Downieville, Virginia City, San Francisco, all were, like the summit of the isthmus, way stations on a journey. Louise smiled in confident anticipation. The wide circle of the journey was almost complete. Soon, thanks to John, she would be safely, triumphantly home.

Chapter XVIII

———◆◉◆———

Homecoming

IN NEW YORK the spring of 1876 was cold and rainy. The little boys grew restless cooped up in the parlor suite of the Everett House.

"Rain, rain, go away," Clarie sang. "Come again another day."

"Don't sing that," Willie said crossly. "Here rain always comes another day. You don't have to ask it to. And that's a baby song anyway."

Clarie's large blue eyes filled with tears.

Eva took Clarie on her lap. "Willie's just cross because he can't go out to play."

"And anyway there's no one to play with," Willie said angrily. "At home we had friends. We had Jimmie and Charlie and Tessie and Birdie and we had all the Roseners and we had——" He interrupted his recital. "Mammy, when will we have friends here? Don't you know any ladies with little boys or even girls?"

Louise turned away from the window. "I'm afraid I don't yet. But soon I will. We have to get settled first."

She turned back to the window and drummed impatiently on the glass. It shouldn't take so long to get settled, to get started.

She had received letters from three of the gentlemen to whom

John had written. The letters were almost identical. The gentlemen were happy to learn of Mrs. Mackay's arrival in New York and hoped they could be of some service to her during her stay. In each case the writer regretted that his wife was out of town for the present, but on her return she would do herself the honor of calling at the Everett House.

It was a week since the letters had come. A week was not a long time, Louise told herself. It seemed long because she was waiting, but it was not long for ladies to be out of town—if they really were out of town. She frowned and stared at the square below her window. Suddenly the wet cobblestones gleamed in the sunlight.

"Look, children!" she exclaimed. "Clarie's song worked, the rain has gone away and there's enough of the afternoon left for a nice drive."

On the way out of the hotel Louise stopped to inquire for mail. A fashionably dressed couple were speaking to the clerk.

"Please be sure," the lady said, "that Mrs. John Mackay receives our cards."

"I am Mrs. John Mackay." Louise took the cards. As she glanced at them she recognized the name. She held out her hand to the lady. "I received your husband's kind letter and I have been looking forward to the pleasure of your visit."

"Charming of you to say so," the lady answered, "but I see that we have chosen an inconvenient moment. You are just going out."

"Only for a drive with the children. Eva and the nursemaid will take the boys out. This is my daughter Eva."

"Charmed," the lady murmured as her hand touched Eva's, "but really we don't wish to interrupt."

"You don't interrupt at all," Louise said gaily. "We can go up to my parlor. It's a little early for tea, but perhaps——"

"Not a bit too early," the gentleman said heartily, "a cup of tea is always welcome on a beastly cold day like this. And I want to hear the news of your good husband."

Louise poured tea and chatted with her visitors. They talked in formal phrases of the weather, of John, of the coming exposition at Philadelphia. This lady, Louise thought delightedly, was exactly like the lady long ago. She, too, lived on Washington Square. She had the same sober elegance of dress, the same reserved manner, the same long aristocratic nose, the same voice.

"How fortunate you are, Mrs. Mackay, to live in California. New York's climate is really perfectly dreadful."

Really. Perfectly. The elegant distortions of *ea* and *er* were just as Louise remembered.

Louise smiled and spoke of New York, of the charms of the new Central Park, of the delightful band concerts. She let fall a phrase in French.

As the lady rose to take her leave she asked, "When are you returning to San Francisco? It's so miserable here I should think you would long for your golden West."

"Worst spring in years," the gentleman said, "but don't let that discourage you and John Mackay from paying us a long visit. I'm looking forward to his arrival. And in the meantime, my dear"—he turned to his wife—"you wanted to invite Mrs. Mackay to your Thursdays."

"Oh yes, of course. On Thursdays at about five I'm always at home. I should be delighted if you would care to drop in."

"Now don't forget, Mrs. Mackay. My wife will count on you next Thursday. I shall not be there as I'm obliged to go out of town on a business matter but I shall not be away long and I shall look forward to seeing you on my return."

On the following Thursday, Louise selected her costume with care. She must be a picture of simple elegance. Some of the ladies, if they knew of her invitation, might be expecting a bonanza queen like poor Eilley Orrum. She decided on her sapphire-blue satin with the lace inserts and no jewelry except her pearl earrings. The lace would be ornament enough. At the last moment she added a small brooch of pearls and diamonds. She smiled across the years at Mrs. Mock. In going to these grand people, she felt that a little piece of jewelry wouldn't hurt; it would give her courage.

In the hope of just such occasions as this, Louise had hired Brown's smartest carriage and pair. When she reached Washington Square she gave her card to her footman. Up the steps of one of these houses she had carried Mémé's packages and now here she was in her handsome carriage, a fashionable lady dressed in satin and lace, with sables to protect her from the unseasonable cold. She was the very lady the child had imagined herself to be when she ran errands for Mémé on a bleak winter day.

Louise was still smiling at the child she had been when the footman's voice interrupted her reverie. "Sorry, madam," he said, "but the lady's not at home. I left your card."

"Oh. Then we'll go back to the Everett House, but first drive around the square and up the Fifth Avenue."

She must have mistaken the day. The line of carriages must be waiting for ladies in some other house. She must be mistaken but she was not. Only in this house were artificial lights already blazing in every room. Two ladies, laughing and talking gaily as though already they were at a party, walked briskly up the white steps. Before a gloved hand could touch the brass knocker the door opened to welcome them.

Louise felt herself shaking with rage. Rage was of no use to her. She tried to hold herself steady. She mustn't let the children see that she was distressed. She would tell Eva that she had stayed only a little while as was the custom in New York on a first visit. Her eyes smarted with angry unshed tears. She would not let that woman make her cry.

"That damned woman," she whispered through clenched teeth. She had often scolded John for his language. But at this moment profanity was better than tears. Tears were what that damned woman hoped for. She counted on Louise being too hurt to reveal the snub she had received. The woman's husband would not be pleased if he knew. Louise frowned. There was no dignified way in which she could let him know that his friend's wife had been turned away from his door.

Louise looked down at her hands. They were no longer trembling. She had herself under control. She could think clearly. She must say nothing of what had happened. The woman, because of her husband, would not dare to say. If no one knew of it, this snub, no matter how much it hurt, would not injure Louise.

She stared with hard dry eyes at the mansions on the avenue. There were other ladies. John had other business acquaintances who would be anxious to return or to earn a favor. She would pretend that this afternoon had never been. She would be patient and await her opportunity to try again.

On the following afternoon Louise was alone. Eva and the boys had gone out with the nursemaid. Louise had excused herself from the excursion on the ground that she must write a letter to John. She picked up her pen and put it down. What could she tell him? She had written about her callers. He would expect her to describe her afternoon in Washington Square. As she picked up her pen again there was a knock on the parlor door.

A boy brought in a card. Louise read the name and address. Mrs. Paran Stevens—244 Fifth Avenue.

"The lady's waiting downstairs, ma'am."

"Please show her up."

Louise remembered Mrs. Stevens. She had met her in San Francisco in '69 or '70. Mrs. Stevens, she recalled, was a large, handsome, dark woman with a frank amusing manner.

Louise tidied her front curls and smoothed her dress. She felt the hard quick beat of her heart. She must, she thought, have been very lonely to be so excited at the arrival of a caller.

"Dear Mrs. Mackay." Mrs. Stevens brushed past the boy. "What a pleasure to see you again after all these years."

"It's very kind of you to remember me."

"Of course I remember you and your delightful husband. My visit to California was before the great bonanza, but even then John Mackay was spoken of as a man to reckon with. And I could see it for myself when he called for you that afternoon at dear Amelia Neville's. I'd have come to see you sooner but I have only just heard you were in New York. Why on earth didn't you put a squib in the paper?"

"I never thought to do such a thing. In the smaller western towns one can't help the local publishing items about one, but it never occurred to me that a lady would deliberately try to have her name in the newspaper."

"Oh, my dear Mrs. Mackay, you have a lot to learn for all you appear such a woman of the world." Mrs. Stevens looked at her hostess approvingly. "You never learned to dress like that in California. Paris?"

"I have spent a good deal of time abroad. I lived in France for more than two years."

"Did you? That was a clever move—not to attempt New York straight from Virginia City. This is your first attempt at New York?"

"Attempt?" Louise repeated coldly. "I'm afraid, Mrs. Stevens, that I don't understand."

"Of course you don't. The trouble with me is that I talk too fast and too much. Or so my lawyer tells me. I've just come from his office. That's why I'm not properly dressed. I don't usually pay a social call in a tailor-made suit. But this isn't precisely a social call."

"I realize that. Would you care to sit down and explain just what sort of call you are doing me the honor of paying me?"

"I think you need a friend in New York. No, hear me out. I'll be frank with you and put all my cards on the table and you must do the same."

"I should be glad to if I knew what game we were playing."

"That's better. At least you're smiling at me even if you believe I'm mad, which I'm not. Nor, I think, are you. I have heard it rumored that you are here not to view the forthcoming exposition, not en route for Europe, but because you mean to settle here. True?"

"I don't know why I should discuss my plans with you."

"Because I can help you. I'm not the best guide there is to New York society but I'm the best that's available. And you can help me. At least your husband can. I'm a businesswoman. I look after my own affairs. I've had to since my husband died. I've plenty of money but at present I'm embroiled in a couple of lawsuits. Also my daughter Minnie's at an expensive age. All I want is John Mackay's advice on mining stocks."

Louise looked thoughtfully at her visitor.

"That's right, don't answer immediately. I'll be frank with you. My husband and I started out as hotelkeepers. We came a long way and since his death I've come further. I'm on many of the best visiting lists. Mrs. Gracie King, for instance, does me the honor of including me. Oh, people laugh at me and lie about me but they receive me and they come to my parties. Almost everyone worth knowing in New York comes to my Sunday evenings. I give them a good time, you see. You'd be surprised at how little fun there is at the parties of the real elite. There's wonderful food and wine and enough of both to choke an elephant, but there's not much laughter. Odd, isn't it, how hard we work to get into a world which isn't after all very amusing?"

Mrs. Stevens laughed harshly. "Still," she continued briskly, "it's the world everyone wants to get into. Amusing or not, those are the best people and that's what counts. But I warn you they are difficult. It won't be easy for you. They don't take kindly to newcomers. They're just getting over the shock of having swallowed a railroad king and a war millionaire. Well?" Mrs. Stevens paused.

Louise thought quickly. This queer woman was friendly. And Louise needed a friend, even a friend who must be bought and paid for. John would not like that part of it but he would do as his wife asked.

"Well, Mrs. Mackay, is it a bargain? Will I advise you and will your husband advise me?"

Louise hesitated only a moment. In spite of John's letters to his acquaintances, this friendship was all that had been offered to her. She would be a fool to refuse it.

"I shall be grateful for your advice," Louise said slowly. "And Mr. Mackay will most certainly wish to reciprocate any kindness shown to me."

"That's all I ask, my dear. As soon as he gets here you shall be guests of honor at one of my Sunday evenings. On his arrival we must have a squib in the paper. This is the age of advertising. Look here." Mrs. Stevens picked up a copy of the *Home Journal*. "And look in your daily paper. Read the guest lists and the little paragraphs of society news. Cutting, Duer, King, DePeyster, Kip, Livingston . . . There they all are. All the proud old New York names. Where do you suppose the journalists get their information? From every New York hostess. And the ladies are right. On my trip West I noticed the eastern and European dispatches in every little paper. New York and London, those are the centers of society. And the only way the elite can maintain their prestige is through the newspapers. Both the Prince of Wales' set and Mrs. Astor's owe their importance to thousands of newspaper readers. Society affects to despise Mr. Bennett and his colleagues but it needs them. So we'll get you into print. First your husband, a dignified little article. Let me think. Mackay, that sounds Scotch. Scotch is much more acceptable than Irish."

"John Mackay can never sound anything but Irish nor wish to."

"Could we say Scotch-Irish then?" Mrs. Stevens pleaded. "The Irish are not at all well thought of. So many Irish Catholic servants, you know. You are both Catholics, I suppose? What a pity."

"To be a Catholic"—Louise's voice shook with anger—"is the highest blessing that Almighty God——"

"Please, dear Mrs. Mackay, let's not get excited about religion. I've nothing against Catholics myself, but these people have. And we must recognize that. Oh, they accept a few French families. And of

Homecoming

course they make exceptions to all their rules. Still it would be easier
if you were Protestants. Then you could become Episcopalians. The
best people are almost all Episcopalians. Aren't you partly French? I
thought I heard somewhere that your mother was of French origin.
Do you speak French?"

Louise nodded.

"Good, good. That's thought a very elegant accomplishment. And
you have two little boys. Children can be exceedingly useful. My
Minnie opened many a door for me through the friends she made on
the beach at Newport. How old is your girl, by the way?"

"Eva will be sixteen in November."

"Perfect. She can be even more useful than the boys. More
immediately useful. We'll get her into one of the fashionable
classes . . ."

"But, Mrs. Stevens . . ."

"Don't worry, my dear. Getting her in will be quite easy. And once
she's in, it will take only a little skillful management to——"

"I won't do it," Louise interrupted fiercely. "I won't use my
children!"

"But they're so young. Even the girl. They won't know what's
going on. Children don't notice the maneuvers of their elders."

"Children notice everything. The boys would know in time and
Eva immediately. I'll not have any of them humiliated. It's for their
sake as much as anything that I have thought of establishing myself
in New York. What will be the good if in the process I injure them?"

"Dear me, you make it very difficult, but I'll do my best for you.
First thing, I'll send you Mrs. Ellet."

"Mrs. Ellet?" Louise asked.

"She writes books. There's one called *The Queens of American
Society*. She'll probably do a special edition for you. It's expensive
but it's worth the money. I tell you everyone believes what they see
in print. So we'll get you into print as elegantly as we can. You'll like
Mrs. Ellet. She's a nice old thing. Well, I must be off, but you'll hear
from me soon. Good-by, my dear, and good luck." Mrs. Stevens took
Louise's hand in both her own. "I like your spirit. I came here because of John Mackay but now I like you. I'd help you for nothing if
I could afford it."

A few days later Mrs. Ellet called at the Everett House. She was a gentle elderly woman. She reminded Louise of Mrs. Meier and Mrs. Kibbe.

"I feel already as though we were friends," Louise said. "You remind me of kind neighbors long ago."

"Then we're off to a comfortable start. Mrs. Paran Stevens asked me to bring you my book. She thought possibly——" Mrs. Ellet hesitated.

"She thought possibly you would be willing to include me in a special edition. I have gathered some material for you, a few little notes on my family and my background and some photographs. This is my father, Colonel Hungerford."

"Oh, a colonel. That's very nice. In the late War of Rebellion?"

"Yes, and he served also as a captain in the Mexican War."

"That's even better. It was a smaller war, you know. Mrs. Winfield Scott is in my book. Perhaps you would care to look through it."

The Queens of American Society was a fat volume. Louise glanced at the chapter headings: "The Livingston Family." "Lady Stirling and her Daughter." "Philadelphia Society in Early Times." "Early Society at the South." "Belles Among the Pioneers of Tennessee." "Mrs. J. J. Roosevelt." "Her Mother, Mrs. Cornelius P. Van Ness." "Types of the Best Class." "Absence of Deceptive Display." Louise turned the thick gilt-edged pages. There were pictures of many of the ladies. Mrs. Roosevelt and Mrs. Coventry Waddell were the most contemporary. The prettiest of all the portraits was the one of Mrs. John Hancock in her lace-trimmed cap and elegant colonial gown.

"You'll notice," Mrs. Ellet said, "that it is not a provincial book. I have included society circles at the South and at the West. And I have not hesitated to mention members of some of our newer foreign families, Mrs. Auguste Belmont for instance."

"I shall be the newest of all if you decide to include me in this distinguished company."

"I shall deem it an honor but I should warn you, it's a little expensive to bring out a special edition."

"Whatever the price, it's worth it to me."

"I hope it will be. It is to me. It's my living. Now if you'll let me have a picture of yourself that I may use."

"This is my husband's favorite. Those gold and ebony earrings and the matching necklace with the cross were among the first pieces of jewelry he ever gave me."

"Yes, this will be perfect. It's very young, very disarming. Now I'll just go over your notes. Hungerford sounds an aristocratic name."

"It is. I believe my father is one of the Hungerfords of Farleigh Castle but I have not yet traced the connection."

"Then we had better not be too specific. I'll just say that the colonel is descended from a celebrated English family of that name. I see you have put down that both you and Mr. Mackay are devoted Catholics. It's a little unusual to mention religion."

"I gather from Mrs. Stevens that it's a little unusual to be a Catholic in certain exalted circles."

Mrs. Ellet smiled. "Don't frown at me. I'm a Catholic, a convert."

"Then you know how I feel. It makes me so angry, I——"

"Many things will make you angry, I'm afraid. Mrs. Mackay, I'm old enough to be your mother. May I speak to you frankly, bluntly even?"

"Please do."

"You are a proud woman. In the eyes of New York society you are, forgive me, an intruder. Fashionable society is not easy on the proud intruder."

Louise stared at her visitor. She had heard those words before. She closed her eyes to remember. She heard Mémé's voice.

"How strange. Those are the very words my mother used before I went to St. Catherine's Academy at Benicia."

"St. Catherine's at Benicia. That's very nice." Mrs. Ellet made a note.

"It's strange that you and my mother should both . . ."

"Not so very strange, my dear. I see from these notes that you were born in New York. Did your mother ever work for New York ladies?"

"Yes. She went out to sew for them."

"And I go out to write for them. Your mother and I have watched and listened to the fashionable ladies. Still, there's no use warning you if you've made up your mind to challenge them."

"But why should I be a challenge to them, Mrs. Ellet? I've been nicely brought up. I'm a respectable woman. Why shouldn't I take my place in the city where I was born?"

"No reason, but society isn't ruled by reason. It makes its choices at random. One newcomer is accepted and another is rejected. Perhaps

your being young and pretty as well as enormously rich will antago-
nize the ladies. And in your case they have what they consider good
grounds for snobbishness. For one thing you're a Catholic. They're
prejudiced against Catholics. They say it's because Catholicism is the
servants' religion. I think the truth is that Catholicism is strange to
them. They don't understand it and they're afraid of it so they affect
to despise it. You won't find it easy to fight that prejudice. Then
there's another thing they'll hold against you. Your husband once
worked for his living with his hands. They look down on manual
labor."

"How dare they?" Louise cried. "How dare they look down on a
man like John Mackay and accept a man who made a fortune selling
shoddy goods to our Union armies?"

"I know the man you mean. But you see he began as a retailer.
That's better than a laborer. Of course they'd like to feel superior to
tradesmen as the English do, but they can't. Too many of them are in
trade, dry goods, furs, real estate, all sorts of trade. I can offer you
only discouragement but I want you to know the truth even if it
means losing your edition of my book."

"You won't lose your edition. I'm not so much discouraged as I'm
angry. And I'm curious. New York is the greatest city in America."

"It's the biggest certainly."

"I'm curious to see if society in the leading city of a republic will
reject a woman because she and her husband once earned their
bread with their hands. I used my hands too. I sewed for my living in
Virginia City."

"I consider that most creditable but I won't mention it in my
article."

"Don't. No use making my upward path any harder."

"I fear you'll find it hard but if you've made up your mind . . ."

"I've made up my mind. This steep ascent is the end of a long
road." Louise drew her soft full lips into a thin determined line. This
would be like the difficult trail between Marysville and Downieville.
The old tune sang in her brain:

> *If we have luck and if we don't*
> *Why bless you, don't you cry.*

"I've come a long journey, Mrs. Ellet, to get to New York. I don't
intend to turn back without at least trying to reach my destination."

When John arrived in New York, Louise told him about Mrs. Ellet and Mrs. Stevens.

He frowned at her bargain with Mrs. Stevens. "Buying a book's all right, but you can't buy friends, Louise."

"No other friends have appeared."

"You mean to tell me that none of those fellows I wrote to—and Dick Dey tells me he wrote to some of his old connections."

"Nothing has come of the letters."

"But you wrote me about the couple who called on you and her invitation to take tea with her."

"That fell through, but Mrs. Stevens has been really helpful. We're to be guests of honor at her musicale next Sunday. And oh, John, she invited me to tea and her daughter and the Viscount and Viscountess Mandeville were there. Minnie Stevens was one of Lady Mandeville's bridesmaids."

"Louise, Louise. You're like all the ladies. You dearly love a lord."

"Certainly I do. He's the son of the Duke of Manchester. Anyone would be excited at meeting the heir to a dukedom. He isn't much to look at," she said regretfully. "Mr. Ralston would have made a much more impressive duke. But the little bride is enchanting. Miss Consuelo Yznaga that was. I took a great fancy to her and she, I think, to me."

"Now about this party of Mrs. Stevens'," John said slowly. "Sure, we'll go if you like, but first we'll give a party of our own."

"Oh no, John. We can't!"

"Why not?" He took her hand. "You're cold as ice and you're trembling. You're keeping something back. Better let me hear it all."

"I only wanted to spare you, since he's your friend. You may as well know."

She told the story of her visit to Washington Square.

"Why that d-d-damn w-woman!" John shouted. "G-G-God d-damn fool of a w-w-woman. I can b-b-break her husband and b-by G-God I've a g-g-good mind to d-do it."

"No, John, that isn't the way."

"What is the w-w-way then?" He paced the floor silently. The red flush died out of his cheeks. His hands unclenched. "I'm all right now, old lady. I lost my head there for a minute. I can't stand to have anyone hurt you. But we'll figure this out together. You say breaking this fellow's not the way, but I can break or make him and others like him and they know it. What's the difference between me using that knowledge and your bargain with Mrs. Stevens?"

"The bargain was Mrs. Stevens' idea, so she doesn't resent it; she just feels she has been quite clever. The wives of men you threatened or bribed would feel entirely different. Even if that handful could force their wives to receive me, what do you think would happen when the story became known to the rest of New York society?"

"I suppose you're right. But I still think we might give a small dinner. Forget the damn woman who was rude to you. We'll invite the others."

"The others haven't called, John. And to invite ladies who haven't called on me is a thing I will not do."

"I'll never get the hang of these foolish female ways."

"They are the ways of the world. And there's sense to them. Unless the ladies had shown me some sign of civility I'd be a fool to invite them. Suppose they all refuse? Suppose they accept and, at the last moment, make an excuse not to come? That has happened. Just the other day there was a bit in the paper about a parvenu who gave a great ball last winter and nobody came. The writer laughed himself sick over it. I don't propose to be that sort of figure of fun."

"They wouldn't dare."

"Any group that considers itself the elite dares do anything it chooses. And remember these fashionable ladies have little to occupy them. Cruelty is one of the favorite pastimes of idleness. Don't you recall in the diggings the loafers setting the dogs to fighting on a Saturday afternoon? For society ladies every day is Saturday. Perhaps I was wrong to come to New York. Perhaps you were right and it's too big a camp for me."

"No place on earth's too big for you, Louise. People have only to meet you to see you for what you are."

"Sunday night will tell the tale. If Mrs. Stevens' guests are all she promises, New York will give its verdict at her party. But whatever they decide, John, you make me feel such a queen that they can't destroy me. They can make me angry, they can hurt me even, but they can never destroy me."

The party had begun when Louise and John reached 244 Fifth Avenue on Sunday evening. The sound of voices and of music came through the open front door as they crossed the red carpet beneath the striped awning. The side curtains were drawn to protect the guests against the light rain. The familiar melody of the "Liebestraum" was welcoming and reassuring to Louise as she slowly crossed the canvas antechamber that led from the curbstone to the door. The carpet flowed smoothly up the stone steps. Like a river, Louise thought, a narrow scarlet Rubicon. What a silly fearful thought. She smiled confidently. What had she to fear? She had been to parties before, to kettledrums and to great balls. At his palatial country estate Mr. Ralston had received the aristocracy of all the world, not of just one city. This little house, this little musicale could not intimidate anyone who had known the splendors of Belmont.

Mrs. Stevens introduced John and Louise to many of her guests as she led them to front seats in the drawing room. They were all here to give their answer, Louise thought, as she bowed and smiled and held her white-gloved hand lightly and steadily on John's arm. These were the names she had read about, these were the faces and the voices she had remembered. They were all here. Tonight she would know their verdict. They would not speak it aloud. If it should be unfavorable they would try courteously to conceal it, but she would know.

When the music ended the guests moved toward the dining room where a large supper table was spread. Gilt chairs lined the walls. Lord Mandeville offered Louise his arm. "Thirsty, hungry work listening to music. I'll fetch us some champagne and supper."

Louise waited uncertainly beside the dining-room door. Several women were seated near her. While they waited for their escorts they laughed and chatted. They were not the solemn sticks that Mrs. Stevens had described. They were having fun. Louise wished that they would look up and see that she was alone.

"Yes, my dear. It's perfectly true." The voice was shrill with amusement. "She must somehow have heard about her Thursdays and she drove up bold as brass in her hired carriage. That's how I heard. You know what an old gossip Brown is."

"And then?"

"Turned away at the door of course. What else can one do if we're not to be drowned in a sea of gold—or silver, I suppose I should say."

"You might say brass." The last voice was crisp and clear. The speaker looked straight at Louise. Then she turned away. "Ah, here are our cavaliers bearing food and wine."

Lord Mandeville came up to Louise. "Sorry to be so long, Mrs. Mackay. Couldn't get near the table, there was such a crush. Shall we ask those good ladies to make room for us and I'll try again. You've met Mrs. van——"

"If you don't mind, I'd rather find Mr. Mackay. Like myself, he's not of New York and he may be feeling something of a stranger."

"Of course, anything you like, dear lady, though to sup with one's own husband is not at all the fashionable thing, not at all."

"But you see, Lord Mandeville, I'm not fashionable."

It was difficult to move in the crowded room. Louise saw John standing beside Mrs. Stevens and Lady Mandeville. Her progress was blocked by a large group. She heard her name spoken by a dark, bony-faced, elderly woman.

"Mackay? Oh, Irish, of course. They don't even pronounce it properly."

"I've heard rumors of washtubs." A young, fair-haired girl giggled. "Mamma was furious at my coming this evening, but I was longing to see what a bonanza queen looked like."

"What did you expect?" a masculine voice boomed. "Diamonds in her teeth? Damn pretty woman, I think, and holds herself straight as a ramrod. Look well on a horse."

"Really, Bertie, that's all you ever think of, horses."

"And pretty women, my dear."

"Pretty or not, one has to draw the line somewhere." As she spoke the older woman looked at Louise without any sign of recognition though Mrs. Stevens had introduced them earlier. "A washerwoman or boardinghouse keeper or whatever she was may be all right in her place, but her place is hardly with us."

"Oh." The young girl gasped as she saw and recognized Louise. "Oh dear." Her cheeks crimsoned. Her forehead was wet with sweat that darkened her pale blond hairline. "Oh, Mrs. Mackay, oh, I——" she babbled.

The man they called Bertie interrupted. "Ah, Mrs. Mackay, won't you present us to your husband and join us?"

Louise turned and saw that John and Lady Mandeville were beside her. John's eyes were cold. He bowed gravely. "It's v-very civil of you, s-sir." He paused for a moment. Louise saw the line of his jaw tighten. "But Mrs. M-Mackay and I want to make an early night of it. We're due in Philadelphia tomorrow to v-view the exposition."

"Worth seeing," Bertie said. "Well worth seeing, they tell me."

"We think it is," Louise said. "It's the reason we came East."

"Oh, really?" the dark-haired woman drawled. "One had heard it rumored that you came East because you are planning to settle in New York."

"No, we hadn't thought of that."

"Oh?" The woman's smile was as hard as the large, rather dirty diamonds that shone dimly at her throat and in her ears.

Louise hoped that her own smile was as cool and untroubled as she meant it to be. "No, Mr. Mackay and I had not planned to settle here, though New York is a delightful little city. As a matter of fact, we have long thought of purchasing a house in Paris. My parents and my young sister are already in residence there. I hope you won't think me rude to say this, but when one has lived much abroad as I have, the most charming American city seems a little provincial compared to the European capitals."

"I wish you would make London your home," Lady Mandeville said. "It would give Mandeville and myself such pleasure to see you there."

"You are very kind, and perhaps I am foolish to hanker after Paris." Louise managed a gay little laugh. "But everyone, I suppose, has a heart's desire and mine has ever been to live in France."

"Fine hunting country around Pau," Bertie said.

"I don't know Pau but I have spent some time on the Mediterranean coast—*le pays où fleurit—où fleurit* . . ." To her dismay Louise heard her voice breaking.

John moved closer to her. She felt his arm hard and strong as a rock against hers. "I don't want to interrupt you, Louise, my dear, but we've an early start on the cars tomorrow. I think we had better find our hostess and say good night."

When John opened the door of their suite at the Everett House, Louise broke into the tears she had so long repressed. Dick Dey was sitting beside the only lamp that was lit. He rose from his chair.

"Some papers have arrived from San Francisco by messenger, sir. I thought you might wish to see them. Permit me to give you a little more light."

"Oh, please, not business tonight, John." Louise had her voice under control but she was grateful for the dimness of the solitary lamp. She did not want Mr. Dey to see her tear-streaked face.

"Whatever it is can wait till morning, Dick," John said brusquely.

"I think there may be something important," Dick Dey persisted. "I know it's hard after an enjoyable evening to——" He hesitated. "I hope it was an enjoyable evening. Two old acquaintances of mine were planning to be at Mrs. Stevens' and I took the liberty, sir, of mentioning our close relationship."

"Don't doubt you meant well, but from now on I prefer that you don't mention my name or Mrs. Mackay's to any of your New York friends. Now put those papers on the table there and I'll take a quick look at them. It may be important, my darling."

In the light of the lamp Dick Dey's face was pale. Poor little man, Louise thought, poor pompous little man. He got on her nerves but he was useful to John. "Closemouthed, dead loyal, and a good head for figures," John had said of him. Poor Mr. Dey. Louise forgot her own distress in pity for him.

As John took her cloak into her bedroom, Dick Dey said softly, "I'm sorry. I seem to have failed you and Mr. Mackay."

His face was almost expressionless. Louise sighed. Poor soul, he couldn't entirely conceal his anger. He must know that the move to New York had been her plan. Because of her he had failed John. He would not easily forgive her his failure.

"Please don't distress yourself, Mr. Dey," she said gently and entered the bedroom to find John in his shirt sleeves.

"I won't be more than twenty minutes with Dick. Then I'll get rid of him and we'll talk."

"Not tonight, John. I'm too tired to talk." She sank wearily onto a sofa. "It's as though I'd been in a race, the desperate, lost kind of a race that you run in a dream."

He put his arms around her. "I was proud of you. You stood up to the lot of them like a thoroughbred."

"I think it was the feeling of being in a nightmare that saved me. I couldn't believe that real people, not people in a dream, could be so cruel."

"Fear makes people cruel, Louise," John said slowly. "Not that that excuses any of them. Least of all the damn woman they allowed to speak for them. But it explains them. I've the notion that these people are afraid. They see all this new wealth pouring out of the mines, out of the railroads, out of all the new enterprises of this modern age, and they're afraid of it. It's too big for them to handle. They can't absorb it as they did the occasional great fortunes of the past. This new wealth can make a new world. It'll act and react in ways we can't foresee, and in the process the smug little importance of this particular elite may be destroyed entirely. We may not live to see the world we're making and they may not know they fear it, but sure as shooting it's coming."

"You always know how to comfort me. You make New York society seem small as the court of cards the little girl dreamed of in that book Eva was reading to Willie."

"Sure, they're only one little circle. There's a dozen others for you to choose from. Europe if you like. Paris if that's where you want your home to be. I know you'd not want to go back to San Francisco."

"I can't go back." She clung to his hand. "You wouldn't ask me to go back."

"I wouldn't want you to, my darling. I understand pride. And whatever world you choose, I'll be there beside you."

"As much as business will allow you. Sometimes I think I hate your business."

"Now that's a silly thing to say and you're not a silly woman. Our fortune is my business. And fortunes don't stand still, Louise. They grow or they shrink and disappear. Good Lord!" He stood up. "I clean forgot Dick and his papers. I'll be gone just the time it'll take you to get ready for bed."

She stretched out her arms to his. "It's all right, I'm not hurt any more. I think there's no weariness or hurt, big or little, that you couldn't comfort."

Chapter XIX

·····━━━◉━━━·····

9 Rue de Tilsitt

"IT'S LIKE COMING home," Louise said wonderingly to John as they drove through the wide bright streets on the evening of their arrival in Paris. "I had forgotten the long twilight. I had forgotten the feeling of space, the look of a city planned for beauty. Do you think I spoke the truth without knowing it and that this is my heart's desire?"

"Another dream, Louise?"

"No, I'll not lose myself in a dream again. Our position in society is my business just as much as our fortune is yours. It's my business and my fight. You said I'd find the equivalent of the California Bank crowd in New York, but I wouldn't listen to you. If I'd used the wits God gave me I could have licked New York, but I went there as unprepared for battle as a six-year-old going to a birthday party. Not that there's any sense to regretting my foolishness. It makes no difference why I was rejected. The simple fact is that I was. So now we must forget New York."

"I'm a pretty good hater, Louise, and so are you. I didn't think you'd forgive so easily."

"I haven't forgiven." Her eyes were dark with anger. "However I mean to forget. I mean to swallow my hate, though it's bitter as gall.

The main thing is that it shouldn't set the children's teeth on edge. I'm a good hater but I'm also a practical woman. I'll build such a position here that Willie and Clarie and Eva can go anywhere. Every door will open before they even knock. You'll see, John. The children of the very people who rejected me will seek the friendship of our sons and daughter and be proud when they achieve it."

"It sounds like another dream, my darling."

"It's no dream, it's a plan. I thought a lot on the steamship coming over. I remembered when we were here before we didn't mingle in society, but those of the aristocracy whom we met in Nice and in the hotel at Lake Como were polite and friendly. Europeans aren't as aware of the fine distinctions of American society as the New York ladies would like to believe. I fancy the American colony here will be less democratic, about Americans at least, than the Faubourg Saint-Germain. But with both groups I'll be cautious and work slowly and patiently."

"Till the vein opens up?" John laughed.

"Till the vein opens up and the local Sharon surrenders. You can laugh but you've told me often enough that people and places are the same the world over. And I think that in climbing as in digging one needs intelligence and perseverance and——"

"I'll not let you call yourself a climber, Louise."

"Don't be silly. It's what I am. Only a child could have believed she could reach the social heights by levitation. And I tell you I've grown up. Judgment you said a man needed in the diggings, well, so will I, and experience—that I got in New York."

"And courage." He held her hand tight against him. "That, my dear, you were born with."

"And luck. You always said one had to have that, too, to succeed."

The carriage crossed the Place de la Concorde. Louise leaned from the window to look at the Arc de Triomphe. "Even so far away it doesn't seem small. Look how square and tall it stands. I wish there was a hotel in that neighborhood."

"I know of no hotel in that district, but maybe we can find a house there."

"Do you think so?" she asked eagerly. "I'd like a house on the Place de l'Étoile."

Within three days John found for Louise the house she wanted.

"It was completed only two years ago," he told her, "but the owner wants to sell. 'Modern Renaissance,' the fellow called the style of it. Anyway it seems a comfortable place. Plenty of room for us all. Mémé and the colonel can have their own suite of rooms and there are two nice gardens for the children."

Louise stepped from the carriage and stared in amazed admiration at the imposing façade of 9 Rue de Tilsitt.

"Plenty of room!" she exclaimed. "Why, John, it's a palace."

"Like it, old lady?"

"Like it! It's better than any house I ever imagined and I've imagined some pretty fine ones."

"Come along. You've not seen the half of it." He led her to the corner of the Rue de Tilsitt and down the Avenue Carnot. "You've got a nice little strip of garden here."

"Why, it's an enormous garden. It's the whole length of the block nearly."

"Wait until you see the one that faces your arch. It stretches right across to the Avenue MacMahon." They walked to the Place de l'Étoile. John pointed proudly to the wide deep garden. "Imagine the parties you can give. You can outdo poor Ralston himself. Imagine you and your grand guests parading up the stone steps onto the terrace and through the french windows. Come, we'll go back to the entrance and I'll show you the inside of the place."

When they entered the court on the Rue de Tilsitt, Louise gasped with pleasure. "A glass-enclosed court! It's so unusual and it makes such an elegant first impression."

"Like the Palace Hotel, only on a smaller scale."

"There's nothing small about it," Louise said as they reached the top of the grand stairway. "But the proportions are so good that the size of the rooms doesn't oppress one."

She walked through the vast, high-ceilinged apartments.

"I think," she said, "I'll make the small salon on the right into an anteroom where I can receive distinguished guests. I'll keep it very simple. No brocade. In a small room brocade is unbecoming to ladies' dresses. I'll hang it in very pale blue satin."

"Anything you like, my darling."

"Of course, the suite of smaller rooms on the ground floor should be done in a more cozy style. We can have our breakfast room there and a smoking room for when you have gentlemen guests. Something in the Pompeian style would be nice."

"Pompeian! Good Lord, Louise, that doesn't sound very cozy!"

"Oh, just frescoes on the walls and possibly a mosaic floor in the hall. And certain lamps and ornaments in ancient style, but the chairs and sofas can be comfortable. You'll see, you'll like it." She looked at him uncertainly.

He bent and kissed her anxious upturned face. "It's all right, I was just startled for a moment. What put Pompeian into your head?"

"Pompeian is thought very elegant. Don't you remember I showed you the Pompeian house on the Avenue Montaigne that Prince Napoleon built? It's much admired, though I think a whole house is rather freakish. But just one suite of rooms as one enters, that would be striking and yet not overdone. I can see it all: first the enclosed court bright with flowering plants, then the Pompeian suite, then, beyond the stairway, the splendid salons looking out on the brilliantly illuminated gardens. Can I really do it any way I want and not count the cost?"

"The sky's the limit, my darling. I want your house to be the finest in Paris."

John completed the arrangements for the purchase of the property on the Rue de Tilsitt before he left Paris. On the morning of his departure he reiterated his wish that Louise should spare no expense in decorating and furnishing her mansion.

"There's only one thing that worries me, John," she said. "The silver service."

"Silver!" he exclaimed. "Why, I sent Tiffany enough silver to equip a palace."

"That's just it. I think it will take some time, two years, they said, to finish the work—with every piece made to our own design."

"Well, buy some silver here to use in the meantime. It'll do for the children later. But for our own table I want a service made from the Comstock silver."

"Something rich and memorable, made of the precious metal from our own mine! Do you think, John, that Tiffany's final designs are rich enough?"

"Hard to tell from drawings. But they looked pretty handsome to me, including that imposing crest you designed for yourself."

"I didn't design it. Father says we're entitled to it, and in America it's quite usual for a lady to adapt her father's crest for her own use."

"You sure couldn't find one on my side of the family."

"But for certain pieces, cigar boxes and such, I thought—I hope you won't mind—I've ordered this."

He took the sketch. It showed a hand grasping a short sword. Below it was the motto *Manu Forte*.

"With a strong hand, John. It suits you. I thought you'd be pleased."

"Hell, old lady, you should have put a miner's pick in the hand. That'd be more suitable. Now, now"—he stroked her hair gently— "don't look so distressed. I was only joking. Sure, if it pleases you for me to have a crest then it pleases me."

"Truly, John? It seemed wrong for me to have one and not you, but if you mind . . ."

"Truly, my darling, I don't. You can have a dozen different crests if you want. All I want is to please you. And speaking of pleasing you"—he opened the top drawer of the bureau and took out a large flat case—"I have a little farewell present for you."

"From Boucheron. But you gave me my pearls. All a lady really needs are pearls."

"I never heard of a lady yet who couldn't use another piece of jewelry. And this is something not just for any lady. It was made specially for you to match your eyes."

She lifted the tooled leather cover of the fashionable jeweler's case. Her eyes opened wide. She could not speak. On the firm white velvet rested a magnificent necklace of matched sapphires set in diamonds. The pendant sapphire was the size of a pigeon's egg.

"And that's only the beginning." John fastened the necklace around his wife's neck. "I've told Boucheron to be on the lookout. In time you'll own the world's finest collection of sapphires. They're your stone; when you're very happy—or very angry—I've seen your eyes darken to exactly that deep glowing blue."

"John, John." Her eyes filled with tears. "Mr. Dale said it long ago to Eva. 'Mr. Mackay would pick that one.' Mr. Mackay would always pick the best and the biggest."

"The best is an investment, in jewels like in everything else. I hope you'll never have to think of your jewels in that light, but if you should need to, stones like these and the others I'm meaning to buy for you are an investment."

She ran to the looking glass. She held her wrapper in the low curve of a ball gown.

"Oh, John, it's so beautiful. The design is so light and fine. You can hardly see the setting. It's as though the stones were held together by magic."

"Now mind you wear it the first time you go to the Élysée Palace."

"I'll get there. I'll meet President MacMahon. I'll meet them all. And to wear a little piece of jewelry won't hurt me in their eyes. Do you remember the jet Mrs. Mock gave me the Christmas Day I met you?"

"I remember, God love her. Wear my necklace as you wore hers, in good health and in good luck."

"John, my dear John."

By February, Louise was settled in her new house. Mémé and Ada and her father were with her. Eva was at school in Neuilly.

Louise insisted that her parents should choose the furnishings and ornaments of their suite. "I want it," she said, "to be your home within mine. There's only one thing I'd like to choose for it. It's something I planned a long time ago."

Louise ordered a glass case bound with gold. Within it, on a bed of antique red velvet, she placed the sword the Sierra Guards had presented to her father.

"It must have the place of honor in your study, Father," she said. "It must be kept bright and shining exactly as I imagined it."

"Well, dearie, if it doesn't seem ostentatious. What do you think, Eveline?"

"I think Judge Taylor and the others who gave it would be pleased to see it so honored."

In that winter and spring Eva brought her schoolmates to the Rue de Tilsitt and Ada entertained the friends whom she had made in her years at Neuilly. The colonel hospitably welcomed old friends who were passing through Paris.

During the quiet winter Louise made two acquaintances of importance. One was Mrs. Edward Follansbee Noyes, the wife of the American minister; the other was ex-Queen Isabella of Spain.

Mrs. Noyes offered Louise an entree into the American colony. She was well informed, also, on French politics and on the intricacies of the Faubourg Saint-Germain.

"It's a complicated society," she told Louise. "It was quite a change to me after Ohio, even after New Hampshire where I was born and raised. To be truthful I was a little nervous when General Noyes accepted the post. Of course, the party owed it to him. He was extremely helpful to them after the last election, presenting the Republican case to the canvassing boards in Louisiana and Florida. Still, I was nervous of this high society but I've made a real study of it. Lucy Hooper, our consul's wife, is quite an expert on those matters, so I'm finding my way. Mrs. Roosevelt has been most kind to me, and the President and his lady too. And since you and I are both newcomers, it will be a pleasure to me if I can help you."

Louise knew that the minister and his wife had welcomed her because of John's long affiliation with the Union party. Perhaps, indirectly, she owed their kindness to Jim Walker's political activities. Whatever the cause, she trusted Mrs. Noyes. They liked each other. They talked comfortably together of the beauty and excitement of Paris, of the opera and the theaters, of Worth, the man milliner. There was much for ladies to admire and discuss in the capital of fashion.

When Mrs. Noyes became homesick for America, Louise listened sympathetically. She mentioned her meeting with Vice-President Colfax and with Miss Bross, the daughter of a lieutenant governor of Illinois.

Mrs. Noyes, a little awed by Parisian society, liked to speak of the familiar western names to which, as a New Englander, she had been able to feel superior. She liked to remember the two years when the general had been governor of Ohio.

Louise was dazzled to find herself acquainted with ex-Queen Isabella. After one meeting Isabella commanded her to call. This was the first of many visits between the ladies.

It was strange, Louise thought, that she should feel so quickly at her ease with the ex-Queen, but as she studied Isabella's warmhearted manner and informal ways of speech with other visitors, she understood. Royalty must learn to put the rest of the world at its ease, or exalted personages would have no social enjoyment at all. The highest-born of the nobility, those who claimed a lineage older than that of any reigning family, were ready to be uneasy in the presence of a queen, even one without a throne. Louise watched admiringly the skill with which Isabella, without losing her dignity, made her guests feel themselves again. And it must be, Louise realized, particularly difficult for an ex-queen who could not permit her royal position to be forgotten for a moment, for fear that it might be forgotten for good.

The Queen never tired of asking questions about America. Gold mines and Indians and enormous rivers and limitless prairies and railroad trains in which one could travel for a week without crossing a foreign boundary, these were the things of which she wanted to hear.

She listened delightedly to a description of the Con Virginia, of the creaking swaying lift that lowered one from level to level, with every level floored and roofed and walled in precious metal.

"And the mules that live and work underground, how do you call them again, poor things?"

"Washoe canaries, ma'am."

"How wonderful! I love it!" The big woman laughed like a child. "And your Washoe zephyr. Only you Americans would call that fierce awful wind a zephyr."

Louise knew that many of the French were puzzled by the Queen's partiality for her. They did not realize that to be with an American was a kind of holiday for royalty. Americans curtsied and said "ma'am"; they followed the ritual that was required, but they followed it with pleasure as children crown a May queen and bow before her and pay her court as though they had no idea that tomorrow she would be a schoolgirl again. Americans were impressed by royalty, they were dazzled by it, they were delighted to be noticed by it, but they were incapable of entirely believing in it. This, she thought, was the secret of their popularity in the palaces of Europe from Marlborough House to the Quirinal.

Louise was pleased by the kindness the two ladies showed her. She enjoyed their friendliness but she did not confuse it with friendship. She knew that what she had said to Theresa was true: from now on there would be no friends, only acquaintances. Even though one called them friends out of courtesy, even though they were charming and kind and welcoming, they were and would remain acquaintances, nothing more. She had Mémé and Ada, and Eva, almost grown now. She did not require love or friendship from other women. Friendly affection and easy kindness were all she would ever ask or need from her new acquaintances.

During the winter Louise received a memento of New York from Mrs. Ellet: a handsomely bound special edition of *The Queens of American Society*.

In her letter Mrs. Ellet enclosed an old cutting from the *Home*

Journal. She had found it among her notes and thought that if Mrs. Mackay had not seen it, it might interest her.

Louise read the article. It was dated June 7, 1876.

"Nevada's Croesus in New York. Mr. Mackay the millionaire miner of the far West whose income is a million dollars every thirty days has been sojourning with his wife and children in the Everett House, this city, for several days. He is probably one of the luckiest men in America. He is of medium height, about fifty years of age, has slightly gray hair and a light moustache, dresses very plainly and exhibits no jewelry on his person. He is courteous and kind and is generally liked. He will visit Washington and Philadelphia and then return to Nevada. N. Y. *Sun*."

Louise crumpled the cutting and tossed it in the wastebasket. Mrs. Stevens' dignified little squib had come too late to be of use. She examined the red-bound book. The frontispiece was the picture she had given to Mrs. Ellet. "Very young. Very disarming," Mrs. Ellet had said of it. Louise laughed. How foolish to imagine that a youthful appearance would disarm the powerful middle-aged ladies! She rapidly turned the gilt-edged papers until she reached her biography. It was a skillful piece of work, but, like the clipping from the *Sun*, it was now of no use to her. She looked thoughtfully at the book. It was too expensive to throw away. She placed it beside some other volumes on a shelf in a small table. It would do no harm, in preparing the Paris campaign, to have at **hand** a reminder of the lost battle of New York.

Chapter XX

Golden Opportunity

IN THE SUMMER Louise learned that ex-President Grant was planning a world tour which would include Paris. Colonel Hungerford brought the news.

"I heard it," he said, "from an old comrade in arms who is very close to the general. And it occurred to me, Louise, that it might be a nice thing if we were to receive him at the Rue de Tilsitt."

"A very nice thing indeed if it could be arranged," Louise said slowly. This could be it, she thought, this could be her bit of luck.

"You see, dearie, the general and I are in a sense comrades in arms. We both served in the Mexican War. To think he was only a second lieutenant then and I a captain! Well, fortunes of war. We never met at the time, but all of General Scott's veterans feel a bond. It would be only natural, only right and proper that I, that is to say that you and your mother and I, should welcome Ulysses Grant to Paris with a splendid entertainment."

"Yes. Yes, it would. This would be a suitable occasion for me to invite the elite, both American and French, to our house."

"So if you like I'll set the wheels in motion. I can write, as one old soldier to another, bringing myself to the general's remembrance."

"Yes. Yes. You could do that. But later, I think. Just before his arrival. He must receive many letters. Yours might never be brought to his notice. I think it will be better if we leave everything to John. He's on the ground. And he's acquainted with the general. He'll be able to arrange this. I'll write to him at once—or perhaps I had better cable. Every hostess in Paris will be trying to capture General Grant." She looked up. "Father dear, you mustn't be disappointed. It's your idea. Having the idea was the important thing. Now it's only a question of carrying it out. John will be glad to do that and he'll be so grateful to you for recognizing my golden opportunity. Oh, Father." She flung her arms around him and kissed him. "Remember when you promised me my own carriage and pair?"

"I don't quite follow, dearie——"

"Of course you don't. I'm too excited to talk very sensibly. It's just that a carriage and pair have ever been my symbol of success. And here I've been waiting for some lucky thing to bring me success and you were the one who found it for me. So it's as if your old promise had come true."

When the last of the golden October leaves had fallen from the trees ex-President Grant and his party arrived in Paris. The November fogs and rains darkened the days, but by night the city was as bright as in spring and summer.

Throughout November there were entertainments for the general and Mrs. Grant. John had arranged that Louise was to have the honor of receiving the distinguished couple on the twenty-first of November. Probably, Louise thought, he had persuaded General Grant to extend his Paris visit in order to make her party possible. The other entertainments, she now knew, had been planned before the colonel had brought news of the impending visit. Her party would be the last; she would make sure that it was not the least. In the meantime, with her parents, she attended the festivities.

At the Élysée Palace, Louise, remembering John's wish, wore her sapphire and diamond necklace. Her dress was of silver brocade trimmed with chenille and silver fringe.

At General and Mrs. Noyes' reception she wore crimson brocade over pale pink silk, ornamented with a profusion of the finest point lace. Both Mrs. Noyes and Mrs. Grant complimented her on her gown and a newspaper spoke of it as "the richest and most elegant dress of the occasion."

The most refined and elegant entertainment, she thought, was that of M. Seligman, the banker. Mme. Seligman was handsomely gowned in heavy lilac silk, cut princess style, opening on a petticoat of white silk covered with ruffles of point lace. Her beautiful daughter, Mme. Bernstein, wore a toilette composed of white silk and green velvet, trimmed with wide point lace. The hostess and her daughter displayed few jewels. Mme. Seligman wore on her dress only a few small diamond ornaments and in her hair a narrow diamond clasp that held a white feather. Most of the feminine guests blazed with diamonds and other precious stones set in large, elaborate necklaces and stomachers and tiaras. Louise knew that the banker's wife possessed a magnificent collection of jewels. How attractive it was, how becoming to a lady not to outshine anyone in her own house. This was an example that she decided to follow.

At last came the evening of Louise's entertainment. Every detail, so long and so minutely planned, was now put together in a brilliant whole.

The ladies' dresses had been chosen with thought.

"Though, honestly, Louise," Ada said, "almost anything looks well in the pale blue salon and the white and gold ballroom."

"That was my plan in decorating every room," Louise said. "Even the dining room. People are mistaken to use red as much as they do. Though, of course, a dining room should have a dignified, masculine air, out of compliment to the host. But my dark woodwork relieved with golden lines and my golden brocaded curtains are becoming to any costume. For tonight, though, the important thing was to have our dresses be becoming to each other as well as to us."

Mrs. Hungerford was in ruby velvet trimmed with point lace. The underskirt was of cream-white satin striped with raised vines of white velvet. Clasping her throat was John's most recent gift, a handsome diamond necklace. For the occasion Louise had presented her mother with a hair ornament like Mme. Seligman's: a feather held by a diamond spray.

Ada wore a simple gown suitable for a young girl. It was of silver gauze over pale blue silk. The skirt was trimmed with garlands of silver flowers.

"You look exactly right, both of you," Loiuse said approvingly. "Mémé as though she had stepped from an old portrait, and Ada the perfect illustration for a fairy tale. And my toilette, do you like it?"

She turned slowly for them to admire her heavy white satin trimmed with lace interwoven with seed pearls. Around her throat were four rows of large and perfect pearls.

"But your sapphire necklace!" Ada exclaimed. "It's so beautiful with white and tonight of all nights!"

"No, not tonight. Not in my own house. I think it's nicer for a lady not to outshine her guests."

Louise took a last look at everything. Once the party began, she must trust to the preparations so carefully made and forget them. She must think only of her guests.

She could find no mistake in the arrangements.

On the upper floor the largest guest rooms had been thrown open so that a lady might, when she wished, retire to repair her coiffure or powder her face. In the old-rose suite there were vases of white flowers. For the bleu Nattier suite Louise had chosen bowls of violets. Costly Indian shawls were hung in lieu of paper or drapery on the walls. The effect, she thought, was handsome and unusual.

Downstairs everything was in readiness. Every flower was in place; every gas jet and candle was lit.

The façade on the Rue de Tilsitt was illuminated so that the street was brightly welcoming to the guests. The glass-enclosed court had been temporarily transformed by a false façade into a magnificent reception hall. It was filled with hundreds of shrubs and flowers brought from the South of France. In the Pompeian suite tropical birds twittered in the aviary and brilliantly colored fish swam in the aquarium. On the broad stairway stood twelve footmen in liveries of red and gold. In the dining room the table was decorated with yellow roses and camellias. At each of the twenty-four places was a menu engraved on solid silver. The dinner guests would include only the general's party and the important officials of the American legation and consulate and their wives. There would be three hundred guests at the reception and ball. There were flowers everywhere. The owner of the finest greenhouse in Nice had come himself to supervise their arrangement. Louise particularly fancied the colossal bouquet of violets and camellias which he had placed in the ballroom fireplace. In the center of the bouquet the letter G was outlined in camellias. Beyond the french windows the garden was decorated with American flags. The emblems were set in a thousand gas jets. John would have liked that. She sighed. Until the last moment she had hoped that he would be able to be present at the triumph which he had made possible. She had thought of him when she had arranged the patriotic display. "You've sure trimmed it up à la fancy," he would say. The effect was rich and elegant, but it would remind the Americans of home. On a November night in Paris they would be reminded of the glorious Fourth as it was celebrated in all the towns and villages from New England to the Pacific states. She hoped the general would be pleased.

At her right at dinner he seemed pleased. He mentioned the garden decorations. He admired the silver menus. He spoke of John. It was, he said, an honor to be the guest of the wife of a man whom he liked and admired.

As the general ate his soup, Louise glanced quickly around the table. They all seemed to be enjoying themselves. Lucy Hooper was, as usual, a center of gaiety. No one could guess from her carefree manner that she was busy noticing and remembering every detail for her newspaper articles.

Louise turned back to Grant. The name suddenly rang in her brain loud and clear as a liberty bell. She had been too preoccupied with the round of parties, and above all with her own party, to think about the guest of honor. This was Ulysses S. Grant. This fleshy, grizzled man was the hero of Appomattox. For a moment the elaborately arranged flowers, the silver menus, the liveried footmen, the whole extravagant display seemed foolish and inappropriate. For a moment she wondered how it appeared to the general. She would speak of her father. His career was something the general could understand and admire.

"My father," she said, "served in the Mexican War as well as in the War of Rebellion. He volunteered and they elected him captain."

"So General Noyes told me. I was a second lieutenant then. Happiest day of my life when I was commissioned."

"And yet since then what a long and glorious road you have come."

He nodded silently. She wondered if he was remembering the dark part of the road; or perhaps even victories were dark to think about when one was solely responsible for them. One had to be a second lieutenant or a newly elected captain to enjoy the glory of war. She wanted to distract him. Probably, like other men, he would be cheered by a well-chosen compliment.

"You know, General, Marshal MacMahon said to me that you were a very learned soldier."

"Well, I'm not. I had neither the genius of Sherman nor the learning of Lee or McPherson. *I only meant to get there.*"

"And you did," Louise said softly.

"I can't talk like Sherman either."

At his sudden warm smile Louise remembered how grave and silent he had been at the festivities in his honor. She had seen him smile broadly only once. It was before the gala performance at the opera house when the people had cheered his arrival and the French orchestra had struggled bravely with "Hail Columbia." He must, she thought, have been more pleased and touched by that spontaneous welcome than by all the brilliant entertainments where hosts and guests honored themselves rather than him, and were disappointed that their lion was a shy, quiet man who would not roar.

This world tour could not be much fun for him. Perhaps Mrs. Grant was enjoying it. At the other end of the table beside the colonel she looked very cheerful, very imposing in her rich toilette of white silk embossed with garnet velvet.

Louise was thankful for the tour which had brought the general to her house. But she could not tell a former President of the United States that he was her bit of luck, her golden opportunity. All she could do in gratitude for his presence was to try to amuse and interest him.

She talked about General Sutter. She described his California mansion and the famous flower garden. She described the general and Mrs. Sutter driving out in their smart carriage and pair. General Grant smiled at the tale of the western horses that were unaccustomed to the eastern trappings and bolted into the river, overturning the carriage and drenching its occupants. He listened attentively to her account of the warm welcome Sutter had received at Forest City on the Fourth of July in '59. That was a year when things were not going well financially for the old soldier.

Louise described the Sierra Guards. They had seemed such amateurs, she told him, in their ill-assorted uniforms, solemnly playing at soldiers.

"And yet, General, those amateurs handled themselves so well in the Piute War that Colonel Hays, the famous Indian fighter, publicly commended them. It was the Guards who gave my father his sword. I think, later, he would enjoy showing it to you."

Louise, with her parents and General and Mrs. Grant, received the ball guests in the blue salon. Presently she noticed that the general was bored and restless. She whispered to her father to take him off and give him a drink and a cigar.

"And I think," she said to Mrs. Grant, "that we ladies, too, have done our formal duty long enough and have a right now to enjoy the party."

The ball was in full swing. Louise moved proudly among the guests: President MacMahon and his wife, who clung to her Bonapartist title and still styled herself Duchess of Magenta; the Marquis de Lafayette—there was a name to please John with his passion for American history. She saw the Duc de Broglie talking to Mémé and heard his strange, cackling apelike laugh. Admiral Gicquel des Touches, the Minister of Marine, was dancing with Minister Noyes' pretty young relative, Miss Lincoln. To watch the French officials one could not believe that they belonged to a ministry that would fall any day. She was thankful that it had not fallen before her party. Gambetta's adherents were far less aristocratic. She danced with President MacMahon, with the Duke Descazes, with Dr. Evans, the fashionable American dentist who was on terms of friendship with half the royal families of Europe.

Suddenly she realized that her father and the guest of honor had been gone for more than an hour. She looked in the Turkish smoking room to which several gentlemen had repaired, but the general and the colonel were not among them. She went upstairs to her father's study. As she approached the open door she heard voices and loud laughter. How surprised the guests would be if they could hear the man whom the French had nicknamed *"Le Grand Taciturne."* She stood unnoticed on the threshold.

"No, Colonel, I wasn't there. We were lined up at——"

"Well, sir, I'll never forget it. It was just after Vera Cruz . . ."

Together, though by separate paths of memory, they had traveled thirty years. She had not the heart to interrupt, to turn the young infantry officers back into the elderly gentlemen whom for a while they had forgotten.

As she moved to withdraw, General Grant saw her and rose heavily to his feet. The incongruously young laugh was cut short. He apologized for absenting himself so long from her splendid entertainment, but an hour passed quickly when one fell to talking of old times. His voice was tired. It was apparent that those brave young times were old and far away again.

Louise forced back an unexpected rush of tears. In her distinguished guest she saw only a weary old man for whom she was sorry. How odd to feel an almost intolerable pity for a hero and statesman whom the whole world delighted to honor.

She took the arm he offered and managed to smile.

The forced smile became real as she heard the ring of pride in her father's voice. "You'll have to forgive us, dearie, two old comrades in arms who got to talking."

Before the general led Louise to the door, he looked at the sword in its glass case and studied the inscription. "Your father's seen a lot of battles," he said. "You must be proud of him."

The general and his party retired after supper, but the ball continued until after five in the morning.

When the last guest had departed and Mrs. Hungerford and Ada had gone up to bed Louise returned alone to the vast, empty gold and white room. There would be many other balls, but none would be like this. Never again would she know the excitement of this first triumphant success.

She walked to a window. The sky was gray in the cloudy dawn. She watched the workmen extinguish the last of the thousand gas jets. They finished and left the garden dark and empty.

Beyond the dark the whiteness of the arch was beginning to emerge. It really did seem to shine with its own light. She remembered how indignant her father had been at the gossip which had accused her of trying to rent the arch from the government in order to illuminate it as a decoration for her party. It was natural for the colonel to be angry on her behalf. The story was not meant to be kind. She opened the window and breathed the cold damp air. In the half light the arch seemed very near, as though it were part of the garden and did indeed belong to her. She smiled. The malicious story was not true but it was not entirely absurd. Like all successful gossip, it had the quality of appropriateness. It was in character. She had a proprietary feeling for the arch. She did not need to rent it. She owned it. It had brought her luck. It was the symbol of her triumph. For a few minutes she watched it shining whiter and whiter at the foot of her garden under the heavy clouds. Then she closed the window and turned back to the white and gold room.

The candles had been extinguished and the gas lamps turned low. She remembered the room as it had been two hours ago. She could hear the music of the city's most famous dance orchestra; she could see the beautiful gowns, velvet and satin, gauze and silk and priceless lace. The guests had worn their best. They had emptied their jewel boxes to do honor to her party. Even the gentlemen had been colorful; many wore uniforms and all who had them wore the wide, bright ribbons and the jeweled and enameled emblems of their decorations.

At her first ball there had been all the names that counted, De Broglie, De Talleyrand, De Lafayette—old as the history books or newly come to prominence, they were all there, De Rivoli, De Rochambeau, De Trohan—dukes and duchesses, counts and countesses, barons and baronesses, Royalist or Bonapartist, they were all there. The leaders of the American colony were present to witness her triumph. She laughed aloud. The most brilliant entertainment of the season had been given by little Mamie Hungerford from Downieville.

Chapter XXI

Promises to Ada

Now THAT SHE was successful, Louise could entirely fulfill the promises which long ago she had made to Ada. She watched her young sister with pride. Ada at twenty had the bloom of youthful beauty without the awkwardness that so often accompanies it. She moved with equal grace on a parquet floor in a wide gauzy ball gown or on the Champs Élysées in a simple fur-trimmed walking costume. In every dress and in every setting she was gay and pretty and at her ease. She laughed and danced her way through the end of the Paris winter season. Then she went south with her parents to enjoy a little of the artificial summer at Nice. They returned to Paris for the beginning of the spring season.

On an April morning Louise watched her sister running down the broad stairs. Ada's violet riding skirt was looped gracefully over the tips of her gleaming black boots. Her black tricorn gave her an elegant eighteenth-century air, though beneath the velvet brim her little face was more piquant, more modern than anything Watteau or Nattier had ever painted.

"Oh, Ada, my darling, you look so pretty but you mustn't run. A lady doesn't run in the house."

"I know. And she doesn't whistle. All the things a lady doesn't do. I can remember your telling them to me as far back as I can remember anything. But you weren't cross about it, just solemn and loving, so I never minded." Ada laughed and kissed her sister. "Watch now how well I've learned." She held her skirt with exaggerated elegance and walked with small dainty steps.

"You can make fun all you like, miss, you and John, but——"

"Louise darling, it's only fun." Ada ran back to embrace her sister once more. "We laugh because we love you and because sometimes you look so little and so fierce and so pretty all at once."

"Go on with you." Louise laughed and hugged her sister and pushed her toward the door. "And don't think John hasn't had a hand in your education. You've acquired a bit of his blarney, though both of you, thank goodness, are sparing in the use of it."

As she walked slowly upstairs to the nursery floor Louise remembered her first sight of her baby sister. She knew she had been jealous and angry, but she could no longer remember anything except the tender pity that had filled her heart when she held the small helpless red-faced creature. She had tried to soothe the squalling infant with songs and promises. "Someday," she had promised, "someday when I am grown a lady——"

The academies at Nice and Neuilly had done their work well, and, before them, the Sisters in Virginia City. But John had done the most for her. From the time she had been ten years old he had cherished her as though she were his own little sister. In his home she had known only love and protection. Thanks to him, she had a trustful friendliness for all the world. She felt welcome and at her ease in any group. The nuns had taught her the rules of deportment. Thanks to John, she had the confidence that enabled her to laugh at the rules and, on occasion, to break them with grace and without embarrassment.

Soon it would be time for Eva to enjoy the pleasures of Paris society. In a year or so Eva in her turn would be the feted princess of the palace on the Place de l'Étoile. It would be best to keep her at Neuilly until Ada's marriage. That, Louise thought, was an event which would not be long delayed. In every ballroom Ada was the prettiest, the most popular of the unmarried girls. Nine Rue de Tilsitt was crowded with her admirers, their flowers filled the salons. Ada would not mean to outshine the niece whom she loved as a sister.

It would happen without her wish or knowledge. Eva's gentle prettiness and charm would fade in the dazzling light of Ada's looks and
her vivid personality. Fortunately Eva was not impatient to be grown
up. She was happy with her books and her music. She was fond of
her schoolmates. Most of all she enjoyed the company of her little
brothers. On her holidays her greatest pleasure was to be with them.

Louise hurried down the hall to the nursery where the boys were
waiting to show her their fancy-dress costumes for Clarie's birthday
party. Her heart seemed really to move and swell with joy when she
thought suddenly of her sons or saw them unexpectedly. She paused
in the doorway as they shouted to her to wait, not to look, in a minute
they would be ready. They were beautiful children. They were fair
like their father, with wide-set, large blue eyes like hers. She hoped
that in time they would both have John's high-bridged nose.

"Shut your eyes," they implored her. "Shut your eyes till we're
ready."

She obeyed and listened to them panting and laughing as they
struggled with their costumes. They were truly carefree happy little
boys. Unlike Ada and Eva they had been born when the hard times
were over; they had never known even the shadow of anxiety. And
they never would, she told herself fiercely.

"Now look! Now look!" Willie shouted. "Look at me!"

Willie in the red and gold of an eighteenth-century officer's uniform, complete with powdered wig and three-cornered hat, was
handsome. At least he would be when both wig and hat were not so
crooked. That could be arranged and the lace ruffles could be
pressed before the arrival of the artist who was to paint the brothers
in costume.

Clarie presented his back to his mother. She laughed with delight
and stretched out her arms to him. He was an adorable miniature
Paris policeman. He waved his arms and said in a thin anxious imitation of Willie's shout, "Now look! Look at me!"

As he turned and faced her, she gasped with dismay. His policeman's costume included a large red false mustache.

"Oh no, Clarie. Not the mustache. At least not for the painting,
darling."

His eyes blurred with tears. "Bu-but I'm a gen-gendarme," he
pleaded. "Please, Mammy, I want to be a real one. They all have
mu-mustaches."

"See," Willie said. "That's what I told you. I reasoned with him and reasoned with him, Mammy, and so did Nurse."

"Please, Mammy, I want to be a real one in the painting." Clarie spoke so low behind the mustache that Louise could hardly understand his words. She could feel the effort with which he kept his voice steady. His long lashes were wet, but he let no tears fall. "Please, Mammy, it's no fu-fun if I can't be a real one."

"Of course, darling. You can." She hugged him. "It's a painting of your birthday. It wouldn't be fair to deny you your first birthday wish." And it was not, she told herself, as if the painting were to be a valuable one. She had commissioned a quite unknown young artist to paint the boys in their finery as a surprise for John in case he did not reach Paris by the seventeenth of April.

"I don't call it very fair." Willie tugged at her sleeve. "I don't call it very fair to let him have his silly old mustache and not let me have Jean."

Jean was the son of the boys' French nurse.

"What has Jean to do with the picture?" Louise asked.

"Well, if Clarie can have his mustache I want Jean. You told Nurse to order him a costume like mine for the party. He's waiting in my bedroom to show you. He's my very best friend and I want him in the picture."

"Come in, Jean," Louise called.

The boy looked very well in his costume. He thanked her shyly in French for his beautiful uniform.

"You ask him," Willie pleaded in a whisper. "You ask him quick so he'll think you want him."

"But I do want him, Willie." She smiled at Jean and asked him if he would sit for his portrait. It would not take long, she assured him. She would tell his mother that in her opinion a group of three would make a more pleasing composition.

The boys shouted with pleasure. They struck attitudes. Each cried, unheeding the others, "Look at me! Look a' me! *Regardez-moi! 'gardez-moi!* Look a' me!"

"Boys! Boys!" Louise grasped her sons and called to the nurse to catch Jean, who was galloping about the room, brandishing his sword. "You must take the costumes off now or there will be nothing left of them for the party or the painting."

It would make an odd-looking picture, she thought, but John

wouldn't mind. Little Clarie in his mustache would make him laugh, and he would be pleased by Willie's loyalty to his first Paris friend. With all his new young acquaintances the boy might by now have begun to neglect Jean.

John did not arrive in time for Clarie's birthday. He cabled Louise that he had been delayed by business in Virginia City and would join her late in May.

Louise wished he might have been present for the opening of the Paris Exposition on the afternoon of the first of May. She went in the morning with her father, by invitation, to view Tiffany's exhibit.

The Mackay silver was prominently displayed. The service was not yet complete, but the fifteen hundred finished pieces formed half of the New York silver manufacturer's entire exhibit. John would be pleased when he came, she thought. Surely nothing in the exposition could be more magnificent than the silver he had given her. Two hundred of Tiffany's expert silversmiths had worked for two years to produce it. It had been brought to France in nine chests, each of which required four men to carry it.

The rich designs were more beautiful than she had hoped. The service was executed in elaborate *repoussé* work; each field showed a different relief ornamentation, but a single fundamental style unified the whole.

"Something memorable from our own mine. That's what I wanted. That's what I have," Louise said. "But even after seeing the designs, I couldn't imagine how splendid it could be."

"And mind you, dearie," the colonel said, "it's thoroughly practical too. Unlike many of these expensive sets, the ornamentation is of a kind you won't tire of, and though it's exceedingly fine it's adapted for everyday use."

It was impossible, Louise thought, to select the handsomest piece. The punch bowl was even larger and more richly ornamented than the one which Mr. Ralston had displayed at Belmont. The great epergnes rose in elaborate sprays and tiers of silver and crystal; filled with fruit and flowers, they would make a dazzling impression. She picked up a knife and fork; they were perhaps a little massive for a lady to manage, but John would like to feel the weight of the Comstock silver in his hands. The prettiest objects were the silver sleighs intended for the serving of claret. They could also be used for flowers in an intimate setting. On a Christmas table they would look charming filled with English holly or red and white camellias.

Her favorite of the entire exhibit was her tea set. She had instructed Tiffany to make it from the first shipment of silver which John had sent them. This was the silver which he had himself carried out of the Con Virginia. He would like to know that it had been fashioned into the tea service that she had so long desired. She would sit in her high-backed chair and before her would be the huge silver tray. She would light the little flame beneath the richly embossed kettle and when the tea was made she would pour it into the fragile Sèvres cups for the ladies, for Mrs. Hooper and Mrs. Noyes, for Lady Mandeville on her visits from London, for the Duchess Descazes and the Duchess of Magenta and for ex-Queen Isabella, who had lately returned to Paris from Spain.

In the afternoon Louise and Ada watched the formal opening of the exposition with Isabella in the Duchess of Magenta's gallery. As the ceremony began, rain fell but it lasted less than a half hour. After the shower the glass palace, its walls newly washed, gleamed more brightly. The flowers and grass on the terrace seemed fresher. On the ramps of the stairs the palms in their blue and white porcelain tubs shone as if their branches were made of green satin. In the distance the Trocadéro Palace loomed softly in the misty air. Louise admired its combination of modern and Eastern elegance. Beside the great bubble of the central dome the little towers resembled Turkish minarets.

Louise had promised to meet Mémé and the children at Tiffany's exhibit. At ex-Queen Isabella's request, she left Ada in her care.

She walked slowly through the exhibits.

The most unforgettable sight was the enormous head of Bartholdi's *Liberty*. It was the only single object that was in scale with the exposition.

Louise paused for a few moments at Boucheron's exhibit where was displayed a sapphire and diamond parure which John had ordered for her. She would return, she assured the manager, to examine further the rich profusion of diamonds and sapphires and other precious stones. Now she must meet her children at the American exhibit.

She walked down the narrow little street of nations on which the foreign pavilions faced. The Spanish façade was Moorish; the Russian and Scandinavian fronts were fashioned of massive, varnished woods.

Beneath Switzerland's belfry she found Eva and Clarie. The boy was standing motionless staring up at the clock. He heard his mother's voice. Without turning, he said, "Wait, oh, wait. In a minute, in a minute you'll see."

Louise waited beside him until the mechanical man in armor struck the hour stiffly with his hammer.

At the entrance to Tiffany's, Mémé and Willie were waiting. Colonel Hungerford, Mémé explained, had gone to view the Pacific coast mineral exhibit. "Since John is paying for it, he thought he should visit it."

"I must do that too," Louise said, "but on another day with just Willie. Clarie's too little for that sort of thing."

"Toys," Clarie said. "In the French part, the man said, there's toys."

The boys and their elders were fascinated by the toy exhibit.

There were mechanical water toys: fish that swam, when one wound a key in their backs, as though they were alive, ships of all sorts and sizes, and mechanical swimming dolls in bathing dress.

There were toy locomotives which had real machinery and went with real steam. There were huge, gas-filled toy balloons in varied and fantastic shapes. They should have waited for John, Louise thought. He should have the pleasure of seeing this exhibit with the boys.

"We'll return to this when your father comes," she said. "He'll know how to choose the best toy."

"A fish?" Clarie asked. "Will he choose a fish?"

Eva smiled at her mother. "Remember my doll from Dale's? She was the first one Father ever gave me. I was six. I've never forgotten." She bent and wiped Clarie's perspiring forehead. She took his hand. "Don't worry, Father will get you the best."

"Can't I have one fish now? Just one fish?"

"Oh, Clarie," Louise said sadly. She wanted to save the pleasure for John. She turned to Willie. "Willie, will you wait for Father?"

"Sure I will." The boy's smile was exactly like his father's. "I understand. You know, Mammy, I'm nearly eight and at school they say that seven is the age of reason."

"Just one fish," Clarie repeated. "That one."

Ollie and Clarie in London,
1885.

Eva and Ferdinand with Bianca
in Paris, 1887.

Ada and Joseph with their children in Rome, 1887.

Eva, in 1887.

Eva, in 1898.

To my dear Mother.

Evelyne

Louise and Clarie, in 1897.

Colonel Hungerford, in 1890.

" . . . you were still angry with
Jim Fair, though he was a handsome man, you said. You said he
could charm the birds from the
trees. And he was a clever man."

Louise in the early 1880s.

Katherine, about 1905.

"Let him," Willie whispered. "He's too little to understand about waiting."

"Very well," Louise said. "Clarie, you shall have one fish, but only one. It's all you can carry anyway. They're as big as our California salmon."

That evening Louise tried to write to John of all she had seen. Her recollections of the exposition were whirling in her head like colored fragments in a kaleidoscope. She would put off her letter until the next day. In the meantime she would sort out her impressions so that she could tell him in an orderly fashion about the wonders she had seen in the palace on the Champ de Mars: the vast-domed bronze and gilt entrance hall brilliantly illuminated by the new electric light, the long glass wings whose crystal-bright walls were supported almost invisibly by cream-colored plaster, the flowered terrace, green and soft as velvet, beside the Seine, the French toys, the jeweled enamels from Russia, the Swiss clocks, the Bohemian glass, the porcelain and jade and embroidered silk from China. Tomorrow she would write all she could remember and urge him to come quickly to see for himself the brand-new splendors of the Great Exposition of 1878. The head of Bartholdi's *Liberty* and the electric lighting would, she thought, interest him the most.

On the night of the second of May, Louise wrote to John. It was late when she finished. She would send the letter off in the morning.

In the morning, before the letter was mailed, a cable came from John bringing the news of Billy O'Brien's death at the age of fifty-two. Louise read and reread the message. She had known of Billy O'Brien's illness but she had not believed in its gravity. Though O'Brien was the oldest, by a few years, of the partners, he had seemed the youngest. He had enjoyed his wealth more than they: its responsibilities had not burdened him. Poor Billy O'Brien. He had enjoyed for such a little time the luck in which, even during the hard years, he had so firmly believed.

Louise tore up the letter she had written. She must write another, a comforting letter. John would be sad and, whether he realized it or not, he would be deeply disturbed by his partner's death. Billy was the first of the firm to go.

Louise shivered and stared at the blank piece of paper. In her letter she would put only love and sympathy. But one day when she was alone with John she would speak again of the long holiday which he was always promising to take and always postponing. Once the lode was exhausted, as soon it must be, surely he would rest. They could see the world together.

When John arrived in Paris he spoke sadly about his partner. "He shouldn't have gone so young. And he'd have stayed young if he'd lived to be a hundred. He enjoyed life, he should have had more of it."

"Poor Billy," Louise said, "but at least no one called him 'poor Billy' when he was alive. He had more fun than any of the bonanza kings."

"He did that. But don't use that expression, Louise, it's never used of us with love."

"People aren't given to loving kings, John."

"Meaning you have to choose between popularity and power? And you and I both will always choose the power and the glory. Still a man gets tired sometimes. It's good to be away for a while from the *Chronicle* and the fool stock gamblers and all the pack that yaps at our heels."

"Can you stay away for the summer?"

"There's times I wish I could stay away forever. But, yes, I can stay for the summer."

"I thought we might take the children to the seashore for July and August."

"I'd like that fine. But meanwhile?"

"There are a few grand affairs in June. You haven't been in Paris since I've reached the top of the heap. The Duke and Duchess Descazes are entertaining and M. Cernuschi, the banker, has invitations out for a ball, week after next, and——"

"Wear your most splendid gown for Cernuschi's ball and your sapphires. I like him and I'd like him to feel that you're doing his party honor."

Louise laughed. "I do honor to all the parties," she said. "Still I'll make a special effort for this party since it's one you care about."

For M. Cernuschi's ball Louise wore her newest and most elaborate gown. It was of *caroubier* faille, richly embroidered with multicolored beads. Her train of pale pink satin was almost concealed by old point d'Angleterre lace. She wore her sapphire and diamond necklace and the matching ornaments. High up on her left arm she clasped John's latest gift, a diamond bracelet in the center of which was a single diamond the size of a hazelnut. Instead of a tiara she wore a diamond wreath in which real roses were twined.

Her maid, Demoutier, clapped her hands with pleasure. "Madame looks like the veritable spirit of summer!" she exclaimed.

Louise turned from her reflection in the cheval glass and smiled at the girl's eager, admiring face. "Thank you, my child. And on your Sunday off you must pin June roses like these in your hair. At your age they're all you need. At mine diamonds are a help."

"Louise! What a thing to say!" Ada stood in the door. "You look lovely without a single diamond."

"My dear, I only said they were a help. I've a few years still before they become essential. Now let me look at you."

Ada turned slowly around. Her dress of white gauze over silver was embroidered with tiny glittering stars. Around her throat was a single strand of pearls.

"Not the pearls, darling," Louise said. "They're not right with that dress. The embroidery is almost ornament enough."

"But the pearls were my Christmas present from John."

"Even so, not the pearls. Fetch the small diamond crescent he bought you at the exposition."

When Ada brought the brooch Louise fastened it in her sister's dark shining hair.

"There," she said with satisfaction. "That's perfect. That's glitter enough. No, wait." She took from her jewel box a narrow diamond band and fastened it on Ada's left wrist. "Since he has given me my new bracelet, John would like you to have this." Louise led Ada to the glass. "See how it all goes together; the diamonds and the sparkling embroidery are all part of a fairy princess' costume."

"Would you like to see me a real princess, Louise? Or at least a marquise?"

"I'd like to see you happy, my darling. Of course, if it could be with a marquis that would be very nice too. But are you serious? I noticed that he sent flowers again today and of course he belongs to one of the first families of France."

"I'm not serious about anyone or anything. I'd like this spring and summer never to stop. Isn't it exciting to be going to a great ball in a Paris garden in June? And me, Ada Hungerford, in the midst of it all! Oh, Louise, I'm glad I can remember Virginia City and even Downieville a little. It makes this all seem more wonderful."

At M. Cernuschi's ball Ada met Count Telfener. Louise noticed him quite early in the evening when for the second time she saw her sister dancing with a heavy-set, dark-eyed, black-bearded man. He was older than Ada's other admirers. He looked to be well up in his thirties. The waltz ended and he reluctantly surrendered Ada to her next partner. Dr. Evans claimed Louise for the polka. At the end of the dance she saw the stranger talking with M. Cernuschi. Dr. Evans would know who he was, she thought. Dr. Evans was a walking encyclopedia of European society.

"Who is the gentleman speaking to our host?" she asked. "I don't think I've seen him before."

"Count Joseph Telfener. Italian, but of Austrian origin, I believe. Said to be extremely rich. Close friend of King Humbert. Heard him well spoken of when I was last at the Quirinal."

"You do know everyone. I believe there isn't a court in Europe where you are not at home."

"I've been fortunate, ma'am, in making connections."

Louise smiled. Over his shoulder she saw Ada dancing again with the Italian count. She must have cut some of her other partners. The child's card was always too full for her to find three dances in such quick succession for a stranger.

At supper Louise sat on M. Cernuschi's right. Count Telfener led Ada to the table.

"There you are, my dear friend," the banker said. "I have saved places for you and your charming partner."

Ada presented the count to Louise. He bowed and kissed her hand. "Your sister has been kind and taken pity on a stranger in Paris. Fortunately for me, her supper partner became indisposed and retired."

Ada kissed her sister and whispered, "The marquis went home in a sulk." She giggled and seated herself beside the Italian.

Louise smiled and chatted with her host. No one could tell that she had a care in the world. As she turned to the partner on her right she glanced quickly at her sister. The whole table, she thought, must see what had happened to Ada. Her eyes were brighter than the diamonds in her hair. Her cheeks were flushed and her lips were softly parted as she looked at her supper partner. Louise could not hear what the count was saying, but Ada listened as though his words were divine revelation.

After supper Louise found John. She disengaged him from the

group with which he was standing. "I want Mr. Mackay to see the view from the south terrace." She laughed. "To be truthful I want to flirt for a few minutes with my own husband."

When they were alone she said, "John, I'm worried about Ada. She's spending the whole evening with Count Telfener."

"My dear, Ada has so many titled admirers, you can't worry about one more. What I'd like to see for her is a good, red-blooded American."

"She has those among her suitors too. But I'm worried about this. Find out about him from M. Cernuschi. They seem to be friends."

"I will if you like, Louise, but I think you're upsetting yourself for nothing. Has the fellow been around long?"

"She never saw him till this evening."

"Well, then, what are you worrying about?"

"I'm worrying about a June night in a Paris garden. And besides, I watched Ada watching him at supper."

"You are worried, aren't you? I'll find out about Telfener. Cernuschi will tell me. But, Louise, Ada's a sensible girl."

"John darling, no girl is sensible. No girl in love at least. I'm desperately afraid Ada is falling in love. He's too old for her and, as you say, he's a foreigner. We know nothing about him. I questioned Dr. Evans but I'd rather have the opinion of a friend of yours. Find out from M. Cernuschi, so that if he's the wrong sort we can stop her before it's too late."

"My poor girl." John took her hand. "We can try, but the old folks have been trying to stop the young from falling in love since time began and damned few have ever succeeded."

"But she loves and respects you, John. She'll listen to you."

"If you're right about what's happening to her, she won't hear a word I say."

When they drove home in the dawn it was quiet in the carriage. Usually after a ball Ada chattered excitedly, but tonight she sat silent between her sister and her brother-in-law.

Just before they reached the Rue de Tilsitt she leaned her head on John's shoulder and smiled sleepily. "Such a beautiful party," she murmured. "Such a beautiful, beautiful party."

On the following day John lunched with the banker. He returned to Louise with a good report.

"According to Cernuschi the fellow's sound enough. Owns a lot of valuable property in Rome and works at looking after it and increasing it. Lord knows that's unusual for a count. I mention his financial position because it means that he'll not be chasing after Ada for the settlement I'm meaning to make on her when she marries. And he's got a good reputation in other ways: he's not a heavy drinking man or a gambler or a woman chaser."

"Did M. Cernuschi mention his age?"

"No, but I took a look at him myself last night and I'd say he's about thirty-five. Somewhere around the age I was when you and I met."

"That was different. I was twenty-three and I was a woman. We've sheltered Ada so that she's still a girl, and sometimes a girl is dazzled by an older man."

"Better than being dazzled by a young fortune hunter's high-sounding title."

"I suppose one can't ask for everything. And, of course, a count is something, but the heir to one of the greatest and oldest names in France is just on the verge of offering for Ada."

"The man himself is everything. You know that, Louise. If Ada is interested we'll get to know Telfener and judge him for himself."

"She's interested. She's expecting him to call and she's changed her dress three times since luncheon."

Count Telfener became a daily visitor at 9 Rue de Tilsitt. He accompanied Ada on her morning rides in the Bois. Her boudoir was filled with his magnificent flowers.

At the end of two weeks his business necessitated his return to Rome.

Before he left he called formally on Colonel and Mrs. Hungerford and requested their permission to join them in Trouville in August in order to pay his addresses to their younger daughter.

The colonel explained that, in accordance with the American custom, Ada would be free to make her own choice.

"My dear Count, for all her twenty years Ada is still very young," Mrs. Hungerford said. "She knows little of the world. She was presented to society only last autumn. I think she favors your suit but I hope you won't urge her to a hasty decision."

"I'm not a boy, madame; I can wait. I love your daughter. I want her to be quite certain that I can give her happiness."

The count also spoke to Louise and asked her to arrange for him an interview with her husband.

"My fortune does not, of course, compare with Mr. Mackay's," he said, "but I have done well and I intend to do better. I am even now returning to Rome to negotiate with the government for property on which I plan to build a theater. I should like to tell Mr. Mackay of my financial circumstances so that he will know that I am fully capable of supporting your sister in the manner to which she is accustomed. Not so magnificently, of course, as Mr. Mackay has done, but comfortably; indeed, without boasting, I may say luxuriously."

John was pleased by his talk with Telfener.

"It's an odd thing about that fellow," he said afterward to Louise. "Outwardly he's a fop with his silk hat and his sable-collared overcoat and his diamond stickpin; and he has all the foreign ways that I've no liking for, bowing from the waist and kissing the ladies' hands, but underneath he's a man. As much of a man as Jim Fair or John P. Jones or any of them. I'd not have said no to him as a partner in the diggings. And I can't say better than that of any man."

In July the Mackays and the Hungerfords went to the Hôtel des Roches Noires at Trouville. John settled them at the hotel before he left for Frankfort to attend Henry Rosener's marriage to Henrietta Rosenfeld.

"I wish I could go," Louise said, "but it wouldn't be fair to leave Mémé with the boys and Ada and Eva. Not with Ada in her present state of mind and with Telfener arriving any day."

"Henry'll understand. I'll give him your present for the little bride and your note."

"And urge her to accept my invitation to them to come here. I'm longing for news of Fanny and Sam."

"Tell the truth, Louise. You're longing to see the girl who could catch an old bachelor like Henry."

"I am indeed. Now you remember every detail so you can tell me."

"Better watch the papers, old lady. You know I'm not much of a hand at describing this sort of thing."

Ada found an account of the wedding in the *Continental Gazette*. "Doesn't it sound romantic, Louise?"

"My dear, I think any wedding would seem romantic to you. Still, this does sound a pretty one." She read aloud: "'The marriage ceremony was solemnized in the presence of a very select circle of friends and relations. At a most elegant *recherché déjeuner* which followed, the floral decorations, intermingled with the dazzling gold, silver and glass set upon the tables, rendered the scene almost fairylike.' And I see there were old friends from the Bay there: Mr. J. W. Heller, for one. John will have enjoyed himself."

"And listen to the nice thing it says at the end, Louise: 'If all the good wishes which were called forth to bless the union of Mr. and Mrs. Henry Rosener reach them in their journey through life, we are sure that they will be a very happy couple indeed, and faithfully commemorate each recurring anniversary of the 19th of July 1878.'"

"It's a long journey, Ada. Don't be in a hurry to start on it."

"But since Joseph and I are so sure . . ."

"Still, wait a little, darling."

When he returned John also advised Ada to wait. "You're married for a lifetime. And you've only one life, so be careful with it."

"And if, next spring, I feel as I do now?"

"Then we'll not say no. But it's like your sister says, it's easy to fall in love in the summer, it's the romantic time of the year. Give yourself the fall and winter too. After that we'll not oppose you. Now let me enjoy my holiday. It's not often enough I have time just for myself and my family."

Late in August, a few days before John sailed, the Henry Roseners came to the Hôtel des Roches Noires to visit Louise.

The bride was only eighteen, Eva's age.

"But she's done mighty well, Louise," John said. "And of course Henry's a bit younger than I am."

"Even if he weren't, she's done well. The Rosener brothers are like you. Perhaps it seems so to me because I saw you together for the first time, but I think it's because they're kind men, as I have good reason to know." She sighed. "I wish Eva might find someone like Henry Rosener. I believe that in marriage kindness is all."

"That's true enough. But don't you be worrying about Eva. Be thankful Ada seems to be choosing wisely."

"I can't help worrying more for Eva."

"Worrying never did a bit of good. So enjoy the end of your holiday."

"I'll enjoy it. I'll enjoy having Henry and his pretty little Henny with me. But when you leave my holiday ends."

"One of these days we'll have a holiday the year round."

"You promise?"

"I can't put a date to it but I promise."

Ada and Joseph were married in Rome, March 15, 1879. The best account of the wedding was in the *Continental Gazette*.

"A succession of brilliant *fêtes* had been expected on the occasion of this marriage, the bridegroom being very popular in Rome; but the exigencies of the Church had, of course, to be taken into consideration, and at the approach of Easter it is forbidden to pious Catholics resident in the city to display much pomp or to manifest too great an amount of rejoicing. The religious ceremony, therefore, took place almost privately at the Palazzo Telfener, formerly a royal residence. Mass was performed by the Superior of the Parish, in presence of Mgr. Capel, placed on the left of the young bride, and of Mgr. Cataldi, who represented His Holiness the Pope, on the right of the bridegroom. After the nuptial benediction a sumptuous *déjeuner* was offered to the guests. At 3 o'clock the guests went to the races which had been specially organized in honor of the marriage, and which took place in Count Telfener's park, situated outside the Salaro gate. The King of Italy, who had made it known that he would honor the races with his presence, arrived on the course at 3:15, accompanied by the Duke d'Aosta and Gen. Medici. As soon as Count Telfener had presented his new family to the King, his Majesty gave up the places of honor to the Countess Telfener, to Mme. Mackay, to Mme. Hungerford, and to the bridesmaids. The other guests remained standing behind his Majesty. Everything connected with this grand *fête* offered to the elite of Roman society went off most successfully, and will leave a lasting souvenir in the memory of all those who enjoyed the happiness of being present. The beauty of the weather, the brilliancy of the sun, the presence of the King of Italy, and the gayety of the noble guests, all contributed to make the day a success and a triumph, auguring well for the future happiness of the Count and Countess Telfener."

Louise read the *Gazette* and remembered the expression on Ada's face during the marriage ceremony. That had been the quietest and clearest moment of the day. She might forget the rest, Louise thought; she would always remember Ada and Joseph standing together at the altar. Still, the festivities that had followed should be agreeable to look back on. King Humbert's presence at the races was something of which anybody would be proud. Except John, she knew. All he cared about was that, in Joseph, Ada was getting a good man. John had been kept in the States by business. Louise sighed. Poor little Ada. She had been so grieved by his enforced absence. She had written to tell him of her disappointment.

"Will this tell him how I feel?" she had asked Louise and had shown her the letter:

Rome 11th March, '79.

My dear Brother!!

By the time you receive this I will be married to Comte Telfener. I cannot tell you how good and kind he is to me, and how he loves me, and how I love and respect him. I can only say one thing that will give you an idea of his character, he is a second John Mackay, in goodness and thoughtfulness, and now my own dear Brother, let me thank and bless you for all you have done for me. I owe you everything, *yes, everything,* and I can hardly tell you how grateful I am, and how I *love you!!!* My constant prayer is that God may bless and keep you, as you deserve.

Kindly excuse this letter, I am blinded with tears of anger, to think I cannot express to you my feelings. I should so much have liked to have you here for the marriage, but you will be present in my mind all the time.

With best love and kisses,

Your little
Ada!

Remembering Ada's letter, Louise knew that it would tell him. An ill wind, she thought, and smiled. The child might not have been able to speak her thanks aloud to John. In her letter she had been able to tell him.

Chapter XXII

·····➤━◉━➤·····

A World for Eva

ON THEIR RETURN to Paris from Rome, Louise told Eva that she had decided not to send her back to Neuilly.

"They were really giving you only a finishing course in these last few months," she said. "Piano, singing, all that sort of thing you can study just as well at home. I spoke about your voice to M. Gounod and he has recommended a private teacher with whom you can continue your lessons."

"Charles Gounod! Do you know him, Mammy? Can I meet him?"

"You can, indeed. You can even sing for him."

"I should be afraid to do that."

"No need. He's a charming man and a kind one. He even listened to Willie play the violin, so you can see he has patience. And he's right, my dear, to encourage the amateurs. Without amateur lovers of music where would the professionals find audiences or patrons? Look at your father and Mr. Piper. There'd be no opera in Virginia City if it weren't for John's love of music."

"I like to sing for Father. But Charles Gounod!"

"You mustn't be shy, darling. I know enough to know you have a very pretty voice. It will be a useful and attractive accomplishment for you. Like little Emma Hueston and her flower paintings. She is, of course, like you, an amateur, but one quite often meets artists in the world of fashion. Singers, painters, writers. You'll enjoy that, won't you?"

"Oh yes. But can't I meet them without going to the parties? Do I have to be part of the fashionable world?"

"Of course you do, my darling. And of course you're a little timid about it beforehand. It's how one feels before stepping out of the bathing hut at Trouville on the first morning. How I dread that moment when the horse is unhitched and I am left practically in the middle of the sea and must step into it."

"The sea is different. At least for me. Because you had me taught to swim, I'm not afraid even on the first day."

"Well, I am," Louise said firmly. "I wish I had Mémé's moral courage and dared refuse to go in at all. You see, darling"—she took Eva's hand—"we're all afraid of something. But you've no need to fear the great world; it's waiting to welcome you. Remember you're a princess, an American princess, the daughter of a silver king. Believe me, that's the best kind of princess to be."

"I don't want to be any kind."

"Darling, what's the matter?" Louise drew her daughter to the sofa beside her. "Ada had her turn, and now that she's happily married it's your turn to enjoy the festivities of the Paris seasons. We'll give a garden party in June to start you off and later, in the fall I think, there'll be dinners and receptions."

"And balls," Eva said. She looked despairingly at her mother. "I can't go to balls. I can't dance. Oh, I know I do sometimes for fun with Father and Grandpa but I couldn't with strangers. I limp. You never speak about it but you know I limp."

Louise's heart skipped a beat, as though in the dark she had stepped on a missing stair. She smiled serenely at her daughter and said lightly: "If I never speak about it, it's because I never think of it. No one does, dear. You swim as well as any girl at Trouville. You ride. You sit your horse gracefully. And—come with me." Louise led the way to her bedroom. "Now walk. Walk to the cheval glass. Slowly—slowly, as they taught you. Now watch that girl in the mirror. Is she limping?"

"No, Mammy, she isn't. At least she is, but with the way this skirt is cut and walking slowly as my dancing masters taught me, it's hardly less noticeable."

"Now look," Louise said. "Stand still and look at that pretty girl. Almost all young girls are pretty, Eva, but they must feel pretty for it to show."

"Am I pretty, Mammy?" Eva flushed with pleasure. "I always thought that Ada——"

"Never compare yourself with anyone. That's the first thing to learn. Look at yourself, darling. Look at the line of your brow. Look at your eyes. You have Mémé's lovely eyes. But you must carry yourself as though you were beautiful. If you don't, your eyes and your wavy hair and your soft young skin will do you no good. You must believe in your own looks, Eva."

"As long as you believe in them, Mammy."

"And about the balls," Louise said gently, "don't be afraid of them. They'll be much easier for you than a kettledrum at home. Here there is always entertainment other than the dance orchestra. And there is conversation. Europeans delight in witty conversation."

"I'm not very witty," Eva said doubtfully.

"Young ladies aren't supposed to be witty, they're supposed to listen. You speak four languages. You can listen in all four and be thought the most accomplished and charming young lady at the ball. Don't be frightened by the thought of a ballroom. It's only one more meeting place for society, like the opera or the Bois or the beach at Trouville. You'll see, Eva. Just trust me and you'll see."

"Of course I trust you." Eva held her cheek against her mother's and smiled at their reflection in the glass. "I know that if you say so I needn't be afraid."

On the mantel the gilded clock struck the hour.

"Heavens!" Louise exclaimed. "It's time to dress for dinner. The Duke and Duchess Descazes are expecting us at eight. There will be only a few people at dinner and perhaps another two dozen to listen to the chamber music afterward." She patted Eva's cheek. "The first little dip into the strange sea, but, as you've so often said to me, 'Once you're in, you'll enjoy it.'"

When Eva had gone Louise did not immediately ring for her maid. She walked slowly up and down the room. Just so she had walked in the months during which she had planned her Paris campaign. Now she must plan for Eva. Within the great world she must make a smaller but no less fashionable and elegant world for Eva. Her house must be not only a center of gaiety but, in the older French tradition, a salon. The artists whom she had met would be a beginning. It would seem quite natural for her to include on her invitation list distinguished exponents of the arts. All who were acquainted with John were aware of his deep enjoyment of music. There should be writers, too, and painters. If she could capture the great Meissonier, that would be a *coup*. The peppery old gentleman was said to dislike society and most particularly to despise millionaires and their wives, but occasionally he painted them. John had suggested that she have her portrait done by Cabanel, but she already knew M. Cabanel, he could wait. She would commission Meissonier instead. She sighed. Meissonier was the most famous of modern artists; he commanded the highest price. The portrait would be a valuable one, but she preferred Cabanel; he always made a lady look so pretty.

The clock chimed the half hour. She must hurry. She must not keep Eva waiting and thus give the child time to get nervous. She walked briskly across the room and pulled the bell tassel.

In the autumn of 1879 and in the winter that followed, Louise entertained quietly for Eva, without great display. She concentrated on dinners followed by musical entertainment and with informal dancing for the younger guests. Eva preferred to remain with her mother and the older people. She felt at ease with Mrs. Noyes and the Duchess Descazes, and she was a favorite of M. Gounod and M. Halévy.

"She grows so slowly in confidence," Louise said to John during his winter visit. "I'm afraid she will miss all the fun of her young years. These should be the holiday years for her before she settles down to the business of living."

"Take it easy, old lady," he said. "You're doing fine."

"She's at her ease in the company of older men. With them she's her natural, gay little self. She chatters about literature with M. Halévy and about music with M. Gounod, but with the young men of position who should be her suitors she's stiff and silent. They seem to frighten her."

"As a matter of fact, Louise, the most of those young fellows frighten me."

"Now, John, you know perfectly well that at nineteen a girl should enjoy the company of young men, whether she takes any of them seriously or not."

"Don't rush her, my dear. Eva's young for her years, in appearance anyway. And she has a sweet childish way with her. No one would take her for more than sixteen at the outside. She has plenty of time. Keep on the way you're doing. Let her go slow, knowing always you're beside her until she feels able to walk alone."

At Mr. and Mrs. Hueston's fancy-dress ball in May, Louise remembered John's words. Eva had not come near her since they arrived. That was a good sign. She should, she told herself, have thought of a party like this for Eva. A costume from another time or place gave a new personality and courage to the shy.

The Huestons' elegant *hôtel* in the Rue de Monceau was a perfect setting for such an affair. The apartments were decorated with a profusion of flowers and all sorts of ferns and palms. The lights and their reflections in the tall, wide mirrors, framed in pale *boiserie*, gave the place the look of a fairy palace.

The hostess and her guests were splendidly costumed. Mrs. Hueston, in pale yellow satin and black lace, was a Spanish lady. Her daughter, Emma, was an eighteenth-century *vivandière* with a full pleated skirt of white cashmere and a corsage of black velvet trimmed with red satin and gold lace. On her powdered head was a black cocked hat. Mr. Hueston, like many of the gentlemen, wore modern court dress.

The handsomest costume among the gentlemen, Louise thought, was that of the artist, M. Horace de Vallais. He was resplendent in the dark armor and jeweled crimson velvet mantle of a Roman emperor. The finest dress of all was worn by Mrs. Noyes. She represented an Egyptian lady of rank. Her gown of white-striped gauze was bound at the waist by a rich scarf of blue and gold, given to her by the wife of the Khedive of Egypt. An elaborate headdress of coins confined her veil. She wore a yashmak, her eyelids were stained with kohl, her finger ends were reddened with henna. Lucy Hooper had decided to impersonate her vocation: her train was covered with newspapers; scissors, paste brush, and ink bottle were hung at her side, and her hair was ornamented by a quill pen; across her bodice was a white satin ribbon stamped with the words: *La Presse*.

Louise, as Marie de' Medici, felt that, compared to her friends, she was rather primly conservative in her pale rose-colored satin embroidered with pearls. Had she, she wondered anxiously, been conservative enough in choosing Eva's costume? One could, in fancy dress, feel so beautiful or such a fool.

When the ballroom floor cleared for an interval between dances she saw Eva near the piano, surrounded by a youthful group. A blond boy sat down and played a ballad. The young girls and their escorts sang to his accompaniment. Louise watched with joy the admiring faces that turned to her daughter as the other singers fell silent and left Eva to finish the song alone. Eva blushed becomingly and gave a graceful little curtsy in response to the applause. She saw her mother and kissed her hand to her across the room before she went with the young people into the adjoining salon.

Her glimpse of Eva had told Louise all she wanted to know. Eva, as Arlecchina, felt beautiful. Her eyes were brilliant above the touch of rouge that in fancy dress was permissible. Her stiff wide skirt of white satin and gauze, trimmed with vivid squares of red and blue, swung gracefully as she moved. In her hair the small flowered headdress was bright with Harlequin's gay colors. Eva, her shyness forgotten, was pretty and bold and unself-conscious as any figure from the *commedia dell' arte*.

After the Huestons' ball Eva slipped back a little into her old ways but she was never quite so shy again. That summer in Trouville, without Ada to help her, she enjoyed herself with the young people on the beach and at the casino. The Telfeners had gone in the spring with Colonel Hungerford to make a tour of California and Nevada.

"I miss Ada," Eva said to her mother, "but it's nice to feel that people like me for myself. I thought in other summers that Ada carried me."

"And now, my darling, you see that you can walk alone."

"But I must walk my own way, Mammy. You do understand that? I don't think I shall ever care for the great world as much as you and Ada do."

"So long as you like it a little—just enough to enjoy the pleasures that are natural to your age."

"And I'm not afraid of it any more. That's the important thing and I don't know how it happened." Eva paused. The room was silent except for the sound of the sea. "Oh, Mammy, I do know," she said. "Of course I know. It was your doing—beginning long ago with the dancing masters and the singing teachers and all the rest. I remember your telling me once that Father promised you the world on a silver platter. Well, you've managed to give it to me too."

In November the Telfeners returned to Paris without Colonel Hungerford. The tour had included not only California and Nevada but Texas and Mexico. Ada had not accompanied her father and husband on the latter part of the tour but had remained with John in San Francisco where she had renewed childhood acquaintances.

"Our trip," Telfener said, "was a business one. Your father knows all that country well and he has splendid connections in Mexico. I count myself fortunate that he permitted me to invest in the New York, Texas and Mexican Railway."

"What's that?" Louise asked anxiously. "And how did you come to invest in it?"

"To answer your last question first: As you know, during your father's residence abroad his financial holdings have been in John Mackay's care. I was happy to advance the necessary funds for the enterprise. As for the company itself, I know something of railways, but my experience has been in South America, not in the States. And I am unfamiliar with American business methods. However your father's expectations are most high, most glowing. He has written about the matter in detail to John."

"John will reimburse you," Louise assured her brother-in-law.

"Only in part, I hope. I should like to retain at least a small interest. It's inspiring to feel oneself a part of the development of the new world. As your father says, we are forging a powerful bond between Mexico and the States, building a vast network of railways through territory that, but a few decades ago, was inhabited only by the red man."

"John will arrange everything. And in the meanwhile it would be well for you and Ada not to say too much about all this to Mémé. Like many ladies, she worries about business enterprises; they are, after all, a little beyond our female understanding."

"Why, Louise!" Ada exclaimed. "John has always said you have a good business head on your shoulders. And Mémé too."

"I think he hardly meant that we could grasp such complicated matters as railroads," Louise said firmly. "In any event you must not speak about this to Mémé, if for no other reason than that it will worry her to think of Father, at his age, taking up such a heavy responsibility."

"But, Louise, he has written to Mémé."

"Not in any great detail, I fancy. So let the details wait until John comes. He can explain them to Mémé so that she won't worry."

In December, John arrived in Paris. He calmed Louise's apprehension in regard to Colonel Hungerford's new venture.

"Let the poor fellow have his fun, Louise. In the end it'll not cost me much more than a few of your grand balls. And I'll see it doesn't cost Telfener a penny."

"But Father spoke, Telfener tells me, of a vast network of railways."

"There'll be no network. It's a little bit of a road. I may in the end be able to unload it on Crocker and his crowd. Meanwhile let the colonel enjoy being president of the New York, Texas and Mexican Railway. The name is the biggest thing about it. Above all let him enjoy feeling like a young man again."

"But, John, Mémé worries. She'll want him to come back."

"You underestimate your mother, Louise. She'll be glad for him to have this last venture. And if she does worry, it'll not be for long. It's mighty lonely dusty country where he is. In a few months I'm thinking he'll be glad to come back to the comforts of home. Soon as we get a hint that he's tiring of it all, you must save his pride by persuading him that it's his duty for Mémé's sake to return. Then I'll find someone to take over the road till I can unload. And if I don't do so at a profit, neither your father nor Telfener will ever know."

The Telfeners had rented the picturesque Hôtel d'Aquila on the Avenue du Bois de Boulogne. Just before Christmas they gave a dinner party in John's honor. After dinner the guests were entertained by singers from the opera.

"They've done every last thing to make it enjoyable for me," John said to Louise. "Even to having a majority of guests who can speak English. But the best of all is to watch Eva. She has found her way, hasn't she? I saw her laughing her head off with some young fellow at dinner."

"She's making friends easily now," Louise said. "And she's making a place for herself in the young world as well as with the older folks. She'll never be the flirt Ada was, but that isn't necessary. All that's necessary to any woman is one serious admirer if he's the right one."

"She's still an innocent little thing, Louise. How will you keep the fortune hunters away?"

"Quite simple. I've made it plain that, according to American custom, no great dowry goes with Eva."

"Anything I've got, she can have. You know that, Louise."

"I know. But there's no need for the mothers of sons to know it."

"I hope it'll be an American she'll choose. I'll tell you who's a nice boy, young Jim Flood."

"She needs better than a boy, John. She needs a man to take care of her."

"She'll find one. Don't you worry. And don't you be in a hurry for him to turn up."

"I'm not. At last Eva is having the fun to which every girl is entitled. With her young friends she's enjoying the pleasures of her age: picnics by the Seine, afternoon tea in the Bois, excursions by carriage to St. Cloud, box parties at the Chatelet—all the small pleasures that are so important to the young. Listen to them now, John. They don't sing very well but my, how they enjoy it."

The artists and the older guests had retired. Six young couples surrounded the piano. To Eva's accompaniment they sang, loud and clear and not very tunefully. They sang ballads of the day and songs they had learned as children. A round of "Frère Jacques" broke up with shouts of laughter.

"Now, Eva," they begged, "now, Eva, before we go, just one American song."

" 'Swanee River!' " someone called.

" 'Camptown Races,' " Emma Hueston suggested.

"Oh yes," they cried. " 'Le Camptown Races' and then 'Le Swanee River!' "

Ada took her niece's place on the gilded bench. Eva stood beside her.

"Remember how they used to sing that western-style?" John asked.

"I remember. 'I bet my money on the ace and king, who dares bet on the trey?' "

As the chorus was reached Ada sang harmony in alto to her niece's soprano.

When the duet ended to vigorous applause and shouts of "Encore!" Louise looked happily at the smiling flushed faces of her sister and her daughter. Two lovely laughing girls, she thought, two pretty girls, neither one outshining the other.

"Look at the beautiful pair of them," John said. "By God, there's no girl in the world can beat our American beauties. And that goes double for you, my dear."

"Sh! Eva's going to sing again."

> *"Way down upon the Swanee River*
> *Far, far away . . ."*

Louise listened with pride and delight to Eva's sweet voice and to the silence that paid tribute to it.

"Well done, old lady," John whispered as he took his wife's hand. "Oh, very well done indeed."

Chapter XXIII

Holiday

New Year's Day of 1881 came and went and John did not speak of returning to California. Instead he suggested to Louise that they give a ball.

"Make it the grandest entertainment ever, my darling, for we'll be celebrating the beginning of the holiday years you've waited for so patiently."

"Do you mean it, John? Do you really mean it at last?"

"I mean it."

"I can't believe it. I've hoped but I've not believed in my heart that you would ever rest."

"What else can I do?" he asked. "The Comstock's about played out. And we have more millions than you and I and the children can ever use. So what's left for me but to share the holiday your heart is set on?"

"Oh dear"—she looked at him anxiously—"I've always wanted it, but maybe it won't be enough for you. Maybe you should have accepted when they wanted you to be senator from Nevada."

"No. That's not for me. I'm glad for Jim Fair to have it. He wants that sort of power, though whether he can handle it, whether any man not schooled in the sharp tricks of politics can handle it, I don't know."

"Still, it's a nice thing for the children to have their father a United States senator and Theresa will be proud. And maybe it will make things better between them."

"So you know there's trouble?"

"Friends have told me. Not Theresa. She says nothing in her letters and I never ask."

"There's trouble. Jim's been acting the fool, poor fellow."

"Poor fellow!" Louise exclaimed indignantly. "Poor Theresa is more like it."

"You're wrong, old lady. Jim's to blame, and if he goes on like this he'll break Theresa's heart. But not all her heart. She has her children. Jim can't destroy her entirely, but if he continues as he's doing he can come close to destroying himself. Poor Jim."

"Don't you call him poor Jim to me. I hear he means to leave Theresa with a pittance. And, John Mackay, if you let him, if you and Jim Flood let him . . ."

"We'll not let him. Don't you worry about Theresa, my dear. Flood and I'll see she gets her rights. Jim Fair's my friend and he's the one I'm everlastingly sorry for, but in a fight, a financial fight between him and Theresa, she's the one who'll need help and I'll be in her corner."

"I know. I know you'll be kind and understanding of Theresa."

"As for understanding, Louise, no one really understands what goes wrong between man and wife, no one on earth but their two selves. Remember that, my dear, and try not to be too hard on old Jim. As for kindness"—he smiled—"it's not my money I'll be getting for Theresa, but Jim's."

"He'll not easily forgive you for that."

"It could make a break between Fair and me for a while anyway. Maybe for good, but I think not. We've been partners too long. Anyway let's hope it doesn't come to a divorce or even to a separation between him and Theresa. Let's hope they start a new life together in Washington." John was silent. He frowned and pulled his mustache. "It's strange, mighty strange, to think of me and Fair away from the Comstock, him trying his hand at the game of politics which sure isn't for amateurs, and me put out to pasture."

"Perhaps you'll like the pasture, John. Remember how you used to yearn for the peaceful green fields of Ireland? And you needn't be completely idle. There's the Nevada Bank."

"Sure. Sure. Though banking was always more to Jim Flood's taste than mine. Still, I'm not meaning to be entirely idle. There's quite a few enterprises besides the bank I've an interest in. There's a pile of investments to watch. Like I've told you, a fortune, even the biggest, doesn't stand still. I aim to keep ours growing. But that will take less than half my time. The rest of it I can spend with you and the children. Finally, after all our years, I'll have time for my family. I never had it, not in Virginia, not at the Bay. There was never time for you and the children."

"Or for yourself, John. All the things you've wanted to see. All you've wanted to do."

"We'll see them and do them together. You and the boys and Eva and me." He relaxed and leaned back in his chair. "It's been a pretty long pull at that and I can stand a rest."

Louise brought him his before-dinner drink of bourbon and water. He lifted his glass to her.

"Here's to us, Louise, and to our family and to time, to this peaceful bit of time in which we can take a holiday together."

The holiday began with a ball and ended with a coronation.

The ball was given by John and Louise on the twenty-eighth of February, 1881. Singers from the opera and actors from the Comédie Française were engaged to entertain the guests in the white and gold ballroom. For those who preferred to dance there was constructed a temporary ballroom that covered the entire garden on the Place de l'Étoile. Eight gilded columns supported the roof; eight immense mirrors with garnet velvet hangings adorned the wall; between the mirrors were eight Gobelin tapestries. Below the mirrors palms and rare ferns and flowering plants concealed the heaters that gave warmth to the vast room. From the silk-covered roof hung twelve bronze chandeliers, each with a hundred and twenty lights. Beneath them the parquet floor gleamed like polished metal.

Louise, with John beside her, made a tour of the house to see that all was in order. Then they returned to the bedroom where Demoutier was waiting with the diamond tiara and the long white gloves which would complete her mistress' toilette.

"Are you pleased, John?" Louise asked. "Are the arrangements as grand as you wanted?"

"Sure are. And it was a smart move to turn the regular ballroom into a music room and theater. You never stop thinking about Eva, do you?"

"So long as no one realizes it but you."

"They don't. They just think you want to give the fanciest affair of the year, to top them all, even the official ball at the Élysée."

"I want to do that too. And I think I shall. Doesn't the entrance look beautiful with the new lighting effect and the medieval halberdier to announce the guests? Oh, John, I love it, every bit of it, from the eighteen footmen on the stairs to the bowls of out-of-season violets in the blue salon. I'm proud that Queen Isabella is my friend and is coming tonight, but I'd rather be me."

"You should. It seems you're a more lasting kind of queen."

"They can't dethrone a bonanza queen and I'm grateful. But what I enjoy is the contrast to the old days. Poor Isabella and the rest have never seen anything but palaces or, at the least, an elegant villa or suite of apartments. I can remember the hall above Craycroft's saloon and Mr. Sharon's Nevada residence. They both seemed pretty grand to me in their time."

"You seem pretty grand to me always. Stand still and let me look at you."

Louise's gown was of white moiré covered with point d'Alençon lace. The lace had been ordered by the municipality of Paris as a gift for the Empress Eugénie, but the empire had fallen before the gift could be presented. John had bought the lace for Louise. She turned slowly for his inspection. The only touch of color in her costume was a cluster of red roses that looked as if it had fallen by accident on her train.

"Do you like me?" she asked.

He bent and kissed the top of her head and looked for a moment at her slender white reflection in the glass.

"Black as ebony, white as snow," he said. "I can remember like it was yesterday you reading that story to Eva. Here." He thrust a hand into his pocket. "I know you'll not wear your sapphires in your own house so I've brought you something simpler but with a sparkle to it. Pearls are fine, but I like to see my girl sparkle at night."

He unfolded the tissue paper and held up a long chain of small but brilliant diamonds. The shining length of it reached to the floor.

"It's beautiful. Let me think how I'll wear it." She unclasped her pearls and studied her reflection in silence. She held the chain against her hair.

"Demoutier," she called. "Come quickly. I know what to do. Don't look, John, till we're ready."

As the maid followed her directions, Louise unfastened her bracelet and removed a brooch from her bodice. John's unexpected gift was the symbol of their holiday; she wished it to be her only ornament.

When Demoutier had finished, the long chain bound the curls on the crown of Louise's head; from there it descended in many glittering coils around her neck and fell in wide loops to her waist where it was fastened by a clasp representing a dove with outstretched wings.

"Now look, John"—she laughed—"I sound like Willie and Clarie. 'Now look! Look at me: look at me.'"

"The stones become you. You're beautiful enough without them, but they sort of light you up."

The ball was the most talked-of event of the Paris season. The newspaper reports agreed that it would be difficult for any hostess to equal it. Even the *Figaro's* Étincelle, who was not friendly to Louise, could find no flaw in the magnificent entertainment.

"None of them can beat you," John said proudly.

"Maybe not, though I think Mr. Bennett means to try. But since his party is in our honor, I don't mind if he succeeds."

In May, James Gordon Bennett gave a huge reception and ball for John and Louise at his estate at Pau. He engaged private express trains to transport from Paris and other cities a brilliant company of guests. He engaged the most popular Paris orchestra and he also brought from Vienna the famous Kapellmeister Strauss and his entire company.

Louise was delighted by the splendor and the extravagance of the decorations and the entertainment and by the elegance of the guests who had gathered from almost every European capital, but her greatest pleasure was not in these, it was in John's enjoyment of the company of their host. On the morning after the ball while she breakfasted on the balcony outside her bedroom she watched the two men, deep in conversation, walking in the garden. She was happy that John had come to know the newspaper magnate. He was the kind of man whom John understood and admired. An acquaintance like Mr. Bennett would increase John's enjoyment of their holiday.

The holiday years slipped quickly by. In all but the swiftness of their passing, they were like time retrieved from childhood. There was no nagging anxiety; there was no driving ambition. The days and the months moved imperceptibly with the seasons. The seasons were gentler than the remembered ones of childhood, for now one could escape them. In the summer Louise and John cruised on a yacht in cool northern waters; in the winter they could, when the short Paris days grew too dark and cold, escape to the warmth of Nice and Monte Carlo.

That dream too, Louise thought as she lay awake in their room at 9 Rue de Tilsitt on a soft May night. "The land where citron-apples bloom / And oranges like gold in leafy gloom."

That, too, she and John had enjoyed together and the land had been as she had first pictured it, with no shadow to darken the golden shore.

Louise moved carefully to her side of the wide bed so as not to disturb John. She sat up and leaned against her pillows. It was hard to believe that it was more than two years since John had announced to her his virtual retirement. She had not quite believed, she still could not quite believe. . . . She listened to his peaceful breathing and held her own breath in a long sigh of contentment. He had not, as she had feared, grown restless. He had made only brief business trips to the States. For most of each year he had enjoyed with her their holiday. It was high time for him to have such enjoyment; he was past fifty. In sudden astonishment, she thought of her own age. In December she would be forty. How strange it was that the most lighthearted of all her years should come when she was nearly forty.

There had, in those years, been small annoyances but none was grave enough to reach and trouble Louise's heart.

She had been almost frightened when Don Philippe de Bourbon had, for a little while, been attentive to Eva. Don Philippe was not young, but he was not unattractive and he was of royal birth. The possibility of such a marriage might turn a girl's head, even though Don Philippe's reputation was not one that would make him a desirable husband. Even his cousin ex-Queen Isabella wrote to Louise.

March 29, 1882

My dear Madame MackKay:

I remember very well what you told me about your intentions with regard to your daughter's marriage, and for
this reason, when the newspapers talked about a marriage between my cousin Philip and your daughter, I not
only gave no credence to this rumor, but I declared to
my friends that there could be no question of this union.

You may be sure, dear Madame, that I shall take every opportunity to do what is agreeable to you, by denying this entirely fabricated rumor.

I hope to have the pleasure of seeing you soon, for
you know, dear Madame, how happy I am to assure you
in person of my sincere and friendly affection.

                                  Isabelle de Bourbon

John had laughed at his wife's anxiety. "What the fellow hasn't
reckoned with is that Eva doesn't give a snap of her fingers for any
of this society rigmarole."

"But, John, she enjoys the company of her young friends."

"Sure, because they're young and they're her friends. And she likes
the older ladies, the Duchess Descazes and Mrs. Noyes and Lady
Mandeville and the rest, because they've been kind to her, and
Charles Gounod and little Emma Nevada because she shares their
love of music. But don't worry about this paunchy prince. She'll not
bother her head over him."

"Please God, you're right."

John had been right. Eva had appealed to her mother. "Oh,
Mammy, you'll have to get rid of him for me. He's talked a little
foolishly sometimes, but I didn't pay much attention. You know how
foreign gentlemen are, they often do say silly things and I knew you
wanted me to be polite to this one because you're so fond of his
cousin, but I couldn't marry him. Ugh!" She made a grimace. "You
don't mind, do you, Mammy?" she asked anxiously.

"Mind? Oh, my darling." Louise kissed her daughter and was for
the first time grateful for Eva's complete lack of worldly ambition.

A lesser annoyance had been the portrait. Meissonier had turned
out to be a difficult man to deal with. He had demanded innumera-
ble sittings and, in the end, the picture had been a disappointment.

Perhaps, Louise thought, if she had concealed her dismay, if her acquaintances had not repeated her comments, the likeness would
have been a more flattering one. She should not have said a word to
anyone. She might have known that the artist, used for so long to
adulation, would be angry. He had allowed his anger to appear only
in his painting. His letters had been polite enough. She remembered
how courteously he had expressed his regret at her dissatisfaction.

> 131 Boulevard Malesherbes
>
> Dear Madame:
>   Yesterday Monsieur Petit told me he had heard from
> one of your friends that you were dissatisfied with me; he
> had not been informed, he assured me, of the cause of this
> dissatisfaction. I have always attached too much impor-
> tance to being agreeable to you, and I have tried too hard
> to put all the talent I may possess into the work of doing a
> portrait of you such as I had never done before and no
> doubt shall never do again, not to be completely dis-
> tressed by such a report. This can only be a misunder-
> standing which will be easily explained, or if, quite
> against my will, it is something else, let me know. I shall
> express my regrets to you, and you will forgive me.
>   Believe me most faithfully yours
>
>   E Meissonier
>
> November 14, '82

Meissonier's greatest difficulty had been with Louise's hands. He
had done them over and over. Before the final sitting he had written
to ask her to bring a pair of gloves.

> 131 Boulevard Malesherbes
>
> Dear Madame
>   Would you kindly, when you come today, bring along
> a bit of black lace that we may add to the hat, and long
> buttoned gloves, preferably suede. I want to try a position
> of the hands that has just occurred to me.
>
>   Faithfully yours
>   E Meissonier

When Meissonier had shown Louise the completed portrait, she

had seen with astonishment and anger that he had substituted another woman's hands and wrists for hers.

"The hands are the last straw," she had said to John. "I'm prettier
than the portrait. Still, they say one has to put up with that from a
celebrated artist. But the hands are unpardonable. Great gnarled
things, three times the size of mine and with big bony wrists. I might
have known he's painted too many Napoleonic horses. I should have
had Cabanel to begin with. I'll have him now anyway, to remember
myself properly by. I thought Meissonier would be an additon to my
salon and then he never came."

"Poor Louise, but we'll have to pay him for the portrait all the
same."

"I won't. Let him sue us."

"You don't want a lawsuit dragging through the courts."

"I hate giving in. Why should I when I'm right?"

"The French courts will find for him. He's their country's oldest,
best-loved artist. We wouldn't stand a chance. The best thing will be
to pay for the picture, put it away, and forget it."

"I suppose in the end I'll do as you say."

"Sure you will, and you might even come to like the portrait. He's
painted a terrible pair of hands on you, but since anyone can see
they're not yours, you needn't care. And he's got your eyes down pat
and your expression. He's not got your prettiness except for the eyes,
but he's got your cleverness and your determination."

"What woman wants a portrait like that?"

"None, I guess, not even one as pretty as you. But in the end we'll
have to buy it."

"You make the arrangements and keep it out of my sight." Against
her will, she had smiled. "Until I ask for it. You know perfectly well
that one of these days when I'm over being angry I'll hang it up
somewhere. I'm too practical a woman to let you pay all the money
he's asking or even the half of it for a Meissonier and then leave the
portrait in a bank's cellar forever."

Louise moved uneasily against the coolness of her linen pillow
cover. She tried to turn her thoughts from Meissonier. He had done
her no real harm. He had provoked in art circles and in the French
press a storm of criticism of her refusal to accept the portrait, but after
more than six years in Paris she was used to newspaper criticism.
She smiled as she remembered the fabrications that had been

printed: the renting of the Arc de Triomphe, the cloak made of feathers of hummingbirds, her offer to pay the Franco-Prussian war debt as the purchase price of the Bois de Boulogne. Even John had not escaped. "Il Conte di Mackay" was the headline of the *Argonaut* story that John was seeking a papal title. There had been so many stories: Meissonier's quarrel with her was only one more.

In the dark room the silk curtains swelled and rustled in a cool breeze. The dawn could not be far off. She would think of little pleasant things and so fall asleep. She must not be tired for the long journey to Moscow that would begin today. The President of the United States had appointed John a special envoy to the Russian coronation.

She thought of her small triumphs in which John had taken such pleasure—*L'Abbé Constantin*, M. Halévy's novel in which she and Ada were charmingly portrayed, had passed its fiftieth edition.

Lucy Hooper had dedicated *Under the Tricolor* to Louise in six stanzas of flattering verse.

Best of all had been R. M. Daggett's novel, *Braxton's Bar*.

John had smiled at the likeness to himself in one of the characters. "It's kindly meant," he said. "Daggett and I are friends from way back."

"Kindly meant and well done," Louise said. "I know you were in Downieville; we've talked often enough of your years there, but I never really imagined you in the time and place I knew. Now Mr. Daggett's done it for me. He's described the miners and the diggings better than I ever knew them. It was the town itself I mostly knew and the townsfolk; the Meiers, the Taylors, the McDonalds, the Kibbes . . . Now, thanks to Mr. Daggett, I can picture you and Jack O'Brien and the others just a little way along the Yuba."

"Seems a pretty good book to me, though I'm no judge of novels and I feel a bit uncomfortable to meet myself as a character in one. Still and all he meant well, and even had he made me look a fool I'd not have minded for the sake of this."

John picked up the book and read aloud the dedication: " 'To one whose girlhood songs were chorded to the minstrelsy of the pines casting their shadows dimly through these pages, and whose dreams by the golden waters of the Yuba were realized in the land of deserts. To Mrs. John W. Mackay

This story of pioneer years in California is respectfully inscribed by The Author.'"

"I dreamed of lots of things beside the Yuba," Louise said. "Mostly of gold and glory and me in my own carriage and pair, but never of being happy as we are. Of course I couldn't." She looked thoughtfully at the book that had brought the old days back to her mind. "One can't when one's young. One can't imagine this kind of happiness, long-sustained and unafraid." Her eyes filled with tears.

"Why, Louise, my dear. You don't look very happy."

"It's that I can't thank you or even speak of what's most important. I can thank you for things: for my jewels and my clothes, for my house and my private railway carriage. I can thank you for the others, for keeping my promises to them, to Ada and to my parents; it wouldn't be much of an old age for Father and Mémé without you. I can thank you for the charities you made possible to me, the contributions to the Church and the gifts to old friends that must never seem like charity. The one thing I don't know how to thank you for is my happiness. I can no more find words for it now than I could imagine it then." She touched the title page of *Braxton's Bar*. "All one can imagine when one is young is the fairy tale beginning: 'Once upon a time there was a goose girl or a princess.' One scarcely notices the end: 'And they were married and lived happily ever after.' Though that final sentence is, of course, the story, all the rest of the tale is only prologue. I didn't know that then. The young don't know, the poor young."

"You and I know, Louise."

"And the knowledge still surprises me. I can't get used to happiness that lasts. Isn't it a little unexpected to you, too, to be this happy at our time of life?"

"Happiness has a way of being unexpected, like sorrow."

"Don't say that, John, it could be unlucky. Sorrow is all behind us." She rapped the painted wooden arm of her chair.

He kissed her gently and for a moment she felt as young as she had been in Downieville.

"Enjoy your happiness, Louise, now while you have it. I remember my mother telling me once that all anyone has is now. So enjoy while you can."

Louise remembered John's words as she watched him sleeping beside her. Now was all they had. This now, this day, this year. Their years together surrounded her, the fifteen that were past and the ones that waited. She could enjoy the present without fear. Long ago she had known that with John a woman would be happy, safely happy. It was at Theresa's house that she had first dimly known. Poor Theresa. It was impossible for a happy woman to imagine the kind of betrayal that Theresa had experienced.

Louise slipped quietly under the covers and moved closer to the warmth of John's nearness.

Theresa wasn't the only one, Louise thought. Few were driven as Theresa had been to leave the shelter of marriage, but to many it wasn't much of a shelter. Among Louise's acquaintances were many married couples who lived together in empty friendliness. She shivered as she imagined the cold silence of their houses after the parties were over and the guests were gone.

"Enjoy," John had said, and she did. She enjoyed jewels and furs and lace. She enjoyed dinners and receptions and balls. She enjoyed the whole elaborate panoply of wealth and position, but without happiness enjoyment was nothing at all. The heart of the matter was in this quiet room.

On May fifteenth according to the Russian calendar, Alexander III was crowned in the Cathedral of the Assumption in Moscow. Louise remembered the white wooden Church of the Immaculate Conception in Downieville where she had tried, without knowing how, to imagine ecclesiastical grandeur. Here it was, as she had not dreamed then, nor seen since, even in Rome. As she watched, she slowly realized that she was seeing something more unusual in these modern times than grandeur, however magnificent. At the heart of the overwhelming pomp and ceremonial was a religious rite in which the Russians believed, the Emperor and his nobles, the Metropolitan and his archbishops, the crowd shouting in the square outside. Even the foreign guests, Louise observed, seemed moved as if they, too, at least while they watched, believed what they saw. This was to the participants more than a coronation, it was an anointing.

The slim figure of Maria Feodorovna seemed tired from the weight of her sweeping silver robes. She was pale as she knelt before her husband while he touched her forehead with his crown. For her sake Louise was glad that the long ceremony was almost over.

When they came out of the cathedral, Moscow blazed in sunlight.

Louise stared at the domes and the minarets and at the crowds of curiously dressed people who had gathered from every part of the empire for the coronation. It was all as strange to her eyes as it had been when she had stepped from the train and seen it for the first time. After the familiar or at least recognizable magnificence of the interior of the cathedral, Moscow seemed stranger and more barbaric than ever.

She had been proud that the President had sent John to the coronation. She had enjoyed the splendid reception and balls. She would paste the invitations in an album.

When she got home she knew she would not really remember or believe any of it. Except the coronation. She would remember clearly only the coronation itself, not Moscow. She had always been a great one for travel, but this city was too far a journey, across centuries as well as miles. She admired the extravagance of the architecture but her admiration was without warmth. All the time she had been in Moscow, even though John was beside her, she had felt uneasy. She had noticed that Demoutier did not seem happy in the place. The maid was unusually silent when she dressed and coifed her mistress.

"Don't you like it here?" Louise had asked. "It's an interesting place, even beautiful in its own way."

"It is as Madame says. It is beautiful, it is interesting. I shall never see anything like it again, but I do not like it."

"Why, Demoutier?"

"Since Madame asks, I will say. The masters here are all, and the people are not even slaves, not even animals. They are nothing. The handsome horses are more."

It is, Louise thought as she stood beside John in the sunlit square, as Demoutier says. At the parties the Russians had seemed like any other aristocratic, rich group except that they were richer, more brilliantly jeweled. Her sapphires had barely held their own. But under the light, smiling, French conversation, there had been something unfamiliar, something disturbing. After Demoutier had spoken, Louise had known what it was. It was something she had never seen or heard before. These people were not an ordinary elite or aristocracy, they were a ruling class that believed it had total, unlimited power. Louise shivered. She would be glad when she and John were back in Paris.

It was on their way home that John spoke to Louise of the plans which he had made with James Gordon Bennett. They had changed trains at Berlin and were installed in their private railway carriage.

"Sit a while," John said after they had dined. "I've been meaning to tell you of my intentions but I hadn't the heart to spoil the end of our holiday."

"So the holiday is over."

"Do you mind very much, Louise?"

"I mind, but not too much. I never quite believed in our holiday."

"Then you were smarter than me. I thought I was out of harness for good. But Bennett has a proposition I couldn't turn down. It'll be a fight like the old fight for the Comstock against Sharon and the California Bank crowd. It's hard for an Irishman to turn down a real good battle royal."

"I understand."

"It's like this. Bennett and I were riding in the Bois not too long before this Russian trip of ours and he was speaking of the murderous rates that the cable monopoly charges. In the end, he said, they'll pretty near put the newspapers out of business. Then he developed an idea and I was right behind him. We mean to break the monopoly. Between us we've got more than the capital we need. Though we'll let some old friends come along. We'll lay another Atlantic cable and we'll lick Jay Gould and his Western Union crowd. What do you think of it, old lady? The details aren't worked out yet, but what do you think?"

"There'll be some pretty bothersome details," Louise said thoughtfully. "What will you do about land lines to connect with your cable?"

"You've hit the difficulty. But it's not too bad. Among my holdings is a small telegraph company that operates between New York and Chicago. George Roberts got me into it. It's not much but it's a start."

"Trench's Mill was a start," Louise said. "When you and Fair were up against the Union Mill and Mining Company."

"I'd give a lot to have Jim Fair with me on this, but there's not a chance. He's still sore over the settlement Flood and I got out of him for Theresa. And Flood says he has enough with the Nevada Bank. Besides, he says we're getting too old for new enterprises. And in another couple of years he'd have been right, about me anyway. With my work finished I'd have got old pretty damn quick. Here's the plan: By the time we get the cable laid we'll have that little land company reorganized and expanded. We'll lay lines down the Atlantic coast. We've got some pretty good friends in Canada. They'll come along and . . ."

While John talked Louise observed the change in him. There was a sudden look of youth about him. His expression, the set of his shoulders, the thickening of his brogue, all reminded her of the young Irishman whom Sharon could not drive out of Virginia City. What a fool she had been to think that such a man could be content to lead a woman's life.

She had been wrong about him and she had been wrong about herself. It was not only because of him that she had been unable to believe in their holiday. Reluctantly she recognized the truth: the leisurely, easy existence had not been enough for either of them.

She had achieved all that she had ever desired. Her position was brilliant and impregnable. Eva moved easily in the gilded circle that surrounded her, and gave every promise that when the time came she would choose a husband wisely. Willie and Clarie were doing well at Vaugirard. They were getting the kind of education and making the sort of friends that she wanted for them. Mrs. Hungerford had persuaded the colonel to settle down to the assembling of his memoirs at Rome in the handsome residence which John had purchased for them. Ada was happy with her babies and her devoted indulgent husband.

Louise had no wish for herself or for her family that was unfulfilled and yet in her, as in John, ambition had been secretly waiting for another opportunity.

"So it'll be a battle," John concluded, "a grand battle worth the fighting and the winning. We'll have old friends along. Henry Rosener is coming in."

"It's always the men of the Comstock you turn to, isn't it?"

"They're men to count on in a fight. And this'll be a rare fight. But I love a fight and so, by God, do you. And how about you, Louise? Is Paris enough for you? You're at the top of that heap."

"Sometimes I've thought—that is before our holiday—sometimes I thought about London. People were most kind on the occasion when we visited Consuelo Mandeville."

"London, eh? That's quite a place to tackle."

"I haven't planned it or even thought seriously about it, but if you're going to be so busy . . ."

"Sure am. I'll be with you when I can and someday there'll be another holiday, but meantime it doesn't matter much which end of the cable you settle yourself and the children at, London or New York. Either one will suit me."

"It'll have to be one of them pretty soon. It's time to think of an English-speaking school for the boys. I rather incline to Beaumont, the Jesuits' school at Old Windsor, but the boys will have to wait until Eva is settled."

"You'd not like to give New York a try for her?"

"Throw that lamb to those she-wolves? Oh no, John. They're meek as lambs themselves when they come over here. I've met a few of them, some I'd even met before, though I don't let on nor do they. I've not received any of them, though some rather strong hints have been dropped that certain New York ladies would not be averse to visiting the Rue de Tilsitt." She laughed. "I've no need of them. But it amuses me to note the change that's come over them. Nowadays I'm that charming Mrs. Mackay of the Rue de Tilsitt, and my mother is so distinguished with her snow-white hair—one would think she had stepped out of an ancestral portrait—and the dear colonel and the dear countess. Still, I fancy, the change in them is only a sea change. I wouldn't trust Eva to them in their own hunting ground. They'd tear her to bits and destroy all the confidence she has so slowly gained. Here she has friends and a place of her own and our Renaissance palace solid against her back. We'll not disturb her when all is going so well for her, but in a year or two when she's settled I'd like to try London." Louise's eyes sparkled.

"You see, old lady, we're both too young for a permanent vacation."

She smiled at him absently. "I'd rent a small house first, nothing pretentious. It would seem natural for me to have a *pied-à-terre* in London while the boys are settling into a new school. And then, later, if I have luck . . ."

"It takes more than luck, Louise, more than money, though both are mighty handy. It takes brains and driving ambition. Never think I haven't recognized the work and the intelligence that made possible the easy-seeming way you've brought yourself and your family to the top of the European heap."

"It must seem a very little victory to you compared to the ones you've won and mean to win."

"No, it doesn't. What other field is there for a woman? And how many women, even with millions of dollars behind them, have succeeded as you have? I'd like to see you take a crack at London. It's the biggest camp of all."

"It's odd that it should be. Europe is so big." She gestured at the curtained window. "And England so small. The English don't think so, of course. Remember the London headline, 'Continent Cut off by Fog'? I wonder what makes that little island so big. The empire, I know, but it's more than that. It's the long and glittering history. And the Crown. And a royal family. They're history made visible in a modern world. A queen and princes and princesses give society a shape that's plain to see." She pushed back the small stiff curtains. "I'd like to have a try at London. It'll be more difficult than Paris. That pyramid is steep, and money won't mean as much. The English are too rich to be impressed by American millions."

"Like I said, it always takes more than money. But you have more, much more." He put his arms around her and watched with her the moving landscape folded darkly against the faint starlight. "We've seen a hell of a lot of this old Europe together, Louise: Germany, Austria, Italy, Norway, Russia, France. It's been a good holiday." He kissed her and held her close to him.

She stood silent in the shelter of his arms and listened to the jolting rhythm of the wheels. It was an impatient, hurrying noise, she thought, the sort of noise that time would make if time had a sound. She pressed her face against his sleeve so as not to watch the darkness rushing past them.

"A good holiday, dearest John," she whispered. "Do you think we'll ever have another?"

"Sure we will. I promise it to you, old lady. My darling old lady."

Chapter XXIV

••••◦➤◉◄◦••••

An American Princess

WHILE JOHN AND Louise were in Russia they had learned that Theresa had won the suit which she had unwillingly brought against Jim Fair.

Before John sailed for America he received from San Francisco cuttings from the *Examiner* and the *Chronicle*. He showed them to Louise.

"There it is," he said. "Poor Theresa and, though you'll not believe me, poor Jim. This isn't good for him. And not only because it finishes his career in the Senate."

"A Divorce and Four Millions for Mrs. Fair," the *Chronicle* headlined the story.

Louise held the cutting in her hand. Two columns in the *Chronicle's* well-remembered format made the unhappy story real and near at hand.

"Virginia, Nev.—May 12. The long-talked-of divorce suit of Theresa Fair vs. James G. Fair came up in the First Judicial District Court this morning at 10 o'clock."

"Poor Theresa," Louise said. "To go back to Virginia for this. I think it would have been a little easier for her to bear at the Bay. She liked Virginia City, you know. She said she was happy there."

"She can still be happy in a way. She has custody of the girls and Charlie."

"Why shouldn't she have them all? Why should young Jim be with his father?"

"The boy's twenty. It was a small sop to Jim's pride. After all it's not pleasant to him to transfer the Yellow Jacket to Sharon to realize cash for Theresa's settlement. That'll hurt. The idea of it, I mean."

Louise did not answer. The name of Dick Dey caught her attention. What part, she wondered, did he have in this sordid business? ". . . Inez Leonard, an important witness in the case who had arrived in this city under an assumed name. Miss Leonard was formerly keeper of a house of prostitution in this city and is one of the parties named in the complaint with whom the defendant is alleged to have committed adultery. Dick Dey, one of the old confidants of Senator Fair, appeared and escorted Miss Leonard to the Court, where her testimony was taken."

Louise pressed her lips tightly together. Dick Dey, confidant and dirty-errand boy. She mustn't say anything. Dick Dey was useful to John. She bent her head to hide from him the anger in her eyes. She need feel only anger on Theresa's behalf, not fear on her own. Dick Dey could not harm her or her marriage. The corruption was in Jim Fair. It was there for Dick Dey to pander to and to use. There was no corruption in John. He was faithful in marriage as in all things. There was nothing dark or secret in his heart through which her own could be broken as Theresa's had been.

She didn't realize she was crying until her tears fell on the paper and blurred the print.

"You feel bad for her, old lady, don't you?" John asked.

"Poor Theresa," Louise murmured, and remembered the young Theresa on a winter afternoon in her parlor in Virginia City. Theresa had been kind and softly pretty. She had blushed like a girl and her laughter had bubbled like a child's.

"What a fool," Louise said abruptly. "What a blind fool I've been. With Theresa before my eyes, what a fool I've been about Eva."

"Eva! What on earth?"

"Don't you see? Eva is like Theresa. She can be hurt. Oh, we all can, I know that. But some women have a trustful innocence that makes them more vulnerable. Theresa has always had it. Even when I first knew her. She was a married woman but she was as gentle and unarmed as a girl. And Eva is a woman. She seems young but she's not really. She's twenty-three almost."

John patted Louise's shoulder. "I well remember you once telling me that twenty-three was a great age, but surely you don't still think so."

"Eva's not a child. A mother can't always tell when a child is grown up. A child can grow up at fifteen and a mother not see. But Eva's nearly twenty-three and I've let things drift. Lulled by our holiday, I've let things drift. 'In a year or two,' I've said. 'When Eva's settled,' I've said. I've been a fool, John; Eva's one that needs help. Like a fool I've waited for her to make her own life, but she needs help. I've always known that."

"Eva's stronger than you think, Louise."

"I know she is. Or I'd not have been able to help her at all. But she's not worldly. She's untouched. For all her cheerfulness and her friendliness she's more like one of the novices at Neuilly than a young lady of fashion."

John frowned and pulled his mustache. "Eva has a wisdom of her own, an armor, too, I'm thinking. Like the novices, like the Sisters."

"John!" Louise stared at him. "You're not suggesting. You don't think——"

"That Eva might become a nun? It's crossed my mind. She was always happy with the Sisters here and in Virginia. Would you mind so much, my darling?"

"It's for her I'd mind. No, that's not true. I'd mind for me. She's my only daughter. I can help her to make the right choice. At least I can try."

"Sure, you can try." He kissed her. "And if you fail, comfort yourself with the thought that the right choice isn't too damn easy to recognize for any of us."

All through the summer at Trouville and during the following winter Louise kept her worry over Eva to herself. That winter Louise's hopes for Eva were high. The heir to one of the oldest and noblest Catholic families in England made no secret of his admiration for her. He came often to Paris. The possibility of an engagement was spoken of on both sides of the Channel and was rumored in the English press.

"You like him, don't you, Eva?" Louise asked casually.

"Oh yes, Mammy. But not—well not the way Ada did Joseph from the very first. Do you remember how she knew right away?"

"I remember. The *coup de foudre* that the French speak of so often, though they're too practical a people to act on it more than occasionally."

"Love isn't practical. It's romantic."

"Practical sounds a harsh word. Let me put it this way, Eva. Marriage is many things. It's love and romance if you like. Though, believe me, romance can come slowly as well as quickly and be just as sweet. Sweeter sometimes. But marriage is also a whole life, a career."

"Oh, Mammy, you are being solemn! We haven't got that far. He just likes me. For myself, I mean."

"His family is rich enough for your father's fortune not to count," Louise said thoughtfully. "Or at least," she added, "not to count too much." She stood up. "Come and I'll take you to Worth to fit your new gown so they'll have it ready for Saturday. You must dazzle this young man a little even if he loves you for yourself. A beautiful gown never hurt."

"I only said he likes me. I hope that's all, for it's all I think I could feel for him. Though to please you I would try to love him."

"My darling, it's no good trying with the heart. But I'll tell you one thing about marriage . . ." Louise did not finish her sentence. She opened a wardrobe. "My navy blue, I think," she said. "It's a beautiful morning. We can walk as far as the Rond-Point and have the carriage meet us there."

"What one thing were you going to say about marriage?" Eva asked.

"No one thing is true about marriage. But what I was going to say is that though it's desirable to have both love and liking, if I had to choose I'd put liking ahead of love. Well ahead. Love all by itself can be a bitterly lonely emotion, Eva. Marriage is something that either grows or doesn't, and no generation has ever managed to explain to the next the why and the how of it. People marry for so many different reasons: love, affection, romance, money, safety. And some of the marriages succeed and some fail and no one can foresee which will be which. It's not what you have to start out with, it's what you have to go on with that counts."

"Sometimes the very idea of marriage frightens me."

"Does it, my darling? Then think of the feeling you have when you hold Ada's little Edna in your arms. That should give you courage." Louise kissed her daughter. "And now," she said cheerfully, "we must get ready if we're to be at Worth's before noon. Whether this young man is *the* young man or not, he is coming all the way from England for the theater and the musicale and reception on Saturday and he deserves to see you in your new frock."

As she watched Eva and the Englishman at the theater and later at the musicale, Louise realized that this young man was not and could not be Eva's choice.

The boy knew. Louise saw it on his face and heard it in his voice as he said good-by to her.

"It is good-by, rather, I'm afraid, Mrs. Mackay. I shan't be coming to Paris for a while."

"We shall miss you."

"Thank you. You've been kind, most kind, Mrs. Mackay, and I'm grateful. But it wasn't any good, was it?" He smiled and was gone.

In May, Louise decided to send Eva to visit Ada. The change would do her good. Rome in May and June was beautiful and it would be a change from the Paris season. And most important, she thought with satisfaction, it was a long way from Neuilly. Louise did not discourage Eva's visits to the Sisters. That would do more harm than good. But she remembered the May processions at Benicia. There had been flowers and candles burning ever brighter in the swiftly darkening twilight. If romance was part of a vocation, then May was a dangerous month in this as in all that concerned the heart.

On the night of Eva's departure Louise knelt at her prie-dieu. She would say a rosary for Eva's safe journey. Eva was safe enough with Demoutier to look after her, Louise thought, it was not for the train journey that she must pray, it was for the longer journey that waited for any girl of twenty-three. The silver cross hung motionless, the black beads, tightly clasped, were still. Louise imagined Eva's arrival. She saw her surrounded by Ada's happiness. Eva would see and share the shelter that Ada had found with Joseph Telfener and their children. It was a different shelter from the one the nuns could offer, a warmer shelter. Surely, a warmer shelter? Louise looked questioningly at the ivory Madonna that stood on the bedside table.

"Please," she whispered. "Please. She's my only daughter."

While Eva was still in Rome, Theresa Fair came to Paris with her daughters, Tessie and Birdie.

Louise entertained at a dinner and reception for Theresa. For the children there was an afternoon party in the garden on the Place de l'Étoile.

There were excursions by train to Versailles and Barbizon and Fontainebleau. They drove in the carriage to Armenonville and the Pré-Catelan.

Clarie and Birdie preferred the Pré-Catelan to any of the sights that Paris had to offer. And on the Fairs' last afternoon they drove to visit the farm and to take tea in the rustic outdoor restaurant.

While Louise and Theresa were still sipping their tea the children wandered off. Birdie and Clarie to visit once more the farm and the cows; Tessie and Willie to walk sedately in an allée under the trees.

"She's almost a young lady, your Tessie," Louise said. "And you were right about her. She's growing into a beauty."

"And you were right about Birdie. She has a special charm of her own."

"You still call her by her baby name. Birdie suits her, but Virginia Fair is beautiful."

"I thought so."

"Virginia Fair. It has the sound of poetry. There's something like it in a poem, if I could think——"

"I thought of no poem in naming her, only of the town where I was happy."

The smooth flower-edged grass, the tall green trees whose leaves scarcely stirred in the light breeze, the clean pebbled path to the farm, the whole elegantly pastoral scene vanished like one of Mr. Piper's transparencies, and Louise remembered the violent colors of mountain and desert and the roar of wind and of machinery and the bitter scent of sagebrush.

She started and with a gloved hand pushed the vivid memory away. "The soft loving way you spoke of the town, Theresa, brought it back so clearly it seemed for a minute I was there."

"My dear, you'd not like that. But I would. And we're both right. I to want to stay and you to want to leave. You to be glad of the change and the vast fortune and I to be afraid."

Theresa's hand trembled and she put in its saucer the cup she had been holding. The light clatter of china on china was loud in the silence between the women.

Louise put her hand on Theresa's. "I haven't spoken, Theresa, because in the old days when I'd have minded pity you never spoke."

"There's no use speaking about it." Theresa clung to Louise's hand. "And it's not so bad any more. It was much worse in the years when I was afraid, but still hoping."

"You've nothing to be afraid of now, Theresa darling."

"No. It's over and done with. Fear and hope, I'm done with both of them."

Theresa looked across the lawn at the green-shaded allée where Tessie and Willie were pacing slowly in decorous imitation of the fashionable couples who surrounded them. "What about them, Louise?" she asked. "What about them, the little loves? I guess we're never done with hope and fear as long as we have children."

"No need to fear for our children." Louise's heart seemed to move in her breast as it always did when, thinking of other things, she unexpectedly saw one of the children. In those sudden, single moments each child was for an instant the best-loved, the only one. Willie walking with Tessie was almost a young man, a handsome charming young man, and a clever one. She could imagine him in ten years' time at John's side. He had a good head for figures already, John said. More important, he was a good boy, Louise thought. He would be a good son to his father.

She turned back to her friend. "Look at them, Theresa." Her voice was husky. She paused and swallowed the emotion that constricted her throat. "Look at them. They've nothing to fear. They've the whole world ahead of them."

Theresa lifted her cup in a steady hand and smiled at Louise. Together they watched their son and daughter solemnly playing at being grown up.

"Two weeks is a miserably short visit to pay me, Theresa."

"I know. Too short after all this time. But I want the girls to see more of Europe. Italy in particular—the Saints preserve us! Will you look at the pair of them!"

Birdie and Clarie ran across the grass. Both children were dirty. Clarie had lost his straw sailor hat and his crimson tie. The torn flounces of Birdie's embroidered frock trailed behind her. The children pushed between the tables in the crowded restaurant. Chairs fell and silver clattered in their wake.

"Oh, Mammy, I was nearly scared for a minute." Clarie flung his arms around his mother's neck. His voice was steady but his body was trembling. Louise held him reassuringly close.

"The man chased us, Mama," Birdie cried. "And we weren't doing a thing! There wasn't any sign to say keep off. But Clarie was wonderful, he shouted right back at the man, in French too."

"Birdie's the wonderful one," Clarie said. "You wouldn't ever think she was a girl. Up that tree and up to the roof. I could hardly keep up."

"What tree? What roof?" Louise and Theresa asked in frightened unison.

"We just climbed this tree, Mammy," Clarie explained. "And then we climbed onto the roof of the barn and then this man came and yelled at us and chased us."

"No well-brought-up child climbs a tree in a place like this, especially not a girl and well you know it, Birdie Fair," Theresa said severely. "Climbing trees is for Lake Tahoe."

"I wish I was at Lake Tahoe right this minute. No, I don't, Mrs. Mackay. I'm sorry I said that. I love visiting you and seeing Clarie again and Willie when he and Tessie don't act like they were fifty years old. But I bet I'll hate all that Italy and Lake Como and everything."

Louise laughed. "Mr. Mackay would agree with you. He always says Lake Como isn't a patch on Tahoe."

"Then why do we have to go to Italy?"

"For one thing you'll see Ada again," Louise said. "Do you remember her, Birdie?"

"I remember her a little when she came back to San Francisco. She wasn't one bit proud, even though she was married and a countess. Not like Tessie and Willie. They think they're just about a hundred years old. They're so proud they make me sick."

Tessie and Willie had come up to the table. Tessie's pretty face was scarlet with embarrassment, her bright chestnut curls were damp with perspiration.

"Oh, Mamma," she said. "How could you let them? I'm mortified. I'm just absolutely mortified."

"You mad too, Willie?" Clarie whispered anxiously.

"No. Like to have been with you." Willie's answer was too low for anyone but his brother to hear.

"I apologize, Mrs. Mackay," Tessie said. "I simply apologize for my sister ruining the afternoon."

"It's not ruined, Tessie," Louise said. "It was time to go home anyway. And it's hard for a child to be on her best city behavior for two whole weeks. It's different for a young lady like you."

"Of course, that's true. I should be patient, I'm older." Tessie smiled forgivingly at Birdie and Clarie. "Come, children. Come, Willie. We'll find the carriage for Mrs. Mackay and Mamma."

Willie turned and winked at his mother before he followed Tessie in search of the coachman.

As Theresa rose from the table and gathered her belongings she frowned at Birdie's bedraggled figure. Unconscious of her appearance, the little girl was skipping happily across the grass.

"Oh dear, Louise. I can't help worrying about that child. Sometimes I think she'll never turn into a proper young lady."

"Yes, she will. She was just showing off in front of Clarie. Boys are annoying just because they are boys, when one is ten. And if Clarie had really teased her . . . But he wouldn't. He's a kind little boy. But if Birdie met a boy who wasn't kind, who was mean and bullying, she'd fight him."

"Oh no, Louise."

"Yes, she would. I did when I was her age."

"She's like you at that. Though who she's really like is her father. The good in him, I mean. She has his spirit and his humor and the charm that can draw the birds right down from the trees. There's lots of good in Jim Fair."

"You, Theresa Fair, are a saint, a perfect saint."

"Well, if I were, you shouldn't sound so angry about it. But I'm not. I just know Jim better than anybody does except maybe John Mackay."

"But John was on your side, Theresa."

"Sure, he was. But it's Jim he loves and so do I, Louise. And if you won't think me foolish to say it, I'm sorry for him. That's why I don't mind him having the boys."

"I thought he only had young Jim."

"I let Charlie be with him too. I don't think he'll do the boys any harm and I can't bear for him to have nothing."

"Theresa. Theresa." Louise put her hand on her friend's arm and they walked in silence to the carriage where the children were waiting.

As they drove through the park and past the lake, the children chattered while their mothers listened. Tessie forgot her grown-up airs and joined with Birdie in begging for a balloon from a vendor on the Avenue du Bois.

"The balloons here have real gas in them," Willie said. "They'll fly higher than a kite if you let them go."

"Bet you they won't," Birdie said.

"Try and see," Willie urged.

Tessie and Birdie released their balloons. The bright, diminishing globes floated high overhead and melted in the distance.

"Remember the boys flying their kites in the spring in Virginia, Louise?"

"I remember," Louise said, but she did not remember Virginia City. Its image no longer was, as it had been earlier, present in her mind. It was a dot on the map, a place invisible in the past.

"And you're never homesick?"

"For what should I be homesick, Theresa? Not for Virginia City, not for the few years in San Francisco, not for the New York I invented from a child's remembrance of St. John's Park and a doorstep on Washington Square. Only for Paris I might, I think, feel nostalgia. Even if I go to London and have real success and am presented to the Queen, I'll never leave Paris entirely. I'll always come back to it. It's my city."

On the morning that Eva returned from Rome, Louise could see that the visit had been a success. There was a brightness about her, an air of lighthearted happiness that reminded Louise of Ada in her first Paris season. It reminded her of more than that. It reminded her of Ada at M. Cernuschi's ball. And before that, long before . . . She looked questioningly into her daughter's face. She remembered the mirror in the little room that once she had shared with Ada. She remembered standing on tiptoe to look into the mirror, to look in wonder at her own softly smiling face.

"Eva, my darling, tell me."

"But you know. Without my telling you, you know. Ada said you would."

"I know something has happened, Eva. But I'm not a Washoe Seeress. Tell me."

"It's like a fairy tale, Mammy. A prince comes riding. He wasn't actually riding. We met in an entre' acte at the theater. He asked to be presented. He didn't know who I was."

"And who was he?"

"Don Ferdinand Colonna, Prince of Galatro. When his uncles die he will be Prince Colonna di Stigliano, head of the Neapolitan branch of the great house of Colonna. I don't care about all that. He could be plain Don Ferdinand or not even Don for all I care. But I knew you'd be pleased. You are, aren't you?"

"My dear, I don't know enough yet to be pleased or not pleased."

"He saw me and he didn't know who I was. Even after he was presented my name meant nothing. He had never heard of Father. It was me he saw, me whom he wanted to meet, me—Mammy, I'm almost afraid to say it, me whom he loves and did when he saw me sitting in Ada's box."

"And you, Eva?"

"Oh, I, of course. Any girl would."

"What is he like?"

"He's handsome, but not flamboyant like so many foreigners."

"Tell me what he is like. Not what he looks like."

"He's young. He's two years older than I but he's still a boy. Of course he's never had responsibility, but that will come. He's—oh, Mammy, I can't tell you. You'll have to see for yourself. I only know he's what I've waited for. Ever since I grew up I must have been waiting."

"When did you meet him?"

"Two weeks ago."

"Then, my dear, don't be too sure. I mean——" Louise hesitated as she searched for the words to express her warning. She sighed. There was no pleasant way to express such a warning. She forced herself to speak. "Italians are flirts, Eva, most Latins are. Most men for that matter."

"Oh, Mammy." Eva laughed and hugged her mother. "Don't be afraid for me. Really you needn't. He's not a flirt. And even if he has been in the past, this isn't a flirtation. He has asked me to marry him. Of course, we both know he must ask you and Father for it really to count."

"Your father will be here next week."

"I know. I told Ferdinand. He's coming to see you both."

"But, darling, this is too fast. Of course we'll want to meet the young man. But this is much too soon for him to pay his addresses seriously."

"We'll wait. I told him we'll be in Trouville in July and August. He's coming there so you can become really acquainted with him. And we'll wait. We'll wait until the autumn."

"The autumn!" Louise exclaimed. "But it's nearly the end of June now."

"Mammy, aren't you happy for me? You sound . . . You sound——"

"I'm afraid, my darling. It's all so sudden. A boy I never heard of. Don't you understand?"

"I understand. And when you meet him you'll understand how I feel."

"And Joseph?" Louise asked. "Does Joseph know him? A man's opinion . . ."

"Joseph doesn't know Ferdinand himself. But he knows the family. And so can you." Eva took from the bookshelf a squat red volume.

"See, Mammy, it's all in the Almanach de Gotha. Here are the uncles. The present prince born in 1808 and his brother born in 1809. And here's Ferdinand. Read, Mammy, it's all there."

Louise took the book and read: "IIème ligne: Colonna-Stigliano. [Résid.: Naples.—Princes de Galatro (royaume de Naples) en 1688; Princes de Stigliano en 1716; Princes d'Aliano en 1716; Marquis de Castelnuovo en 1716; Grands d'Espagne de 1ère classe 1764 . . .]"

"The titles are all there," Louise said. "And so is Don Ferdinand Marcantonio Giuliano Colonna, the heir to his childless uncles. But it's Ferdinand himself whom I want to know. And you must take time to know him too, Eva. It's your whole life you'll have to live with him if you marry. You mustn't be careless with your whole life."

"Oh dear." Eva replaced the Almanach de Gotha. "I thought you'd be pleased to have me a princess. So did Ada. And I've heard Father tease you about titles."

"I'd not be truthful if I didn't admit I've wanted an important marriage for you, a position in the world. A title? Yes, I've wanted a title for you. But I've never wanted it for you without happiness. Remember, I didn't want Don Philippe."

"Oh, Mammy," Eva laughed. "What are you imagining? Ferdinand is the farthest thing from that old reprobate you can think of. As Grandpa says, he looks like a choirboy. Wait till you meet him."

"I'll wait. And you must wait until you're sure."

"I am sure. But I'll wait. Even till next year, if you say."

"I think your father will say next year. At the earliest."

"He'll like Ferdinand. I know he will. And it'll please him that Ferdinand admired me and had himself presented to me and called several times before he knew about my family."

"Yes. That will please him." If it's true, Louise thought. It might be. It just might be. "He knows now, doesn't he?" she asked. "About your father's fortune, I mean."

"Yes, he does. There was something in the Italian papers about the new cable."

"And was he pleased?"

"Of course, Mammy. But mostly on account of his uncle. He was afraid the old Prince di Stigliano would be angry at his having fallen in love with an unknown American. That's natural, isn't it?" Eva looked pleadingly at her mother. "Please be happy for me. I've waited a long time. And you can trust my judgment. I'm not a child, I'm twenty-three."

"Oh, my darling." Louise took Eva into her arms. What could she say? What had Mémé been able to say? What in her turn would Eva someday find to say? The young heard only their own hearts, they did not listen to the old, they could not. She held her daughter close as though Eva were still the little lame girl for whose happiness Louise would have bargained with the devil himself.

The day after John reached Paris, Don Ferdinand presented himself at the Rue de Tilsitt. Louise and John waited in the blue salon to receive him.

The butler stood in the doorway. "The Prince of Galatro, madame."

As the prince entered, relief filled Louise's heart with warmth. This was no threatening stranger, this was just a beardless boy. He was slender and of medium height, and his manner, as he greeted his host and hostess, was gentle and pleasing. He was unusually handsome. Eva had been right, Louise thought, any girl would be drawn to this beautiful aristocratic young David. She smiled as she listened to his modest account of himself. He had no fortune, he admitted, but someday there would be the revenues of the family estates. In the meantime his uncle was prepared to make him an allowance.

"Whoa there, boy, slow," John said. "We've plenty of time to be thinking of allowances and revenues. It's yourself we're anxious to know about."

"I? Oh, sir, I'm nothing. There's nothing very good or very bad to know about me. I realize I'm not good enough for Eva."

"Mrs. Mackay and I'll be the judges of that," John said. "And if there's anything, even a minor matter, on the record against you, now's the time for you to speak out. Right now."

Don Ferdinand looked hesitatingly at Louise. "Well, sir, if you mean—ah, ladies. There have been a few."

"Must have been. You're a good-looking youngster. The important question is: are these ladies in the past? Is there any present entanglement?"

"No, sir."

"Good. Tell me, what are your interests?" John asked. "How do you occupy yourself? Go in for sports, gambling?"

"I have gambled. You have the right to know. It was a bitter lesson. At twenty-one I came into a little money from my grandmother. It seemed to me a fortune. I—I lost it at the tables. And that is not all." The boy appeared to be finding it painful to continue. "I—my fortune was not so great as I had supposed. My uncle was obliged to help me to settle my debts."

"How long ago was this, Don Ferdinand?" Louise asked. Her voice was sharp with anxiety.

"Oh, madame, do not worry. I am not a gambler at heart. That was a boy's folly. I have disliked telling you of this affair. But for me it was a good thing. This happened almost two years ago. I vowed then never to frequent the tables again or even in a private house to indulge in high play."

"Depends on your definition of 'high,'" John said.

"I can define it, sir. Any stake is high that one cannot easily afford. I learned my lesson and I don't think I touch a card a dozen times a year."

"We've no right to cross-examine you, but it's best to have everything in the open. By the look of you, I'd say you're not a drinker. Am I right?"

"You are, sir. I'm fortunate that for me that has never been a temptation."

"Good, good. Well, my boy, you've been frank and I'll be frank in return. You seem a nice lad but you scarcely know our Eva. Don't ask to pay serious court to her yet."

"But, sir, I must. It is only honorable that I ask your permission. Since already I have asked Eva to marry me."

"All right, young fellow, you've done the honorable thing in asking. But I think Mrs. Mackay and I will just withhold our answer till we get to know you better. Eva is precious to us. We want to be mighty sure that you're the right one for her."

"I hope you may come to think so. I cannot, not ever. I know I am not good enough for Eva. There must be many who are more worthy of her. She has all Europe to choose from. Only this I can say." The young man held his head high. "Nowhere on the Continent nor in the British Isles will she find a prouder name to bear than mine."

"In our country," John said slowly, "a man makes his own name. It's the man Eva's getting we're interested in."

"If you don't care about my name you leave me with nothing to offer your daughter."

"I've no doubt it's a fine name and Eva, like any girl, would enjoy being called Princess. The ladies dearly love a title. But it's not your title, my lad, nor your name that can make Eva happy. It's only yourself can do that."

"May I hope then that in time you will give me your permission to pay my addresses to your daughter?"

"You've barely met the girl. See what the summer brings. The fall will be plenty soon enough for us even to think of talking seriously."

"You grant less than I had hoped, but more than I deserve. May I have your permission to have a word with Eva? I passed her on the stair as I arrived. She said she would be in the garden."

"Sure. You can go this way." John led Don Ferdinand through the ballroom to an open french window. Eva was standing on the grass at the foot of the stone steps. She looked anxiously at John.

"It's all right, Eva. We haven't eaten your young man alive. Now you run along with him. Take a drive if you like. Enjoy yourselves. That's all your mother and I ask: enjoy yourselves and let the future wait a while."

When John returned to her Louise looked questioningly at him. "What do you think of him?" she asked.

"I don't know. And you?"

"In a way I'm relieved. I was much more frightened of Joseph when I saw him at M. Cernuschi's."

"Poor Joe, he does look like anyone's idea of a dark and sinister foreigner."

"That's it. There's nothing sinister about young Colonna. He's just a boy."

"A boy's harder to judge, Louise. Besides, this fellow may look a boy, but he's a man or should be. And what kind of man, be damned if I can guess. Joe was easier for me to know. This young fellow of Eva's comes from an entirely different breed of cats."

"It's a fine breed, John. That much is in his favor. They've produced statesmen and generals and princes of the Church."

"I'm not saying they haven't. And black sheep, too, I'll bet. The thing that bothers me is what's this fellow? Black sheep or white? Strong or weak? His kind have been trained for a thousand years to show the world exactly what they want to show and not a jot more."

"He was honest about his having gambled and he was as frank as he could be in my presence about women."

"There was nothing he said that I couldn't find out for myself, as I intend to do through Joe. The boy would guess that." John sighed. "Eva's set on him, isn't she?"

"I'm afraid so."

"You are afraid, aren't you, Louise? So am I. Why? What's wrong with this boy?"

"Nothing." Louise could not bring herself to put one small humiliating thought into words: Eva was sweetly pretty. She had a gentle charm that attracted, but it attracted slowly. She had had suitors, but none had fallen in love with her at first meeting, at first glance as the child thought Colonna had done. Many beautiful women must have been in love with Don Ferdinand. It was hard for Louise to believe he had been drawn so quickly to Eva.

"It's a little hard to believe, isn't it?" John asked. "Him falling in love so quick with our girl."

Louise nodded. There had been no need to speak her doubt. After a while married people thought together as easily as they talked.

"That's what I want for Eva, John. A marriage like ours."

"No two marriages are alike, old lady. And maybe we'll see this young fellow differently when we know him better."

"I hope so, because I think she's made up her mind. I've never seen her so determined before. But, John, if this is wrong for her, isn't there some way to prevent the marriage?"

"How? Threaten to cut her off? You'd only hurt her and he's too smart to think we'd go through with it, as indeed we wouldn't. Nope. You've got just one thing to work with, Louise: time. Put things off, slow them down."

"Perhaps if we took her away . . ."

"Take her away to dream of that boy's beautiful face! That's no good. Besides, where can you take her that he can't follow? He's got no job to tie him down. And I bet the whole damn Colonna clan will be happy to finance this courtship."

"If only you could stay over for the summer. She might listen to you."

"I can't and she wouldn't. And it might be that she's right. He may be better than we think."

Their hands went out to each other. Their eyes met questioningly.

"Do you believe, John, that this might be all right for Eva?"

"I hope. That's all either of us can do, my darling, just hope."

Joseph Telfener's inquiries confirmed Ferdinand's account of himself. He was abstemious. He had never been known to be drunk. There had been women, but not more, Joseph thought, than one could expect with a handsome, idle young man.

"His lack of occupation is the problem, Louise, though it's common enough in his class. Once he is married, I hope the old prince will give him a greater part in the management of the estates."

"And his gambling?" Louise asked. "It's a vice I fear and detest."

"Apparently it's not a vice with the boy. As he told you, he behaved stupidly when he came into what seemed to him a fortune. But since then he hasn't played at all."

"He scarcely touches a card, he told us."

"Never, according to my informants. But perhaps he could not hope you would believe that."

"What do you think of him yourself?"

"I scarcely know him. He's an attractive, good-looking boy. He bears a fine name."

"And those who do know him? What do they say? What do they say of him in Rome?"

"In Rome?" Joseph laughed. "They say he's a Colonna. And they think that Eva's family should be grateful for the attentions of a prince of that mighty house. Any weakness in the boy himself they excuse because he lost his father when he and his sister Donna Amalia were little children. Donna Amalia is much admired. She is a beautiful, charming creature. All Rome expects her to make an important marriage. At least Don Ferdinand has a splendid situation in society to offer Eva."

"That's something. His title is something. But the boy himself is everything. And we who love Eva don't know him."

"You'll get to know him, Louise. Have him to stay at Trouville. Don't worry so, my dear. Eva is your ewe lamb whom you have always protected. I think you wouldn't willingly entrust her to anyone."

"There's a young Englishman whom I would have liked for her."

"But Eva wasn't in love with him. She is, I think, with Don Ferdinand. Be grateful that I could find nothing to his discredit."

Time was all she had to work with, John had said, and Louise had agreed, as though time were a changeless element that one could measure, as though they weren't both old enough to know the varying and unexpected speed at which time could move.

The summer of 1884 was swift. The individual days beside the sea at Trouville were long and leisurely, but the weeks melted away. It seemed to Louise that July could scarcely have begun and yet here they were in mid-August.

Eva's engagement was not announced; Louise refused to consider it a fact, but the world of fashion was aware that there was an understanding between the Italian prince and the American heiress. The world approved and it took Louise's approval for granted. For Eva's sake Louise betrayed no doubt of Don Ferdinand. She said only that nothing was settled, since the young people had known each other such a short time, but of course Don Ferdinand was a charming boy.

"Such a good-looking boy, Mrs. Mackay," the ladies said. "Such a fine name."

Louise nodded and smiled. She caught herself now in the mirror nodding and smiling as Demoutier brushed and combed her hair before dressing it. Louise frowned. She could imagine the talk as the ladies sat at tea or on the beach. "How pleased Mrs. Bonanza Mackay must be." "My dear, she was delighted enough to capture Count Telfener for her sister. She must be beside herself at the prospect of her daughter becoming a princess of the house of Colonna."

Let them say what they like, Louise thought, only let this be right for Eva.

Her eyes met her maid's in the glass. Impulsively she spoke. "Demoutier, tell me——" She hesitated. She had never tolerated servants' gossip. If they gossiped to her they would gossip about her. She knew that well enough. But Demoutier was loyal. Demoutier, her mistress knew, had been approached by newspaper writers and had laughed at their offers. Demoutier would not even accept from the tradespeople the commissions that were her due. Demoutier was a young woman of independent heart and mind.

"Tell me, Demoutier, what you think of Don Ferdinand? You spoke your mind to me about the Russians when we were in Moscow."

"Oh, madame, the Russians are different from the Italians."

"All Europeans are different from Americans, so we aren't able to judge them. Tell me what you, as a European, think of this boy."

"Madame does not understand. It is difficult, almost impossible, for me to form an opinion of a young gentleman of the nobility. It is hard to judge anyone from another class. Madame cannot understand because in America there are no classes."

"No permanent ones," Louise laughed. "I'm hardly the one to deny that, but my compatriots would not agree. They spend half their time with Europeans explaining the importance of class distinctions in our beloved republic."

"Oh, a republic, madame! France also is a republic. But that is of no importance to the nobility and the rich. I had thought perhaps it was different in America."

"It is. We're younger, our country is bigger. We move up and down the ladder more easily. And there are more ladders. But all this isn't what I want to talk of. And I'm not asking for gossip either. I want your opinion of the prince himself."

"What Madame asks is difficult. He is a good-looking young gentleman and he has a fine name."

"You too," Louise murmured.

"Madame says?"

"Nothing. Only that you say what they all say. Go on."

"About the Prince of Galatro I cannot say more. I see only what Madame sees, what all see: the charming manners of Monsieur le Prince and the beautiful proud face. Oh, madame, it is the pride I fear. Madame will forgive me."

"Go on, Demoutier, I asked you."

"I have seen that pride too often not to recognize it. The aristocrats do not think of the rest of us as quite people. And perhaps—and this is my fear for Miss Eva—perhaps they do not think of Americans as quite people either because of those ladders of which Madame speaks."

"Count Telfener is not like that."

"Monsieur le Comte is good, and he loves Madame la Comtesse. It does not matter in what foolish theories a kind and loving man believes."

"And the prince, Demoutier, is he kind and good?"

"I do not know. He does not reveal himself, that young gentleman. I have seen many like him since I have been in Madame's service and before. They flocked around Miss Ada, and Miss Eva, too, has had her share. They learn so young the smooth manner, the charming expression that conceal the man, like—like . . ."

"Like armor, Demoutier, and a helmet with the visor down."

"It is as Madame says. And yet often there is nothing to conceal except the young man's fear of the great world in which he finds himself."

"And Don Ferdinand?"

"He is not afraid, he knows always that he is the Prince of Galatro and the world has spoiled him. Particularly the ladies, I think. But I also think that now that he knows her he must love Miss Eva."

"Now? What of that first meeting, Demoutier? You were with her in Rome when they met."

"I heard the story. It was talked of belowstairs. But, madame, all Rome knew that Mrs. Mackay's daughter was visiting her aunt, the Countess Telfener. Still, if the prince has now come to love Miss Eva he probably believes himself that he admired her at first glance when he saw her in the theater. Any man knowing her must love her and be kind to her."

"That is what I try to think, Demoutier. At least it's what I hope."

"Hope is all that is possible for any mother, madame." The maid's deft fingers were gentle as she combed Louise's curls and dressed them in a high dark crown.

Early in the New Year, Eva's engagement was announced. John and Louise were uneasy. Neither they nor any member of Eva's family knew Don Ferdinand any better after six months than at first meeting, but they had learned nothing to his discredit. Eva's unwavering determination prevailed against their uncertainty.

"She is twenty-four," John had said to Louise.

"And she seems so sure of the rightness of her choice. It's hard to stand against such certainty."

"It's hard to refuse her anything. We never have and we don't know how to start now. That's what licks us, Louise. That and not having anything specific against him. He even got himself a job."

"I don't know how much work is involved in being attached to the household of the Duke of Aosta."

"I don't say it's my idea of work but maybe it shows he's trying."

The engagement was celebrated by a dinner and musicale. The party was arranged with no thought except of Eva's pleasure.

The house was brilliantly illuminated. In the glass-enclosed courtyard there were orange trees and tall stands of mimosa. In the Pompeian suite there were palms and orchids and other exotic plants. The ballroom and the salons were decorated with huge bouquets of Eva's favorite white roses and with bowls of violets and of lilies of the valley.

Louise had engaged a concert orchestra. The rest of the entertainment would be the spontaneous offering of friends. M. Viterbo and Signor Perugini would sing, as would Emma Nevada.

The Hungerfords and the Telfeners had come from Rome, bringing with them Don Ferdinand's sister, Donna Amalia Colonna.

Donna Amalia was a handsome girl who held her tall slender body as straight as an arrow. Tonight, Louise thought, she did not seem any lovelier than Eva. Eva and Donna Amalia and Emma Nevada were standing beside the piano. Emma was small and graceful; her heavy-lided eyes were almost the same color as the Parma-violet satin and tulle of her gown; her expressive little face with its turned-up nose was framed in a cloud of curly nut-brown hair. Emma and the queenly, olive-skinned Italian beauty were a becoming contrast to one another. Eva held her own between them. Eva, in Worth's flower-embroidered white tulle, looked no more than nineteen.

"Her charm," the great dressmaker had said, "is a youthful one. We must emphasize that clear-eyed, dewy look of innocence. Nothing, madame, is more enchanting than a radiant young girl. And nothing is more difficult to dress. However I shall not fail her for this important occasion."

He had not failed. But his success was not his entirely. A newspaper writer had said of Eva, "No more than Miranda does she conceal the impression Don Fernando has made on her heart." Perhaps, Louise thought, Miranda on her lonely island was, despite Prospero's arts, less beautiful before her Neapolitan prince arrived.

M. Halévy claimed Donna Amalia's attention. Eva and Emma laughed and whispered together like schoolgirls. They had scarcely known each other when they lived in Nevada. Dr. Wixon had only occasionally brought his motherless daughter from Austin to Virginia for the theater or a Fourth of July celebration. Eva and Emma did not remember each other as children, but they remembered the same childhood and this, Louise supposed, as much as their love of music, had made them friends.

The ballroom was filled with Eva's friends. The white and gold walls had framed more elaborate and larger entertainments but never one quite like this. It was, Louise thought, as if one could feel the affection and the loving wishes for Eva that united the guests as though they were a family gathered for a country Christmas instead of the members of a fashionable and artistic Paris soirée.

Emma Nevada concluded her program with Gounod's "Ave Maria."

When she had finished, the composer spoke to Louise. "You must be proud of your little protégée, madame."

"Our goddaughter, monsieur, since last winter."

"I take only a small part of the credit. It was you who brought her into the Church."

"I think it was, rather, the memory of her Irish mother."

"You are too modest, madame, about your convert. Though that doesn't astonish me. The true woman of the world, like royalty, is always clever enough to be unassuming in speech and manner. But what does surprise me, if you will permit such frankness from an old man who is also an old friend, is that you should be so devout. No"—he frowned—"that's not the right word. Madame is zealous. That fits you better. Madame is fiercely zealous for all she loves: her Church, her children—and tonight you must be very happy for your daughter. Her joy shines brighter than your hundreds of candles and softer than your roses. She is in great beauty. And it's a pleasure to see how proud the Prince of Galatro is of her."

"He should be. Her beautiful look of happiness is his doing. I'll grant him that."

"He's a handsome boy, madame, and, of course, the house of Colonna is a very great one."

Don Ferdinand bent over Eva's chair and whispered to her. She blushed and shook her head.

"He wants her to sing. He's proud of her voice. She will later."

"The Prince of Galatro is right to be proud, madame. There are not many amateurs who can sing in the same salon as Emma Nevada."

"Little Emma Wixon. I can remember going to Austin to hear her sing Cinderella in a school entertainment. I never dreamed that she would do so well. Nor that I would." Louise laughed. "We've both come a long way from Nevada."

"It's fortunate that she took the name of your state with her. Wixon is completely unpronounceable by Europeans."

At the end of the evening Eva sang. She began with a duo of "Fleurs d'Amour" with M. Viterbo. She concluded her program with "Perles d'Or."

As she finished there was long and loud applause.

Don Ferdinand took her hand and drew her gently forward. When he had withdrawn and the audience was quiet Eva announced her encore.

"I shall now sing '*Connais-tu le pays.*' I know that Mignon is Emma's role and I shouldn't dare to attempt this song in her presence, but it's Mammy's favorite and I want to sing it for her."

When the song ended Louise wiped her eyes. "Forgive me for being so foolish, M. Gounod. But that song has always been for me a sort of symbol and promise of happiness. I knew and loved the words first," she said tactfully, "and I know it isn't the finest song in the world except for me."

"Any song, madame, that promises and recalls happiness is the finest song in the world. None of us write many of those."

M. Gounod offered Louise his arm and led her to the dining room where supper was to be served.

Louise stood beside John while the company toasted Eva and her prince.

"He's only a boy, after all," John said almost inaudibly. "Maybe we've been too fearful for Eva."

Louise smiled at him uncertainly. She looked hopefully across the room at the boy and girl who seemed to see only each other. She did indeed look like Miranda and tonight he looked like that other Ferdinand, gentle and loving and tenderly possessive.

As the ladies never tired of repeating, he was a handsome boy and he bore a name that was known the world over. Louise remembered the New York ladies. They and their like could never touch a princess of the house of Colonna. Ferdinand's name would be a shield for Eva. The Princess of Galatro would be safe from the world's cruelty. To that one certainty Louise lifted her glass as the guests confidently toasted Eva's happiness.

Since John could remain abroad only until the middle of February, the wedding date was set for the twelfth. Louise determined to give her daughter a beautiful and elaborate wedding.

"Have it beautiful, Louise, but not big," John said. "Otherwise you'll have a three-ring circus on your hands. American heiress marries Italian prince. You know what the papers will do with that."

Eva agreed. "I'd rather have a small wedding," she said. "I don't want *tout Paris* to see us married, just our families and the friends we love. But I'd like a beautiful wedding. Can it be beautiful and small?"

"It can, it will be, I promise."

Only fifty-three guests were present for the ceremony at the papal nunciature in the Rue de Varenne. The throne room was transformed into a chapel. On the altar there were lilies, white and tall as the candles that filled the candelabra. All the floral decorations were white, even the violets that were strewn on the floor.

Louise's dress and bonnet were of electric blue. She wore two sapphire bracelets and at her throat was a sapphire brooch. Mémé's dark costume was relieved by a cabriolet bonnet, plumed in green. Ada's old-rose satin gown was looped at the side with a chain of rubies. Little Edna Telfener was almost lost in her ruchings and flouncing of lace.

Louise was pleased to observe the admiring glances that Ferdinand's aunt, Donna Cecilia, gave to the American ladies' costumes.

The bridesmaids, Egidie Descazes and Amalia Colonna were charming in diaphanous draperies of pale pink China crepe.

The most beautiful dress was Eva's. M. Worth and Louise had agreed on complete simplicity. The specially woven ivory satin was rich enough to need no ornament except the embroidered orange blossoms that bordered the long train. Eva wore not one inch of lace, not a single diamond. Her veil was of tulle wreathed in fresh orange blossoms. She was the bride that every girl imagines, the legendary, romantic figure whose white gown is undisturbed by fashion's changes.

John stepped back from the altar and took his place with his wife and his sons.

The nuncio, Monsignor di Rende, gave a solemn talk to the young couple. He expressed his happiness at blessing the old world and the new in the persons of the bride and the groom. He was edified, he said, to note that frivolity and fashion had been excluded from today's ceremony.

At the close of the ceremonies the nuncio asked the company to join him in silent prayer for the bride and groom.

If prayers and a papal blessing could bring happiness, Eva would be happy, Louise thought. She knew that Eva believed they could. Ferdinand, as he knelt beside his bride, looked as though he, too, was awed by the solemnity of the occasion. He looked, indeed, like a choirboy. He looked like the gentle, devoted Ferdinand in whom Eva believed.

"The monsignor's taking an awful long time," Clarie whispered to his mother. "I've run out of prayers."

"Just say them again, Clarie. Say them for Eva's happiness."

Clarie shut his eyes tight. His lips moved earnestly.

If any prayer could do it, Louise thought, it would be a prayer like this one: young, undoubting, unafraid.

After the ceremony there was a reception for the wedding guests at the Rue de Tilsitt. The entire house was magnificently decorated with flowers. The most elaborate floral pieces were in the large tapestried salon where the young couple received. Below the tapestries were footstools of orchids. At each end of the long room was a tall pedestal of white roses, ornamented with the Colonna coat of arms and surmounted by a coronet fashioned of yellow and crimson roses.

"Eva looks exquisite," Mrs. Morton said to Louise. "And every inch a princess."

"Madame la Princesse, mes homages." The Italian ambassador bent over Eva's hand.

"Madame la Princesse."

"Princess."

"Principessa."

The voices were the voices of friends and relations and yet still the title rolled richly on every tongue.

To be a princess means something, Louise told herself fiercely. In the time and place in which we live it means a lot.

"Mammy, Mammy darling." Eva's arms were around her mother. "It's been a beautiful wedding, just as you promised. And I'm so happy I can hardly believe it, but I do. And you do too now, don't you? You do too?"

"Of course I do, my darling. You're the princess from the fairy tale who lives happily ever after. And now you must finish greeting your friends and then Demoutier and I will help you to dress for your journey."

"Imagine it, Mammy. Imagine me a married lady, setting off with my husband in a private car for the Riviera. I'm glad we're going there."

Below the babble of voices, Eva hummed the melody that promised happiness:

"Connais-tu le pays où fleurit l'orangier . . ."

Chapter XXV

·····➤◉◈·····

A Visitor to England

SOON AFTER EVA's wedding Louise decided to arrange for Willie and Clarie to enter Beaumont in the spring.

Before he left Paris, John had urged Louise to rent a house in London. His new enterprise, he had said, would necessitate his going often to England.

His new enterprise consumed most of his time and energy. This battle seemed to Louise as hard and as all-absorbing as the old fight against the California Bank for the Hale and Norcross. John, she thought, must miss the firm. Cheerful hopeful Billy O'Brien was gone. Jim Flood in his handsome chocolate-colored mansion on Nob Hill felt himself too old and too tired for new endeavors. Even the affairs of the Nevada Bank seemed too much for him, but he had confidence in the management he had installed, and John had faith in Flood's judgment. Jim Fair had withdrawn from his former associates. He had not forgiven them for standing with Theresa.

John liked Mr. Bennett and admired him. James Gordon Bennett, he had told Louise, was a good tough fellow to have along in a tight spot.

"And make no mistake, Louise, Jay Gould means this spot to be a tight one for us."

"Like Mr. Sharon in the old days in Virginia?"

"No, it's not like that. Not entirely. This means a hell of a lot to me, to my pride mainly. But it's not an all-or-nothing gamble like Fair and I were in before we uncovered the bonanza. And in other ways, too, this is different. All that's the same is that I'm in a fight and I mean to win it."

Louise knew that in one important respect this cable war was different from the old battle for the lode. In Nevada rivals, even enemies, had in a sense been comrades. She remembered the sound of John's voice when he spoke the names: Jones, Sharon, Sutro, Walker, Fair . . . friend or foe, they were the men of the Comstock.

Jay Gould and his associates were men from another world, as was Mr. Bennett even though John respected and trusted him.

Louise did not doubt that John would win his battle. The new cable and telegraph companies would in the end equal and perhaps surpass their long-established rivals. She also realized that this would be neither a short nor an easy struggle. It comforted her to think that in the fight John would have a friend from Virginia beside him. Henry Rosener was a member of the board of directors of the Commercial Cable Company.

The house in the Rue de Tilsitt was lonely without Eva. London, too, would be lonely. John would be there only occasionally, and when he came most of his time would be spent in the City. London would be lonely but it would be a challenge. The siege of London society was a project worth attempting.

> *If we have luck and if we don't*
> *Why bless you, don't you cry.*

She smiled as she looked back on the long road they had come. "We've sure made the riffle," she whispered.

She frowned. Her black brows met in a single level line as she paced slowly back and forth across the velvety flowered carpet of her brocaded, rose-colored boudoir and considered her plan of attack.

Her trip to take her sons to their English school would be only a visit. She would make that quite clear. She would ask Lady Mandeville to find her a house.

"Something small will do, Consuelo," she would say. "I just want a *pied-à-terre* in London so I can be near the boys while they're still new at Beaumont. They can spend their vacations in France. I shan't need a London house beyond the first of the year at the longest."

She would ask Mémé to accompany her. It would be a comfort in a strange city to have her mother with her. And Mémé would be a wise and unflustered counselor in London as she had been in Paris and in Washoe and in Downieville. She was not awed by high society. Like John, she believed that people were the same everywhere.

Mémé would also be an impressive chaperone for an American in London. Louise smiled at the thought that a woman past forty should need a chaperone, but she had read *Truth* and other English newspapers. She had seen some of Cockaigne's malicious London dispatches in the *Argonaut*. No more than youth and innocence were age and the married state a protection against the cruel and poisonous tongues of the gossip writers.

Deliberately she broke the train of her thought. She must not think of settling in England. She must think of herself as a visitor, she must be, inwardly as well as outwardly, a visitor until such time as she considered it wise to allow herself to be persuaded to remain.

Lady Mandeville rented for Louise a house in Hamilton Place, Piccadilly. Louise was pleased with her choice. The house was charmingly furnished. It was not large, but the drawing-room floor would open up well for entertaining. One could give a dinner or even a reception.

Lady Mandeville watched anxiously as Louise inspected her new residence.

"Of course, flowers and a few of your own things will make all the difference."

"It's just right. Exactly what I asked you to find."

"Lord Sudeley's house might have suited you better. It's the largest and most elegantly furnished mansion for rent in London. But you said you didn't want a mansion."

"I have a mansion in Paris. I don't need one in London for those few months."

"This will do for a beginning. Don't frown at me, Louise. I know you mean only to visit us but I mean to change your mind. All London is longing to receive you. First of all you and your mother are to dine with me tomorrow evening. Mandeville is still in the States, you know, but perhaps he'll be here for part of the season. The American minister and Mrs. Phelps are coming. And Lady Randolph

Churchill. Lady Randolph is quite our most beautiful American. It will be a small party. You'll not have many such cozy evenings. The season will soon be under way, and you with it, my dear. You'll be dancing at Marlborough House before midsummer."

"My dear Consuelo, I shall love to see as much as a visitor can. But please don't try to launch me like a battleship."

"I only want to see you queening it here as you do in Paris."

"Well, just remember that a bonanza queen does better on her first appearance without too loud and too sudden a flourish of trumpets. Let me do as I wish. Let me be a quiet visitor to your London scene."

"London won't let you be quiet. London will fete you. But we'll try to do it your way. After all, your way has been a pretty wise one."

"Not always," Louise said sharply. Then she smiled and took Lady Mandeville's hand in hers. "Please don't think I'm ungrateful. I'm not. I'm looking forward to your hospitality and that of your friends. And, naturally, I shall want to make some return."

After Lady Mandeville's dinner Louise received many invitations. The silver tray in the entrance hall at Hamilton Place was filled with cards engraved with the names of distinguished callers.

Mrs. Phelps called on Louise and asked her to name the evening on which she would dine at the legation.

"The minister and I are so anxious to make your stay in London an agreeable one. Anything we can do. Of course Lady Mandeville tells me that you have many English friends, Mrs. Mackay. Having lived so long on the Continent, you are probably better acquainted in English society than even the minister and myself.

"But there are also some charming Americans here. I was speaking only yesterday with a delightful American couple who regret so much never having met you on their visits to Paris or the Riviera. At least she's American. He is of English birth but he lived for many years in the western states, a Mr. Bonynge."

Louise moistened her lips and forced a smile. The poor fools, John had called them, crowding the muddy wooden sidewalk outside the brokers' office. Outside Bonynge and Hawkshurst and the rest. The poor, poor fools who had made Mr. Bonynge and the other brokers rich.

Mrs. Phelps was still speaking "—an unusual name. I felt sure you would remember it, though it's some time, I think, since he was in Nevada."

"Yes. I remember the name. He had offices in San Francisco but he was, I believe, at one time a broker in Virginia City."

"She's a charming woman and received in the best circles. She is quite intimate with Her Royal Highness, Princess Christian."

Louise smiled and poured another cup of tea for her caller.

"And so," Mrs. Phelps continued, "I thought perhaps you would allow me to bring Mrs. Bonynge to call. Or better still, I can invite them to dine with you at the legation."

"You are too kind. And I am distressed to realize that I am very much booked up for the next few weeks. A little later I should be honored to accept an invitation to the legation. But I do hope that you will honor me by dining here. I am planning to ask a few friends the week after next to return some of the kindness that has been shown me. May I send you a card? It would give me a very special pleasure to have you and the minister present at my first little entertainment in this city."

The conversation turned to other festivities that were planned for the season. The American concert for the benefit of the National Relief Fund for Sick and Wounded British Soldiers would be given in June. Louise said that she had already promised Lady Randolph that she would take a box.

The name of Bonynge was not mentioned again.

When Mrs. Phelps had gone Louise told her mother of her visitor's suggestion.

"I'll not accept an invitation to the legation until she has time to forget her notion of inviting me with a C Street broker and his wife. You remember the name, Mémé?" Louise asked, harshly. "Bonynge. Bonynge and Hawkshurst was the firm."

"Louise, my dear, calm yourself. It's all so long ago. You must forget."

"I don't forget. I don't forget easily. You know that, Mémé. Why do I love Theresa Fair and Fanny Rosener and a handful of others from Virginia? Because I remember. But my memory works two ways."

"Suppose you meet. Folks may think it a kindness to bring you and the Bonynges together since they, too, are from the West. What will you do?"

"I'll behave. I'm not a child, Mémé. I'm a sensible middle-aged woman. Just for a moment, hearing the name so unexpectedly, I was young and angry again."

"And frightened again, my poor darling."

"Yes, of course." Louise smiled at her mother. "John says most hate comes from fear. Not that I hate Mr. Bonynge. There were so many of them all along C Street."

Louise stood up abruptly and shook her skirt and brushed it with her hand as though there were dust or caked mud on the smooth silk.

"Don't worry, Mémé. I'll not make a fool of myself. If we meet, I'll be civil. But more than that I can't do. I'll not give kindness where none is owed. And I'll not have a C Street broker in my house."

Louise's dinner was small, but she looked proudly around the flower-decked table at the guests whom she had assembled. The newspapers were full of the cable-rate war that was beginning. It pleased Louise that at the same time her own first engagement promised success to her London campaign.

Secretly she acknowledged that the American guests gave her the greatest satisfaction. The American minister and Mrs. Phelps were of the company and Lady Mandeville, once Consuelo Yznaga of New York. Her Spanish ancestry made her different from other New York ladies and she was Louise's friend, that was the important difference. Mr. Fred Beach was from New York and Miss Emily Yznaga and Lady Randolph Churchill. One could still hear in Lady Randolph's voice the crisp accent of her childhood. Lady Randolph, olive-skinned and dark-eyed, was, as Consuelo had said, London's most beautiful American. She was tall and slender with small bones and tiny feet. Her laugh and her gestures were quick and impulsive. In body and in manner she was completely American.

Maria, Marchioness of Ailesbury, was a reminder of another era. She had been present at the coronation of young Queen Victoria. She had not Mrs. Hungerford's white-haired dignity. Her flower-trimmed peacock-blue gown was ill-suited to her years. Her dyed hair was puffed and frizzed around her face, but she was witty and friendly. One forgot her garish appearance and accepted as gallant her stubborn battle against old age.

Mr. Boulatzell, Mr. Delacour, the Honourable Mrs. Sterling, Lord Marcus and Lord William Beresford, Lady Molesworth, Sir William Gordon-Cummings, the Earl of Dunraven, Mr. and Mrs. Alsopp. It was a gathering in which any hostess could take pride. It was a group in whose company Louise was pleased to go to a ball in one of London's greatest houses.

Mrs. Hungerford did not go to the ball.

"Wait up for me," Louise whispered to her mother. "So I can tell you about it. It will be a grand affair. The whole Prince of Wales set will be there and very likely His Royal Highness himself."

It was just after one o'clock when Louise returned.

"My dear." Mrs. Hungerford's voice was anxious as Louise entered the upstairs sitting room. "Are you all right? To be back so soon!" She turned the gas full on. "I can see you are. Your eyes are as bright as your sapphires and you are grinning like a Cheshire cat."

"It was wonderful. Royalty does give a tone. Real, unexiled royalty. Poor Isabella always made one feel a little sad under the excitement of knowing a queen. This is different, even the unroyal titles. They still have the power, I guess that's what makes the difference between the English nobility and the French."

"And were they all there?"

"They were indeed. Dukes and duchesses and the Lornes. She is Princess Louise, you know. And the Prince of Wales. Of course he's not so young as I pictured him when I read about him in the eastern dispatches the time he visited the States. But then I'm not so young myself any more."

"You look young enough to be your own daughter."

"I keep my figure, that's the main thing. And it's a struggle. When I'm an old lady I'm going to eat and eat and eat."

"And did you dance with the prince tonight?"

"No, but he was pointed out to me. And I think I was pointed out too. He sent an aide to invite me to his table for supper."

"But I thought his supper party was always arranged well ahead of time."

"So it is. And of course there was no reason for me to be invited beforehand. Still, even so, it was a pity about my headache."

"Your headache? You look blooming."

"It seems to be gone now. But, yes, I had this headache and so I had to ask to be excused. Wasn't it a pity?" Louise kept her face grave, only her lips quivered.

"But, my darling. Could you refuse? He's the Prince of Wales."

"I don't know if I could but I did."

Louise's laughter echoed in the small room. Mrs. Hungerford smiled.

"I knew you'd agree, Mémé. Least of all from the Prince of Wales could I accept a last-minute invitation. The prince is the Sharon of London. And when Mr. Sharon decided to accept the Irishmen he sent us a proper invitation, or Theresa and I wouldn't have gone with Jim and John to the reception for Vice-President Colfax. That seemed such a grand party. I can still see them all: Mrs. Colfax and Miss Bross and Miss Calhoun. The Prince of Wales is really Mr. Sharon and Princess Louise is Mrs. J. P. Jones. When I remember that it helps me to keep my head."

"And how is your poor head?"

"It's screwed on tight, so you needn't tease. And sometime I'll be presented properly to the Prince of Wales and to the Princess of Wales. She's my ideal of a fashionable, beautiful lady and yet she's out of a fairy tale too. To be presented to the old Queen would be like stepping into a history book. And it would be a triumph." Louise's eyes sparkled. "The biggest triumph of all for little Mamie Hungerford."

Louise attended the American concert at St. James Hall on the evening of the ninth of June. She wished that John could see the patriotic display in the heart of the English capital.

From the organ gallery behind the orchestra was suspended a huge American eagle in white on a blue ground with thirteen stars curving over his proud head. A huge lyre made of white carnations was hung in the center of the stage and American and English flags entwined, draped each corner.

The audience rose as royalty entered. The Prince of Wales and his princess came first, followed by their three daughters. The princesses, with their hair loose about their shoulders, were, Louise thought, like a picture in a child's book. Long ago she had admired just such fair, restrained young girls standing on tiptoe on an illustrated page. Alexandra was like a child's dream of a princess—no, not quite. A child would not imagine for a princess the simplicity of dress that was suited to a modern, royal public appearance. The Princess of Wales was the most dazzling figure and the most quietly dressed woman in the hall. The elegance of her costume consisted in the richness of its material and the suavity of its line.

Princess Louise and the Duke and Duchess of Edinburgh completed the royal party.

The entertainers were all Americans and many of them were amateurs: Mrs. Ronalds, Lady Mandeville, little Miss Nettie Carpenter, Lady Randolph Churchill, Mrs. F. A. Post.

The one perfect performance was given by a well-known professional singer, Miss Antoinette Sterling, a fat, badly dressed, uncorseted woman whose appearance seemed all the more grotesque in contrast to the society beauties. But as she sang, the hall was still.

The roar of applause died away. The distinguished guests began to circulate. The intermission had begun.

Louise waited with her mother and her guests. Presently Consuelo Mandeville approached Mrs. Hungerford.

"If you will come with me, Mrs. Hungerford, you and Louise. Their Royal Highnesses have expressed the wish that you be presented to them."

Louise's heart thudded as she approached the scarlet-covered sofa where the Princess of Wales was sitting. The prince, standing beside his wife, extended his hand first to Mrs. Hungerford, then to Louise as they curtsied. They curtsied again to the princess and to her daughters.

"You have a charming daughter of your own, Mrs. Mackay, I believe," the Princess of Wales said. Her voice was unaccented, the carefully trained voice of royalty that must be at home in strange lands. As she spoke she cocked her head slightly to one side.

Louise remembered that the princess was a little deaf. She answered, not loudly, but slowly and distinctly.

"I have, ma'am. She is newly married and I miss her. Their little royal highnesses remind me of her just a few years ago."

"But your sons are still with you?"

"They are at Beaumont College, ma'am. That is why I am in England."

"And I hope that we shall also have the pleasure of welcoming your husband to England, though I know he is much occupied by his new cable company."

"Fortunately, ma'am, the cable company will necessitate his coming often to London."

"And we shall hope"—the princess extended her hand in farewell—

"to see you soon, and Mr. Mackay when he comes to England, at Marlborough House."

As Louise curtsied she marveled at the skill with which royal personages mastered each small detail of their parts. Quick studies, Emma Nevada would have said. They were told in advance about each stranger but, as they spoke, the words were so spontaneous and natural that, though one knew it, one could not believe that this was a lesson learned by heart.

Before they withdrew from the royal party Mrs. Hungerford and Louise were presented to Princess Louise and to the Duke and Duchess of Edinburgh.

Louise looked about her. The intermission was in full swing. Less than ten minutes must have elapsed since she had left her box.

She touched her mother's hand. Its unexpected warmth told her that her own hands were cold.

"I guess I'm a little excited, Mémé."

"Naturally, my darling. This is a triumph for you."

Louise remembered the eternity that had ended the evening at Mrs. Stevens'. That, too, must have lasted less than ten minutes.

"I think I'll scarcely have to use my hard-won wisdom. I think the walls of this city are tumbling down without a single blast of my golden trumpet, or should I say silver?" Louise laughed. The New York hurt was not forgotten but it was eased. Suddenly it didn't matter any more. Alexandra had put the New York ladies in their place.

Consuelo Mandeville's prophecy came true. Before the end of the season Louise was dancing at Marlborough House.

The elite of London was gathered and Louise was among them. Her white satin gown, specially ordered from Paris for the grand occasion, was cut and draped to give her the illusion of height. The high heels of her tiny slippers were jeweled. Her tiara and her necklace were of large and brilliant diamonds. Bracelets glittered on her white-gloved wrists.

The Prince of Wales danced with her. She made him laugh, though she could not afterward remember what she had said. She was as excited as a child at a birthday party, not at one of the birthday celebrations she had known, but at the ones she had imagined behind the bright windows on St. John's Park.

The Princess of Wales spoke with her for several minutes after supper. The princess inquired for Eva.

"You must bring the Prince and Princess Colonna to England, Mrs. Mackay. One hears such charming things of her and of him, too, of course."

"It will not be possible this year, ma'am." Louise hesitated. But even from a royal personage she could not keep back her happy news. "She's at present in a delicate condition."

"And you look so happy, Mrs. Mackay, and not at all as if you could be a grandmother."

"Your Royal Highness is too kind. And I am happy. The daughter of my daughter. That's what I hope for, though for Colonna's sake I suppose I should wish for the boy."

The party swirled around Louise. The prince danced with her once more. The Marquis of Lorne claimed his dance. Lord Charles Beresford, the Earl of Kinmare—partners with names from the pages of history. Sir William Gordon-Cummings, Mr. Arthur Wilson, names from here and now, names of modern importance because those who bore them were members of the Prince of Wales' set.

When Louise returned to Hamilton Place, Mrs. Hungerford and Demoutier were waiting in her bedroom.

Demoutier unfastened the tiny hooks and listened in silence as her mistress described the glories of Marlborough House, her two dances with the Prince of Wales, and a dance with another royal highness.

"His Royal Highness, the—the——" Louise laughed. "Think of me meeting enough royal highnesses to forget one of their names!"

When Demoutier had gone, Louise and her mother talked about Eva.

"All through the soiree my heart was a little with her and with her news. Mémé, were you this excited when you knew I was having her?"

"Yes, my dear, I was."

"Why didn't you tell me? Why hasn't a single friend told me that it's exciting to become a grandmother?"

"Perhaps they tried and you didn't listen. No one listens to a grandmother except other grandmothers."

"Isn't it nice that one really good thing, one really exciting thing, is saved for one's latter years?"

"The best is yet to be? Sometimes that's true, Louise. This is one of the times."

"Oh, Mémé, everything's going so well that it almost frightens me. So many blessings I can't count them. I'm too happy. Eva sounds truly happy. Even in her letters before she wrote about the baby. And the boys at their new school. I was a little afraid Beaumont might be hard for them, speaking as they do, Parisian French and American English. Children can be wicked to anyone different. Grownups too. But their schoolmates like them and they're such nice boys. Frank Woodlock and Evelyn Fitzgerald, he'll be a charmer when he grows up; little Teddie Blount and Don Carlos's son, Don Jaime. And I think they feed them better at Beaumont than they did at Vaugirard. Clarie's gained five pounds."

Mrs. Hungerford laughed softly. "He's your baby and so he seems always the frailest and the most in need of care."

"Well, he did get that awful croup in Paris. I think the English climate is doing wonders for him."

"You're a lucky woman, Louise."

"As long as my children are lucky, I'm lucky."

"And John."

"John lucky? I suppose he is. He says that luck is a part of all success. But with him luck is the least. He's strong, not just for himself but for all of us. Remember the night of the earthquake when, because he was with us, it didn't seem so bad? I can't imagine being afraid with John or for him."

Andrea Marcantonio Ferdinando Colonna was born on the fourteenth of December at 9 Rue de Tilsitt.

She had been wrong to wish for a girl, Louise knew. She had forgotten the pride that was part of the happiness in a son's birth. As she looked at Eva's radiant face she remembered the pride.

John too. Louise smiled as she watched him with the baby. Someday there would be a grandson to bear his name, but in the meanwhile he rejoiced in Eva's accomplishment.

"Well, Granny," John said, "here we are. Whoever would have thought? Grandpa and Granny."

And so Louise had her name for the third generation.

Eva regained her strength quickly. In January, Andrea was christened at the English Passionist Fathers' Church in the Avenue Hoche.

Ferdinand was gentle and attentive with Eva. It's a good thing it's a boy, Louise thought. Why was her thought an angry one? she wondered. Every man was pleased to have a son. Why should she hold Ferdinand's natural pride against him?

It was not until after the christening that John and Louise spoke of their own affairs.

"We're doing what we set out to do," John said. "Getting the rates down. It's a murderous war, but Jay Gould can stand it and so, luckily, can we. In the end there'll be some compromise. Not an agreement exactly, but a letup. And the public will be the better for our battle and so will the newspapers, including the rivals of the *Herald,* and so, please God, will me and Bennett be."

"You've slipped into the old way of speech. Only it's 'me and Bennett' now instead of 'me and Fair.' "

"Jim's still sulking. He wants no part of the bank or the cable company or anything of Flood's or mine."

"They say he's sore as a bear. Fanny Rosener wrote me. And I hear, too, that he thinks you're overextending yourself with Mr. Bennett and he's glad of it."

"Maybe, maybe. But if I was in a tight spot tomorrow I'd go to him, and furthermore he'd help me out."

"You're as bad as Theresa."

"We know Jim. And like I've told you, Louise, there's not such an almighty big difference between a partnership and a marriage. Now tell me about yourself. From the *Argonaut* and your letters I gather you're doing mighty well. You didn't mention it but I saw in the *Argonaut* that you wore your sapphires to Marlborough House. I bet you blinded them."

"As a matter of fact I didn't." Louise smiled demurely. "I had thought of wearing them. Indeed, I ordered a white dress specially to set them off."

"Then why in blazes, old lady?"

"Well, you see, John, the day of the ball I received a message, a command you might call it, though it was put as a request from Her Royal Highness through a lady-in-waiting, that I wear my famous sapphires."

"And so?"

"So I sent a little note to her ladyship explaining that unfortunately the sapphires were locked away in the bank and it would not be possible to get them out in time for the ball. Wasn't it a pity?"

John shouted with laughter. "Good for you, old lady. Oh, my darling old lady, I can't believe that with your nature you haven't got a little bit of Irish somewhere."

"The Irish aren't the only proud ones, John."

"So I see. And I see, too, that you've handled the nobs and the snobs of London just right. Are you meaning to take a house there in the spring again?"

"I am. Lord Sudeley's house at 7 Buckingham Gate is for rent. It's the handsomest furnished mansion to be had in London."

"Then you take it. And I promise you that this year I'll be over more."

"More! Will you be over at all? I have Willie and Clarie nearby. And Mémé will come back with me and perhaps Father in the summer, so I'm not exactly lonely, but still——"

"But still you're hankering after another holiday for the two of us."

"I am."

"It can't be for a while. I'm in the middle of a fight, beside the reorganization and expansion of our companies. I'll have to stick pretty close to business for the next few years. And never in one place, that's the hell of it. But one day . . ."

"And this time not just a holiday."

"Sure. One day when we're both old enough to forget ambition and the boys are old enough to be in charge, the pair of us will settle down. Grandpa and Granny in some sunny quiet spot. Meanwhile I'll come to London as often as I can and you amuse yourself taking the place over."

On the afternoon of March 23, 1886, Louise was presented to Queen Victoria by the Viscountess Mandeville at a Drawing Room at Buckingham Palace. Mrs. Hungerford was presented by the Lady Norreys.

Mrs. Hungerford wore a gown of garnet velvet and brocade, richly trimmed in lace.

For her own costume Louise chose old-ivory satin. The deep creamy tone matched the famous point d'Alençon lace and set off the whiteness of her shoulders. The pointed satin bodice and the underskirt were embroidered with a design of wheat sheaves in seed pearls and silver. The overskirt was a film of lace. The satin train trimmed with velvety ostrich plumes and soft sprays of lilac was also covered with the lace. John would be pleased, she thought, to have her wear this gift as well as her jewels. She wore the most beautiful pieces from her collection of sapphires: her tiara, her necklace and her earrings and, on her left wrist, one magnificent bracelet. In her long veil were three white ostrich feathers. Her bouquet was of snow-balls and white lilacs.

It seemed strange to the American ladies to be dressed in such finery before noon, strange to be part of the slow daylight procession of carriages filled with ladies and gentlemen in ballroom attire.

As she reached the palace Louise found herself beside the American minister's wife.

Mrs. Phelps introduced a young girl whom she was presenting. "Mrs. Mackay, Miss Bonynge."

Louise held out her hand. Her smile and the warmth of her greeting were spontaneous. One could not hold an old anger against this sweet-faced young thing.

"The minister was disappointed," Mrs. Phelps said, "that we have not the honor of presenting you, as well as the Bonynge family."

"It would have been an honor for me, but as you know Lady Mandeville is an old and dear friend and she arranged my presentation even before the minister so kindly offered."

"Mr. Phelps is somewhere about with this dear child's father."

Louise's eyes met her mother's and as the crowd separated them from Mrs. Phelps she spoke. "So after all the C Street broker and I find ourselves under the same roof."

The Drawing Room was a brilliant occasion. The Prince of Wales arrived at the garden entrance of the palace, attended by a detachment of the household cavalry. He was accompanied by his son, Prince Albert Victor, and attended by the Duke of Abercorn.

The military, splendidly uniformed, was much in evidence.

A guard of honour of the Coldstream Guards was mounted in the Quadrangle, and a guard of honour of the 1st Life Guards in the courtyard.

Inside the palace the Royal Body Guard of the Yeomen of the Guard was on duty under the command of Lord Monson. In the State Salons Her Majesty's Body Guard of the Honourable Corps of Gentlemen at Arms was under the command of Lord Sudeley. When

Louise entered the throne room she was dazzled by the magnificence of jewels and gowns, of orders and uniforms.

Princess Christian's parure gleamed with emeralds. Princess Henry of Battenberg wore diamonds. Her dress in shades of mauve deepening to violet was, Louise thought, the most exquisite costume to be seen. Another beautifully dressed woman was the Duchess of Roxburgh in a gown of pale blue satin with a train of sapphire velvet.

Lady Mandeville touched Louise's arm. They moved forward. As Louise rose from her low curtsy, the elegant ladies, the uniformed gentlemen, the royal highnesses, the peers and peeresses of the realm faded into insignificance compared to the old woman in the jet-trimmed black dress. On her breast, set in a brooch, the Koh-i-noor blazed beside the wide blue ribbon of the Garter. In the white veil was a coronet of pearls and diamonds. But without crown or jewel or order one would recognize the Queen, one would know that this was majesty.

Louise made her final curtsy and withdrew. She was obliged to hold her head back and her eyes wide to keep tears from falling. To step even so briefly into the history book was an unexpectedly moving experience.

It was a disappointment to Louise that John reached London after her presentation.

"Though I think," she said, "that it would have been a hard task to get you into court attire to be presented."

"Well, my dear, I'm not very handy at that sort of thing. I'd rather leave it to you."

"But you'll be here for the season? Their Royal Highnesses the Prince and Princess of Wales have promised to honor me by attending a dinner and musicale on the twenty-eighth of June. It would make the triumph sweeter to have you there."

"My girl is sure flying high. You bet I'll be there."

Except for a ten-day business trip to Paris, John spent the months of April, May, and June in England.

He was proudly present at Louise's dinner for the Prince and Princess of Wales.

He had no love for English royalty, Louise knew. He remembered too well the Ireland of his boyhood. She watched him with amusement as he sat beside the princess. The sternness melted from his face. Not John, not any man, Louise thought, could resist Alexandra when she chose to be charming.

At the reception there would be a hundred guests. The company at dinner was small and carefully chosen.

Eva and Ferdinand and Colonel Hungerford had come from Rome for the great occasion. Louise was glad that Sir Arthur Sullivan was a favorite of the prince and princess. She had known that it would give Eva pleasure to sit next to him. On her daughter's other side she had placed Sir Christopher Sykes. He was an amiable and kindly man.

As Louise talked to the prince she unobtrusively watched her guests. Her dinner was a success. The flowers on her table, arranged with ribbons in the new Directoire manner, were a miracle of color and perfume. The Hungarian band played softly. She had ransacked the world for delicacies. But most important for the success of the evening, she had brought the right people together. They talked and laughed not only with their dinner partners but across the table. The entire group from the old Marchioness of Ailesbury to the young Princess Colonna had come sparklingly alive with warmth and gaiety. The mood would last as the small company became big. Her reception, like her dinner, would be a party, not a function.

Louise relaxed and laughed with unfeigned merriment at a royal anecdote. The prince laughed with her and said, "I knew your house would be like this, Mrs. Mackay. Perfect food and wine of course." He smacked his lips. "Pleasure to dine with a hostess who learned her art in Paris. And I knew it would be fun. You Americans have brought fun to Europe. You know what some of our hostesses forget, that the first requirement of an entertainment is that it be entertaining. And I'll wager you have a surprise in store for us later. What's it to be?"

"A surprise, sir, I hope Your Royal Highnesses will be pleased."

It was in the hope of pleasing the princess that she had engaged the famous Russian Choir Singers. They would remind Alexandra of a faraway and beloved sister.

The prince might not care for quite such solemn music but in a room full of pretty women he would be content no matter what the entertainment.

The white and gold music room was decorated with a profusion of white and yellow orchids. The handsomest display was on the mantel where the tallest of the delicate sprays touched the top of the high mirror. The light breeze that came through the open window was cooled by the huge blocks of ice which had been placed on the balconies.

Mr. Edward Oudin, the American baritone, was well received. His performance brought to a conclusion the musical part of the program.

Louise approached the prince. "Now my surprise, sir. Knowing Your Royal Highness' fondness for the French people . . ."

The talk and laughter died away. The guests were silent for a moment and then broke into delighted applause at the entrance of M. Coquelin and Mme. Blanche Pierson of the Comédie Française and Mlle. Réjane of the Vaudeville.

At the end of the performance the prince led the long rounds of applause.

"A fine surprise, Mrs. Mackay. One sometimes gets a little tired of even the best musical entertainment. And to me it's a particular pleasure to see my friend Coquelin again. I should like you to place him at my table at supper."

The party did not fade away. It retained its brilliance and its festive mood until the late hour when the prince and the princess departed.

The last of the guests, while they waited for their carriages, laughed and chattered as lightheartedly as though they were at the beginning of a party instead of at its ending.

Even John, Louise noted with satisfaction when they retired to their room, looked neither tired nor bored.

"That was one fine party, Louise. I didn't expect to enjoy myself but I did. Right from the start. Alexandra may be a princess but she's a hell of a nice woman."

"And the prince?"

"He's a smart fellow, I think. Smarter than he lets on. Hard on him spending his best years waiting around. It's a wonder he doesn't get into more trouble than he does."

"I know these things don't mean so much to you, John, but it's quite an honor to have both their Royal Highnesses. Quite an unusual honor for an American."

"I'm no expert on society but I'm no damn fool either. I was sure proud of you tonight. You're right at the top of the heap."

"The biggest heap there is. There's no place higher to go."

"I know how you feel. After the big bonanza I slowly lost my taste for poker. I'd got too rich to care if I lost or won. Has the fun gone out of this game for you?"

"Not entirely. I still have to prove it isn't beginner's luck. I can keep quite busy consolidating my position. Besides, to be truthful, I enjoy queening it in London. Perhaps if I'd been born to this kind of thing I'd not care about it at my age. Maybe if one's born to it one doesn't care at any age."

"Plenty of born ladies and gentlemen acted like they cared to-night. They get real buck fever at the sight of royalty."

"I guess most of them care. And a good thing for society that they do. Society is like any business; if the members of the firm ever stop caring it'll fall apart and cease to exist."

"And when I cease to care about my business and turn it over to Willie . . . ?"

"Oh, John, that'll be forever. Ten years at least."

"Less than that. Willie's a smart lad. Give him another six, seven years and he'll be ready to step into my shoes. Then will you be ready, Louise, to quit this complicated game of yours?"

"You know I will. However much I enjoy it I never quite believe in it. Mrs. John Mackay of *Truth* and the *World* and the *Argonaut*! I think: This is never me. And I feel like Mrs. Kent and the other actresses riding in their decorated cavalcade from town to town in the diggings."

"There's not an actress then nor a royal highness now can touch you, my darling. A long time ago I told you it would be worth it to make a woman like you queen of the Comstock or any other damn place your heart desired."

Chapter XXVI

••••➤◉◄•••

The Top of the Heap

AFTER JOHN'S DEPARTURE the season continued to be a triumphant one for Louise. She took a house at Cowes for two weeks and was one of those who dined with the Prince and Princess of Wales on their yacht, the *Osborne*.

In September she went with Mrs. Hungerford to Aix-les-Bains to rest and found that the French watering place was filled with the faces she had seen in London, at Ascot, at Cowes. There were English and French and Americans all taking the cure lightly and their social engagements seriously.

Mrs. John Sherwood, the wise and witty correspondent of the New York *World*, was at Aix-les-Bains. Like Lucy Hooper, Mrs. Sherwood knew the people of whom she wrote. She went to their parties and so had no need to invent the festivities, and felt no smarting desire to malign the fashionable hosts or their guests.

In November when she had returned to Paris, Louise received from John two of Mrs. Sherwood's articles that had been reprinted in the *Argonaut*.

Louise was pleased by Mrs. Sherwood's description of her:

"Mrs. Mackay is the best of wives and mothers. She is a very pretty little brunette, very young-looking to be a grandmother; she is bright, with a sense of the ludicrous, describes a scene or a conversation well. She has no troublesome egotism, and is of an amiable, harmless temper."

Louise smiled. Fortunately even the most gifted newspaper-woman was not clairvoyant. She went on reading.

"Mrs. Mackay has a beautiful pair of eyes, a very pleasant nose, not too retroussé . . ."

That was kind of her, Louise thought and closed one eye and rue-fully observed the tilt of her nose.

". . . and a nice mouth and chin," the article continued. "She is little and has beautiful little feet. She writes a perfect note, with a sweeping English hand."

The conclusion of Mrs. Sherwood's remarks about her would do as a sensible summing-up of her London triumphs:

"She appeared quietly and well. She committed no sin except that she succeeded."

At the end of January, Louise rented for Eva a villa at Menton. Eva was expecting a baby early in April and she was not as well as she had been before Andrea's birth. She did not sleep well and she grew tired easily. The doctor advised for her a warmer and quieter place than Rome or Paris.

Louise sat beside Eva's chaise longue in the wide-windowed bed-room. The green and flowered landscape was peaceful; the February air was soft as May.

"Someday," Eva said, "I'd like to own a house on the Riviera. It would be nice for the children to have a quiet country place far from Rome. It would have to be the Italian Riviera, of course. My little Colonnas must have an Italian childhood."

"I can't seem to think of your or Ada's children as Italian."

"They are, you know." Eva laughed affectionately at her mother.

"I know. I know. And Andrea's baby talk is a mixture of Italian and English. But then little Nito's was French and Spanish as well as English. Mine too, I suppose. And so a little Italian doesn't make your son seem like a foreigner to me."

"He is though, Mammy. Or rather to him I am the foreigner. 'My grandmother was an American,' his children will say someday. I'll be foreign and exotic like your French grandmother whom I never knew."

"You don't feel foreign in Rome, do you, Eva? Or strange? Or—or lonely?"

"With Ferdinand? Oh, Mammy, no! If only he could be here with us. But Aosta keeps the poor boy in constant attendance."

"He still seems very young, doesn't he?"

"That's a fault that——"

"Darling, I didn't mean a fault."

"Well, a quality then that time and growing children will remove. And he's so gay. To Ferdinand everything is fun, a ball or the races or a picnic with me and Andrea. Just to hear him laugh. Sometimes in the evening he has gentlemen in to play cards and he laughs so heartily that the sound reaches my boudoir and seems to fill the little room with his warmth and gaiety."

"It's good for gentlemen to be by themselves sometimes. At least they like it. But"—Louise kept her voice low and casual—"I don't know where I got the idea, but I thought Ferdinand didn't play— didn't like cards."

Eva laughed. "You know perfectly well where you got the idea. Ferdinand told you that after that unfortunate experience when he was a boy he gave up all gambling."

"And what changed him?" Louise asked quietly.

"Why, now it's not a gamble. Father has been so generous to us that Ferdinand can easily afford a game of cards or even an occasional evening at a casino. And, as he says, when the stake is low enough or one's income is high enough for losses not to matter, one is sure to win. See." Eva touched the ruby and diamond heart that pinned the lace at her throat. "He brought me this from Monte Carlo in December."

Louise examined the brooch. "It's beautiful. I'm glad he won, not lost, what that center stone cost."

"Don't be afraid. He gambles only for fun. You mustn't fear for me." Eva took her mother's hand. "This is different. I was very little but I remember or perhaps I heard Grandpa or Mémé or Mrs. Mock talking late; grownups forget how much children can hear. I suppose I'll forget with Andrea and the new baby. Anyway, I heard when I was a child and so I understand why you fear that Ferdinand's gambling might be like—might be like . . ."

"Eva, you must never think harshly, never——"

"I don't. My poor first father. He's so young in the picture I have. Younger than I. I just feel sorry."

"I suppose it's all you can feel. He wasn't well in his last years. And they're all you can remember and so you can only be sorry."

"I remember more than that, I think. He was dark and handsome, handsomer than his photograph. Sometimes I think it was remembering him that made me fall in love with Ferdinand."

"Ferdinand is different."

"I suppose he is. It's just something, a look, a beautiful, aristocratic look."

"Your father was a distinguished man, Eva. He was a gentleman and a graduate. And before his—his troubles, he was a successful, indeed a brilliant surgeon."

"I know. I'm only sorry for the troubles and thankful that Ferdinand lives in an easier time and place and that—I don't like to say it but I must, not to hurt you or in any disrespect to him but to reassure you for me—Ferdinand has no taste at all for drink. I know he told you that, but perhaps on account of the gambling you may not believe."

"That's something one can see, Eva. A hard-drinking man can't hide it. The way he holds his glass, the way he looks at the glass he doesn't dare reach for. All the little betraying ways. I've seen enough of Ferdinand to know he's been spared that weakness and I've been thankful."

"You should be. And for so much else. For my happiness. Can't you see that?"

Louise stroked Eva's smooth brow. "Yes, I can. Keep looking like this and I'll come to love your Ferdinand as I do Joseph. Already"— she forced warmth into her voice—"I'm fond of him." In the end surely she would be fond of him and learn to trust him. She should trust him now, she thought, and be grateful to him for the serene and happy expression that made Eva's face almost beautiful.

At the beginning of March, Louise took Eva to 9 Rue de Tilsitt to await the birth of her child. On the twenty-seventh of March, earlier than she had been expected, a baby girl was born.

She could not, Louise thought, have been very early, for she was plump and rosy and unusually pretty. Or perhaps all granddaughters were unusually pretty. No—Louise shook her head as she watched the infant sleeping in the satin-lined basket—no, it was not imagination or a wish, this was a lovely baby. Being a grandmother had not blurred her judgment. She knew very well that though Andrea was a dear little boy he was not in the least pretty. This child would be. Louise murmured a prayer of thankfulness that the looks had gone to the girl. The daughter of her daughter. She was glad that Eva's daughter had a beautiful name: Bianca Amalia Celeste.

"Everything you have will be beautiful, Bianca," Louise whispered. "Everything of the finest, everything of the best. But the best of all will be to have my gentle Eva for your mother. Someday you'll know that, little daughter of my daughter."

For Clarie and Willie the most important event of the London season of 1887 was the arrival of Buffalo Bill and his Wild West Show.

Louise promised the boys that as soon as their father arrived he would take them to the American Exhibition.

"It will be more fun to go with your father. He knows Colonel Cody."

"You mean we can speak to him?" Clarie asked. "We can shake him by the hand?"

"That might be managed too. If you boys will wait for your father to see the show, I'll invite Colonel Cody to the party I'm giving on the twelfth of July. Your father has promised to be here for it."

"But gee! Wait until July!"

"The longer to enjoy looking forward, Clarie."

"And he won't be able to come until after his show and you'll never let us downstairs that late. Bow like little gentlemen and depart before dinner. That's what we do."

"It's what you should do, Willie—at least until you're at the university. But, after all, you're seventeen. And this party is to welcome your father after almost a year away, and so if Colonel Cody comes I think you can make a quiet appearance after dinner for the entertainment and to greet your special guest."

"And me?" Clarie asked. "Thirteen is pretty old too."

"For this once we'll say it's old enough."

"Buffalo Bill in our own house," Clarie said. "They'll never believe it at Beaumont."

John kept his promise to arrive in London for Louise's grandest entertainment of the summer. And Louise was able to keep her promise to the boys. She invited Colonel William Cody and he accepted.

"Do you think maybe Miss Annie Oakley and some of the cowboys might come too?" Willie asked. "Clarie and I were wondering."

"No, Willie. It would be no compliment to the colonel to invite him if I asked him to bring his company. He's coming as an old acquaintance of your father's, not as an entertainer."

The Colonnas and the Telfeners came from Rome for the party. This pleased John more than all of London's high society, though Louise could see that he was pleased for her sake that the gathering was a distinguished one. She had thought of John's pleasure in choosing her guests. It interested him to talk to Sir Albert and Mr. Reuben Sassoon and to Sir Julian Goldsmid and Mr. Alfred Rothschild. He had to take the Marchioness of Londonderry into dinner, but that went well. Lady Londonderry was an agreeable woman, and being herself a successful hostess she knew how to be a charming guest.

Before the concert and the dramatic entertainment began Louise seated John with Fanny Ronalds and Mrs. Arthur Wilson. They would amuse him.

She watched gratefully as he spoke a few friendly words to Mrs. Paran Stevens. He had not forgotten that Mrs. Stevens had tried long ago to be kind. She smiled indulgently as his face brightened at the sight of little Miss Chamberlain. She was so pretty and so unspoiled by her great success that one could not help wishing her well.

Some of the guests Louise kept out of John's way. He hated pretense and he hated snobbery.

"And what beats me," he had said to her, "is that so many of the worst offenders don't need to be. They've got titles or money or both. They don't need to pretend and they ought to be way past snobbishness. Got everything they need, I guess, except brains."

Buffalo Bill, in faultless evening dress, made his entrance before supper. He was the sensation of the evening. The guests and the artists surrounded him.

The younger Coquelin saluted him. "More than a strolling player, sir, you are a veritable hero."

Willie and Clarie hovered hopefully on the edge of the crowd that surrounded Colonel Cody. Clarie caught his father's eye imploringly.

John took the colonel's arm. "You must be tired, Bill, after the performance. How about coming off with me for a quiet bourbon and water and a cigar? I'm sure these folks will excuse two old acquaintances for a little while. See you all at supper." He beckoned to Willie and Clarie. "Time you boys were in bed, but you can come along to my study with the colonel and me for a few minutes."

The boys listened entranced to the colonel's tales of Indian warfare, of wagon trains rescued and redskins routed in the nick of time.

"Pretty big contrast, John. Then and now."

"Pretty big for both of us." John lifted his glass to his guest. "Old times, Bill."

"The best times, John. Still and all I've done pretty well in London. I've got all the big bugs solid, from the Queen down. The Prince of Wales himself gave me a gold horseshoe pin set with genuine rubies and diamonds."

"Doing mighty damn well with your show from all I hear."

"Hard work though. Sometimes I think it was easier fighting Indians. When are you coming to see me? I got a great company. That little Annie is a gem."

"Tomorrow, Father?" Clarie asked. "Can we go tomorrow?"

"If the colonel here can make room for us, we'll go tomorrow. The ladies will want to sleep after these festivities, but I've never got over keeping miners' hours."

"The best seats in the house are yours," Colonel Cody said. "For you boys and your father any time, the best seats in the house."

John devoted his first days in London to the boys. The evenings were spent quietly. Having the family together was a rare treat and Louise refused to make any social engagements while her sister and daughter were in England.

After the Telfeners and the Colonnas returned to Rome, John and Louise and the boys went for a brief visit to Ramsgate.

"And not too many late nights when we get back to London," John warned. "I mean to make this trip a holiday one. The two of us might run over to Paris and Trouville later. But right now I'll be pretty busy."

John's first appointment in London was at the bank which was the English correspondent of the Nevada Bank.

It was evening when he returned to Buckingham Gate. Louise was dressing for dinner. He went to her room and dismissed Demoutier and closed the door.

"Got a bit of bad news, old lady," he said. "I'll give it to you fast.

We're overdrawn at the bank, overdrawn to the tune of about a million. I thought I'd fall out of my chair when the fellow told me. But my poker face from the old days stood me in good stead. He thought we must have some big deal on. I got out of there and sent off some fast cables and it seems he was right. We have."

"You never told me."

"Nobody told me. George Brander, the manager of the Nevada Bank, and two brokers Dresbach and Henry Rosener's brother-in-law, John Rosenfeld, got into a big deal in wheat with bank funds. Oh, all legal, I expect, but Brander allowed enormous loans. Cornering the wheat market, they were. Well, the market collapsed on their heads. Worst part is that Sam and Henry Rosener will be in a bad way. Flood and I are in something of a bad way ourselves. At least right now we are, but it's the Roseners who'll be really hurt. They owe the bank more than they have in the world, I'm afraid."

"But you can help them."

"I can try, once we're out of this mess ourselves, but Sam and Henry won't take charity. You know that. They're not the kind."

"I know. Only the kind to give it, never to accept it."

"I'll have to get back to the States as quick as I can. I've booked passage on the *Servia*. She's due in New York the eighth of August. Meanwhile young Jim Flood is keeping me advised by cable. I'll not be able to go to Consuelo's tonight."

"I'll stay with you. I'll send a message that we can't come."

"That's just what you won't do. Credit's a tricky thing, Louise. You'll go to the party and wear your finest gown and all your sapphires."

"My sapphires, John darling, of course. Why didn't I think? And my pearls and the rest of my jewels. You can have them all and welcome. They'd bring close to a million, maybe more. You said they were an investment."

"Your investment, old lady, not mine, not even if I stood in desperate need, which I don't. We neither one of us will have to touch our investments. None of yours at all and none of my important holdings. Flood and I will find the money. Poor old Flood. This'll be a terrible blow to him. He's not a well man. If he had been, this never would have happened."

"Could—could the Nevada Bank fail, John?"

"It could but it ain't going to. I'll make damn sure of that. Young

Jim will hold the fort till I get back. And don't forget, Flood and I have a pretty good name in San Francisco and in the Atlantic states as well. I'll raise what we need and more without a depositor losing a dollar."

"Where will you get it? Money's always tight after a crash like this."

"Can't you guess where I'll get most of it? Don't you know who I'll go to?"

"You'd never ask Jim Fair for money? Even for the loan of it."

"Sure, I would. And what's more he'll let us have it. Oh, he'll make a few remarks about Flood and me making fools of ourselves on our own. He always fancied himself the brains of the firm. And, by God, he wasn't so far wrong."

"And you think he'll come to your rescue?"

"Sure. Same as Flood and I would if Fair was in trouble."

"It's a long time since you've been partners."

"Partnerships made in the diggings don't break easy. Fair'll help us out. He'll be damn disagreeable about it but he'll do it. Now get ready for your party, Louise, and blaze with jewels, so if I have to I can borrow a million or so in London to tide us over."

The Nevada Bank did not fail, though black headlines foretold disaster.

John, in New York on his way West, refused to talk to the press.

Mr. Whitelaw Reid of the New York *Tribune,* in a sharply worded interview, held John responsible for the wheat deal.

An unnamed associate of John's was quoted by the San Francisco *Chronicle* as saying: "It looks to me as if Mackay would be in the hands of Jay Gould before long, if, indeed, he is not there already."

John said nothing except to issue to the San Francisco *Examiner* a firm denial that he was in any way interested in the wheat deal either personally or through the Nevada Bank, other than that the bank had loaned money to Dresbach and Rosenfeld.

His brief letters and the enclosed clippings brought Louise the story.

Like Louise, the San Francisco papers found it difficult to believe that Jim Fair would go to his former partners' financial assistance, but he did.

When Fair assumed the presidency of the Nevada Bank in place of Flood and, in reorganizing, dismissed Brander, both the *Chronicle* and the *Examiner* interpreted his actions as unfriendly to his old associates. They would be out of the bank before January, the papers predicted. Fair was, in his shrewd and wily way, revenging himself on Flood and Mackay.

Louise smiled as she read the columns of print: It's thought here . . . It's evident that . . . Opinion on Pine Street . . .

The facts were simpler than the editors would permit their readers to believe.

Jim Flood was lying gravely ill at Menlo Park. He could not save the bank. John could not absent himself long from the battle with Jay Gould. Jim Fair took over for them. Thanks to him, the bank would stand, unshaken. The old firm was back in business. Louise found it almost as hard to accept as did Mr. De Young of the *Chronicle*, but the fact was that Fair and Mackay and Flood were partners again.

Louise knew that newspapers were given to misquotation, but one story from the *Chronicle* had the ring of truth:

" 'I've said all manner of hard things about Jim Fair,' said Mackay, 'but I see I wronged him. He's a whole-souled straightforward fellow and I'm not sorry to lose a few millions when I know I've got such a friend.' "

John would never have spoken so intimately to a reporter nor had he ever publicly criticized Fair. It was probably young Flood, Louise thought, to whom John had spoken. The boy must have repeated his words. Young Jim was not experienced enough to be on his guard with even the most friendly-seeming newspaperman. But John, she thought, would not be displeased. He would be glad to have placed on the record his regard and affection for Jim Fair.

John had been right. The newspapers and the rest, including Louise herself, had been wrong. A partnership made in the diggings was not easily broken.

The Nevada Bank stood firm. Jim Flood and John retained their interest.

John and James Gordon Bennett won their fight against Jay Gould and his American and English associates. The young cable and telegraph companies prospered. From 1887 on, the Commercial Cable Company and the Postal Telegraph were competitors with which Western Union and the Anglo-American Cable Company were forced to reckon.

Louise, securely established in London as in Paris, watched her sons growing toward manhood.

Eva seemed as happy in her marriage as Ada was in hers.

When John came to London he and Louise rejoiced together over their respective achievements. All was well with them and with their children. The Mackay family was at the top of the heap.

Chapter XXVII

·····•◉•····

A Little Malice

WITH HER MOTHER, Louise was engaged in planning her two most important parties of 1889. On April third the Prince of Wales would honor her, and on July fifteenth, Princess Louise.

For the Lornes the beauty of the party was all-important. For this dinner Louise decided to erect from the curb to the entrance a new carriageway lined in scarlet silk, lighted with red globes. The house would be brilliantly illuminated with electric light, and stairway, halls, and salons would be banked with flowers.

"Red roses on the stairs, I think, Mémé, white orchids and yellow roses on the dining table and—but I've time still for Princess Louise. Here's my dinner menu for the third. For the prince food is the main thing, even before pretty women. What do you think?"

Mrs. Hungerford checked the menu.

Huitres Natives

Tortue Claire
Bisque d'Ecrevisses à la Mantua

Filets de Truite à la Vénitienne
Blanchaille

Mignons de Venaison à la Cumberland
Oeufs de Pluvier en Bellevue

Selle d'Agneau Printaniere

Sorbet au Kirsch

Cailles roties à la Pompadour
Salade de céleri

Asperges d'Argenteuil, Sauce Mousseuse

Truffes au champagne

Macedoine de Fraises Bordelaise
Bombe à la Esterhazy

Petits Diablotins

Mrs. Hungerford smiled. "I see your chef means to outdo himself. And your guest list? Has it met with royal approval?"

"I had it back from Marlborough House this morning with neither additions nor subtractions."

Mrs. Hungerford scanned the list. "I hope poor old Sam Langton may be looking down on us. Earl and Countess of Lathom, Earl and Countess of Romney, Earl and Countess De La Warr. Names like those were in his books, and pictures of their castles, I expect. Lady Edeline Sackville, Countess of Kilmorey, Viscountess Curzon, Lord Richard Nevill . . ."

Mrs. Hungerford silently finished reading the list and said, "I see you haven't included the Bonynges."

"What on earth made you think of them after all this time?"

"I've thought of them, or at least of him, often in the past year. And Mrs. Phelps spoke to me before she and the minister returned to the States. She thought you would be well advised to include Mr. and Mrs. Bonynge in some of your entertainments."

"She has certainly been persistent on their behalf, but then they say Mr. Bonynge has been helping the Phelps boy in business."

"Mrs. Phelps must be grateful for that, but I think she spoke out of regard for you, Louise. She emphasized the wisdom of not making an enemy of one who should be an old acquaintance. She didn't say much, but I thought her manner oddly emphatic."

"You mean that Mr. Bonynge may be responsible for the little digs that have been appearing in the press from time to time? The anonymous reminiscences of the old days, all aimed at making it quite clear that Mrs. Bonanza Mackay wasn't always so grand as she is now. The world knows that. Still, there have been more unfriendly references to my early years in the last fifteen months or so."

Louise frowned and picked up a red scrapbook in which she kept a collection of newspaper cuttings. She turned to page thirty-four.

"This one from the Virginia *Evening Chronicle* of last March was particularly unkind, though the *Chronicle* reprinted the story only in carrying the staunch denial of Judge Bob Taylor and the rest."

"The denials are not believed, Louise. If one could stop the stories . . ."

"Do you remember this particular one, Mémé?" Louise's voice was harsh as she read aloud:

"'Editor *Evening Chronicle*. Dear Sir: The following basely false narrative of incidents in the early life of Mrs. John W. Mackay . . . has been widely copied by the American and European press:

"'"This is indeed a peculiar world," said a mining expert at the Planters' House yesterday. "Here I pick up the paper and read of Mrs. Mackay's doings in Paris—how she receives the scions of royalty, how she entertains, how she appears at the opera, how she dresses and how she does a thousand other things; and then I can scarcely conceive that eighteen years ago she kept a boarding house in Virginia City. . . ."'"

Louise paused. "Pity it wasn't true twenty-five years ago. It would have made me a better living than sewing and those wretched piano lessons. And the people I know now would, I suppose, think one as ungenteel as the other."

"Perhaps I'm wrong to be anxious about those mean little stories. After all, no nice person reads the papers that print scandal."

"Oh, Mémé," Louise laughed. "You know they do. I do myself. And picturing me as a boardinghouse keeper isn't scandalous but it's meant to tear down my dignity, so I don't like it. But that's not what angered me and angered Judge Taylor and the others who signed the letter. Listen to how the article goes on, in case you've forgotten:

"'"She was a young widow then with an interesting child who has since matured into a young lady and was recently married to an Italian prince of some kind. That little girl has often sat on my knees

Louise in court dress at 6 Carlton House Terrace in 1902.

Bianca

John's first grandchild,
K. Mackay.

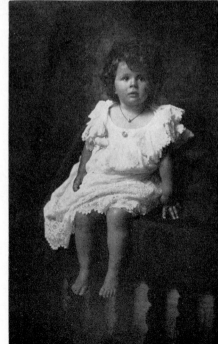

To my darling "Mémé"
Andréa

Andrea.

Marco.

Statue of John W. Mackay by Gutzon Borglum.

Louise in 1928.

Ellin in Paris, 1909.

Harbor Hill from the west terrace.

Louise, Clarie, and Clarie's son Willie, in the Gothic room at Harbor Hill. Painted by Sir John Lavery in 1926 or 1927.

with a little tin can in her hand which contained the contributions of her admirers."'

"That's the part, Mémé, that's the part for which I could kill the anonymous writer. To make a whining beggar child of Eva—— Listen:

"'"She would climb on the boarders' knees, and shaking her little bank, would say: 'Is you lucky today?' This query had the desired effect, and the bank receipts were increased."'

"I don't know why I kept the hateful thing except that it touched me to have Judge Taylor and Senator Stewart and the rest come to my defense. 'The foregoing,' they say, 'is a base misrepresentation from beginning to end.' And they put in about Father in the Mexican and Civil wars. And they say that I was educated at Benicia. It was such a little while. It was good of them to remember." She laughed. "Not that I ever let anyone forget that I went to St. Catherine's. Benicia and Farleigh Castle kept me going when I had nothing else." She looked down again at the cutting and her eyes were dark with anger. "Whoever got it reprinted—I could kill him."

"For Eva's sake there's a milder and more effective way to act. The way that Mrs. Phelps had in mind."

"You really think Bonynge is responsible for these stories? It could be so. But why?"

"You are the most successful and the most talked-of American hostess in London. Others may be envious."

"I know envy breeds a little hate, a little malice. But I don't believe you can buy malice off with an invitation."

"Isn't it worth trying for Eva's sake?"

"I would if I thought it would work. But John told me long ago that paying blackmail never works. Not with people, not with the press, not with anyone."

"Let me put the book away. I can see you are distressing yourself."

"The book? Oh, my cuttings." Louise gave her mother the book and picked up the guest list. "I'm not distressed, just preoccupied with the party. I must do my seating plan. Everything else is arranged."

"I'll leave you to do it in peace."

Louise smiled at her mother. As the door closed, she stopped smiling and stared, unseeing, at the guest list. She had not told Mémé that, for Eva's sake, she had already paid blackmail.

After Eva's second son, Marco, was born at the Rue de Tilsitt in January, Ferdinand had come to his mother-in-law on an evening when she was alone in her boudoir.

"I have not," he had said, "wished to worry Eva at this time but I am, madame, in grave difficulties. I have met with reverses at the tables."

"Eva told me that you had taken up gambling again, but surely with Eva's income . . ."

"In previous and smaller losses Eva has been helpful. She even allowed me to pawn some of her jewels. I know you would wish me to redeem them."

"Her pearls?"

"Yes, madame. And the diamond tiara and the turquoise and diamond parure and some smaller items, but I have had excellent copies made. And in Rome, alas, many of the best jewels are paste."

"For Eva's sake I will redeem the jewels."

"There also is the matter of my more recent losses."

"Can't your uncle help you?"

"Even if he were willing, it would be beyond his means. It's a question of a little over eighty thousand."

"Lire? Francs?"

"Alas, dollars."

Louise was silent. If she paid, he would gamble again. If she did not pay, he would make Eva ask. Eva's pride would suffer more and in the end the result would be the same: Louise would pay.

"I am at your mercy, madame."

And Eva is at yours, Louise had thought and she had shivered, though no draft had disturbed the air of the heavily curtained room.

"If I pay your debts, Ferdinand, you must behave. I think you understand me."

"I promise, madame, that——"

"Your promises are worthless to me."

"I cannot permit even my mother-in-law to speak thus to a Colonna."

"Don't be an idiot. I am your mother-in-law. Remember that fact and be grateful for it. For Eva's sake, whether I like it or not I must help you."

"I'll not ask again."

"You will but don't let your demands be so outrageous, or even for Eva's sake I may grow tired of going to your rescue."

"I thank you, though I know your generosity is on Eva's account. You do this because of her love for me. She does love me, madame." He had been silent for a moment before continuing in an even tone. "She loves me very dearly. You must remember that."

"I do. And just as long as she is happy in her love, I will be your friend. Now give me the pawn tickets. I'll redeem her jewels and then you may return them to her. She'll like it better that way."

"How very thoughtful you are, madame. I believe there is no kindness of which you would not be capable on Eva's behalf."

"And no cruelty either. Remember that and be good to her."

Louise sighed and looked at her guest list. She tried to shut out the recollection of Ferdinand's handsome smiling face. His new fashionably trimmed mustache and small beard made him look no older. After five years he still had the unlined brow of a boy. His voice had been smooth when he spoke of Eva's love for him. There had been no sound of a threat, but the threat had been there. Louise had kept her voice steady. She had answered firmly. But she had paid his blackmail and she knew as well as he that she would pay again. John would be angry when she told him but he would be helpless. Eva's love for him was Ferdinand's weapon. John and Louise, like their daughter, were at his mercy.

On the sixth of April there appeared in the Manchester *Examiner-Times* the following article:

"It is not generally known that Mrs. Mackay who entertained the Prince of Wales on Wednesday night and whose parties will be conspicuous features of this season was once what Americans call a washwoman—what we call a washerwoman. She was a poor widow with two children to support and washed clothes for some of Mr. Mackay's miners out in Nevada. One of the men said to Mr. Mackay one day, knowing that he had a good heart, 'Won't you go in and see poor ——'s widow? She's in great trouble—very poor.' Mr. Mackay went to the cottage, saw the widow, fell in love with her and married her."

The article was reprinted on the same day, in part, in a London paper, the *Echo*.

It was Consuelo Mandeville who told Louise that cuttings from both papers had been sent anonymously to everyone who had been present at the dinner on the third.

Louise, with a steady hand, poured tea for her guest. "They were sent to me too," she said.

"And—and in a separate envelope, but by the same post, there was a horrid little pamphlet telling a slightly different story."

"Every version of a lie is bound to be different, Consuelo. It's hard enough to tell the truth the same way twice."

"I don't like to show you the pamphlet but I think I ought." Consuelo's hand shook as she took from her purse an envelope.

Louise looked at the misspelled, awkwardly written address.

"It's odd," she said, "that this apparent illiterate should have knowledge of my guest list even before it appeared in the *Court Circular*. And to know the addresses too. Very odd."

She took from the envelope and read the cheaply printed pamphlet:

"'Some years ago I met a gentleman, a railroad man who knew the Mackays and boarded a while with them in the mining camp. Mrs. Mackay run the house and washed the miners' shirts, his own with the rest. Her daughter or sister (immaterial which) now Princess Colonna waited upon the table, and Mrs. M., said princess, with all those other seekers after bonanzas sought relief in the "sage bushes" instead of a jasper or allabaster lined, and rose of ottar scented closet.'"

Louise replaced the pamphlet in the envelope.

"I shall keep this if I may. It's possible that its origin can be traced. I regret that you were forced to read such vulgarity, the work of someone not quite right in his mind perhaps."

"Yes, but it's still odd, as you pointed out, that an illiterate or lunatic or whatever he is should have our addresses."

"And strange that this communication should have arrived by the same mail as the newspaper cuttings."

"Louise, you should do something."

"I intend to. I doubt I can do anything about the anonymous pamphleteer. But the Manchester *Examiner-Times* is another matter. There have been disagreeable stories printed before, but they've been in obscure little papers not worth noticing. The Manchester Press is different. It thinks itself respectable. It should be taught a lesson."

"It's not a scandalous article, Louise. I've seen far worse about all sort of well-known people in *Truth* and in your own *Argonaut*."

"It's not scandalous but it's not true. And it's intended to make me a figure of ill-natured fun. It's perfectly respectable to sell fish, but one doesn't care to be called a fishwife. And though there's nothing reprehensible in washing clothes, 'washerwoman' is used as a derogatory term. 'She looks like a washerwoman' was never said as a compliment. Well, since I never was a washerwoman, I think I'll make the great Manchester Press pay for calling me one."

"Louise, you'll never sue."

"I certainly will as soon as I get John's approval. I'll give the money to charity, of course, but I'll have the satisfaction of seeing the publisher of that mealymouthed provincial sheet out of pocket."

"You're angry."

"Wouldn't you be? Suppose they printed some malicious fabrication about the Yznagas in their Cuban days."

"You're right. Someone should stop them."

"I don't suppose I'll stop them but at least I'll give them pause. And more important, I may frighten the gentry who send the scurrilous little stories to the press."

"Why should anyone do such a despicable thing?"

"For money usually. But sometimes it must be from personal spite and sometimes I think it's for the enjoyment of a secret sense of power. 'I got that printed,' the informant says to himself. 'You think yourself so much more important than I, but I got that printed, my fine gentleman, my fine lady.'"

"It's hard to believe you have enemies, Louise. You have done so many kindnesses."

"Only where they were owed."

"Or where it was your pleasure. You never owed me a kindness and yet you've shown me many, so very many."

"You did me a kindness once when you were young and impulsive. It was long before you arranged my presentation at court. It was in New York."

"We scarcely met in New York. I had no chance to be kind but I liked you and I admired you. You may have forgotten this, but we were at a party at Mrs. Paran Stevens' on a Sunday evening and a horrible old gorgon of a neighbor of my family's was there. She always terrified me. 'So distinguished looking,' Mamma used to say, 'and so refreshingly outspoken.' Ugly and rude I always thought her. You stood up to her that night and I admired you so and I wondered if I'd dare to be so brave now that I was the Viscountess Mandeville instead of little Consuelo Yznaga."

"Dear little Consuelo." Louise touched her guest's hand. "You were very brave that evening, offering me your friendship under the angry eyes of your mamma's acquaintance. I hadn't many friends among the elite then."

"You have now."

"And it seems I also have an enemy. But he's secretive and therefore not very courageous, so it shouldn't take much to frighten him, whoever he may be. The suit against the Manchester Press may turn the trick."

John approved of Louise's plan to bring suit against the Manchester Press and on his advice she placed the matter in the hands of her lawyers.

On the twenty-first of June the London edition of Mr. Bennett's *Herald* officially announced that Mr. and Mrs. Mackay had begun legal proceedings against two well-known papers for libel with a view to putting a stop to the periodical attacks of their enemies.

Mr. George Lewis, Louise's solicitor, explained to her that a writ would be served on the London *Echo* as well as on the Manchester Press Company. The suit against the Manchester Press would be the important one and, once it was won, an apology and retraction from the less important *Echo* would suffice.

John had not been able to come this spring to London. The Commercial Cable Company and the Postal Telegraph were doing well. The cable company was showing a handsome profit for the Mackay-Bennett system. But the affairs of the companies, particularly of the rapidly expanding little Postal Telegraph, kept John almost constantly in New York. And when he could leave, his presence was required in San Francisco where Jim Flood's long illness and death had added to his California responsibilities.

Jim Flood had been gravely ill at Heidelberg for months before his death on the twenty-first of February. But its expectedness had not lessened John's grief at the loss of his friend.

Louise decided to go to America during the summer. It was a surprisingly difficult decision to reach. She was astonished that it should be so hard to force herself to return. She had always meant someday to visit New York again. She had not realized until now the strength of the hidden will that had made her postpone her voyage.

She wrote John that she would bring Willie. It would be good for the boy, she pointed out, to meet his father's American associates and employees. It was time for him to become acquainted with New York.

New York in summer, Louise told herself, would not be bad. It would be hot but it would be empty of the elite. It was absurd to think like this, those of New York's elite whom she invited to her London house were delighted to accept. There was nothing to fear. Nor did she feel fear. She felt a different emotion which she tried to analyze. It was a kind of homesickness turned inside out. For more than twenty years of her life she had looked back on New York with nostalgia for the birthplace to which she dreamed of returning. To her young heart New York had been the promised end of all the roads. It had been home. Like all young hearts, her own had been foolish. Now she was middle-aged and sensible. She shouldn't be reluctant to return to the almost forgotten city. She shouldn't be so silly, she told herself angrily, and she instructed her secretary to book passage on the *City of Paris* on the twenty-third of July, the day after her dinner in honor of the new American minister and Mrs. Lincoln.

The party for Princess Louise and the Marquis of Lorne was as successful as Louise had hoped. None of the invited guests had been frightened away by the newspaper articles or the anonymous pamphleteers.

It pleased Louise that on this grand occasion there should be present old acquaintances from the West. Mrs. George Hearst was there and Mr. and Mrs. Michael de Young.

The bonanza firm had in the past been bitterly criticized by the San Francisco *Chronicle* and Louise supposed that De Young would again attack Fair or Mackay if it suited his paper's purpose.

"It's all in the line of business with newspaper fellows like that," John had said to her. "And it never really hurt us."

"You say that now, but you used to be angry enough at De Young."

"Sure. Sure and I could be again. Still, I kind of like Mike and I enjoy talking with him about old times on Comstock. There's not so many of us left who remember."

Louise felt less forgiving toward Mr. De Young. Still, it could do no harm to have him see one of her famous parties. And she liked

Mrs. De Young. She was proud to have Princess Louise and the Duchess of Newcastle and the rest of her distinguished English guests see American women like Mrs. De Young and Mrs. Hearst. They were not brilliantly fashionable like Mrs. Ronalds or Mrs. Potter. In the eyes of Lady Randolph and her mother, Mrs. Jerome, the western ladies were representative of a raw and uncivilized part of the States. But Louise thought that the princess and the duchess and many others would recognize and admire an old-fashioned gentility that in the new world, as in the old, was deeper rooted and more enduring than the ever-changing, restless elite that surrounded Mrs. Astor or the Prince of Wales.

As the *City of Paris* steamed toward the New York harbor, Louise told herself that she had been silly and childish to be unwilling to return.

Willie banged on her cabin door. "Hurry, Mammy," he shouted. "I'm going on deck. I don't want to miss the first sight of the harbor."

Louise smiled at the eagerness in the boy's voice. She had accomplished for her son what she had intended. He was happy and excited at the prospect of seeing at last the country and the city that he thought of as his own. He would not be disappointed. Willie now, and his brother later, could feel sure of a welcome anywhere in their native land.

Louise smiled contentedly and unhurriedly continued to eat her breakfast. As the hour of landing drew near, she began to understand more clearly her reluctance to return. She had been reluctant to make a journey in time as well as in space. She had not wanted to acknowledge that her childhood dream was gone entirely. She had invented a paradise and called it home. It was foolish to miss it but it was impossible to replace it. Neither London nor Paris was home. Perhaps someday she and John would find a place to make their own, but it would be a holiday place. Home for him had been the green fields of Ireland and for her, 9 Grand Street and the glimpses of St. John's Park and Washington Square. Home had been a dream for both of them, invented in poverty and in the exile of the early western years.

She sighed. Not for anything would she be young and vulnerable again.

Willie was back outside the cabin door. "Hurry, Mammy, we're just coming into the harbor. It's the finest thing. As Father says, there's nothing in Europe to beat America."

"Go up on deck. I'll join you in a few minutes."

To watch and to listen to Willie was pure joy, Louise thought. He hadn't a care. The world was his. And Clarie's too, though at present Clarie was going through a solemn stage. He was very serious about his school activities. He had overdrawn his pocket money to buy a new curtain for the theater. He studied, she thought, no more than necessary, counting on his French to raise his average and win him a prize to please his parents. He worked hardest on the cricket field. His highest ambition was to play for Beaumont.

Clarie had been disappointed not to come to the States, until his mother had offered instead to send him to visit his beloved grandparents. A cricket-playing Oxford graduate had accompanied the boy to Italy. Louise had stressed the tutor's skill in cricket rather than in mathematics, though she hoped the young Englishman would manage to find time for both.

This American trip, she had explained, was Willie's. He was, after all, nearly nineteen. But it was not for Willie's sake that she had brought him alone, it was for John's. Without his younger brother, Willie would seem older. If John were minding, as deeply as she feared, the death of his old partner, the presence of a grown son should be a comfort to him and a strength.

John met them at the pier and drove them to the Windsor Hotel.

Willie glanced impatiently around the handsome parlor of the suite. "Can't Mme. Demoutier unpack without you?" he asked. "We don't want to stay cooped up in this hotel all afternoon."

"There's a young fellow from my office waiting downstairs for you," John said. "Henry Rosener offered to show you around, but for a sight-seeing trip I figured you'd have a better time with a fellow your own age."

When they were alone John put his arm around Louise and held her shoulder in a tight grasp. "It's good to have you here, old lady. Glad to be home?"

"Home? Where you are is home, John. *Wo Du bist, bin ich zu Hause.* I don't like Germans or their poetry, but that always stuck in my head. Being a wanderer, I guess it suited me."

"It feels pretty good to have you quoting poetry, even foreign poetry, to me after twenty-two years." He kissed her and drew her to a window and studied her face in the bright light. "How do you do it, Louise? You look like a girl."

"Only in your eyes. Your loving eyes that have always flattered me. And in mine you're still the fair-haired young Irishman who was bound and determined he'd be master of the Comstock."

"Not alone. I couldn't have done it alone. It took Fair and Flood." He sighed. "It's selfish of me to be mourning Jim Flood's death. Sure it was a mercy he was taken and his suffering put an end to." He was silent for a moment. "Two of the Irishmen gone. And Sharon too. Funny, how one forgets hard feeling and only remembers old times."

"Even in the old times, even when you were battling him, you always had a sneaking respect for Sharon."

"Nothing sneaking about it. Both Jim Fair and I had to respect the man even when we were fighting him. Poor Jim, he was looking old the last time I was in San Francisco. Well, we're none of us growing any younger. Your fair-haired Irishman is getting pretty gray."

"Gray hair is distinguished. You're not old, just sad over Jim Flood and tired from too much work. What you need is a vacation."

"And I mean to give the pair of us a bang-up one."

He told her his plans: Willie would remain for the most part in New York in Henry Rosener's charge. He would learn something of the New York end of the cable business and become acquainted with the workings of the Postal Telegraph.

"On his next trip I'll send him West. We're planning to run lines along the Atchison, Topeka and Santa Fe to California and we're building lines through Oregon and Washington territory and connecting interior points with all the large cities on the Pacific coast. Mind you, I mean for the lad to have his fun too. After all, this is his vacation. Henry and other friends will invite him out of town for weekends. Staten Island, Lakewood, Asbury Park. Lot of nice places for him to go. And for us I've chartered a yacht. We're going to cruise, just the two of us, up the east coast. A real holiday."

"Like the time we went to Norway. I'll like that."

"I've planned a little gaiety for you too. We're stopping off at Bar Harbor. We'll stay at the Louisburg Hotel, be a change from the boat. We're invited to meet President Harrison. On the way home we'll put into Newport for a weekend."

"Oh, John. Bar Harbor and Newport don't seem like your idea of a holiday."

"Ordinarily they wouldn't be. But just for once I'd like to show my girl off at our American resorts."

"I didn't expect——"

"Sure you did. Look at the pile of trunks you brought. You enjoy society, Louise, and you might as well see what it's like on this side of the water. I figure we'll make Bar Harbor in time for the Floral Parade. They say it's quite a sight. We won't get back to New York until just before the September sailing that'll get Willie to Oxford in time."

"It's a short holiday."

"Only kind I ever get. But I'll be in England in November and I expect to stay over for two or three months."

"That won't be a vacation. In London you'll be in the City till all hours and you'll be going back and forth to Paris and to the Irish cable station and to Bristol."

"Someday I'll let Willie take over. Meanwhile let's make the most of this short holiday. As Mrs. Mock used to say, enjoy, Louise, enjoy."

The visits to Bar Harbor and Newport were a success. Louise was pleased for John's sake. His pride in her was gratified by the cordial welcome they received. But after Paris and London, after Aix-les-Bains and Homburg, the American resorts seemed to her provincial. She used in calm appraisal the adjective which once in anger she had flung at New York.

At Bar Harbor, John and Louise attended the Floral Parade in the company of President Harrison.

The carriages and carts were decorated with flowers. It was not so handsome a floral display as Louise had seen at Nice, and the American ladies were not so elegantly attired as the French beauties of the *monde* and the *demimonde*. But the simplicity, even the provincialism, of the scene added to its charm. If a country fair in a little village could be fashionable, Louise thought, it would be like this.

Louise wore a gown of lavender silk with an overdress of silk muslin.

Mrs. Blaine complimented her on her costume. "It looks as though you had chosen it with just this occasion in mind."

"I've worn it only once before, at Marlborough House at a garden party the Prince of Wales gave for the Shah of Persia. I thought I would put it on for the next time for my first meeting with my own ruler."

"Oh yes, Mrs. Mackay, we heard about that garden party!" young Miss Blaine exclaimed. "We heard that the Shah wanted to buy you, that he even sent some awful little man to tell you so."

"Yes, my dear, he did. But it wasn't an awful little man who acted as interpreter, it was the Persian minister, whom I know and who is charming. But under the royal eye he had to carry out his peculiar commission. I told him to tell his master that the lady was not for sale. Poor man, he was very embarrassed to be sent back to ask me why I wasn't for sale."

"I'm sure," Mrs. Blaine said, "that you put him in his place and made it quite clear that American womanhood is not bought and sold."

"No, I just said to the minister, 'Tell him the lady is too rich.' That put an end to the negotiations."

"Oh my!" Miss Blaine said. "Nothing like that ever happens in Bar Harbor."

John and Louise attended several entertainments in honor of the President: a small luncheon given by Mr. and Mrs. Howard, a dinner by Mr. and Mrs. Gurnee, and a large and brilliant reception at the Valley Club.

"Have you enjoyed?" John asked as they drove home from the reception to the Louisburg Hotel.

"I've loved it. And you know why? Of course, it's an honor to meet the President of the United States so intimately and informally. But one doesn't always enjoy an honor. I think the fun has been that those entertainments have reminded me of the first grand party we ever went to together, the one Mr. Sharon gave for Vice-President and Mrs. Colfax. Here we are back with the political elite: President Harrison, the Secretary of State and Mrs. Blaine, Secretary Tracy, Senator and Mrs. Hale, and Congressman Henry Cabot Lodge."

"You'll meet a different kind of elite at Newport."

"They do keep their elites in a lot of different compartments over here, don't they? There's no one top group made up of all the worlds: politics, the arts, finance, the aristocracy, such as exists in England. There's not even one all-important place like London."

"Not New York?" John asked gently.

"Apparently not, except in its own estimation. Mr. Lodge was explaining to me about Boston. And there was a Mrs. Somebody, I can't think of her name. She was born in Richmond, she said, and obviously felt that that statement needed no adornment. She listened to Mr. Lodge with courteous attention, but I'm sure she wondered why anyone should bother to distinguish between northern cities."

"Oh, those elites." John laughed. "All alike the world over and all thinking themselves so different."

"Still, they're not so entirely alike but that I'm curious to see Newport. The Bar Harbor ladies have hinted that I shall dislike it. Such ostentation, they say. Why leave New York at all, they ask, only to reproduce it in every detail from white-wigged footmen in knee breeches, to gold plates, to ballrooms banked with orchids."

"I think they're right at that. It hardly seems the place for a country holiday."

"It doesn't mean to be. And I shall enjoy seeing it, gold plate and overdecorated ballrooms and all."

Newport was what Louise had been led to expect: an elaborate little city, beautifully placed on the edge of the sea. The setting had none of the mountainous grandeur of the Maine coast, but the cottages made up for the simplicity of the landscape. They were palatial and the entertainments offered within their walls were as ostentatious as the Bar Harbor ladies had prophesied.

The most elaborate soiree that John and Louise attended was given by Mr. James Van Alen at his Elizabethan villa. Among the two hundred guests Louise found acquaintances from London: Sir Julian and Lady Goldsmid, Lady Selkirk, the Countess of Shrewsbury. The distinguished Americans who were present included more new names than old: Mr. and Mrs. Cornelius Vanderbilt, Mrs. William Waldorf Astor, Mr. and Mrs. Henry Clews, Mrs. Leiter. John had been right when he had prophesied that the brilliant new wealth would dim the century-old light of the long-secure, smug little elite.

In September the vacation ended where it had begun, at the Windsor Hotel. John and Louise spent the last evening alone together. Willie had gone out with some of his new acquaintances.

John showed Louise an album he had received from the staff and employees of the Commercial Cable Company.

"It belongs with the silver globe of the world they gave me last

Christmas. But the boys only presented me with this just before you arrived in New York."

"I cut the picture of the silver piece from the *Electric Age* last January and pasted it in my scrapbook. And here's a fine account of your receiving the album." Louise picked up the *Electrical Review*. "I'll put this with my other cuttings."

She cut out the article. "I keep lots of cuttings, some kind, some unkind, some true, some false."

"I bet you even have that damn Manchester *Times* article in your scrapbook."

"I have. The children may be interested to read those things someday. They'll easily discern which are true and which are false. The accent of truth is unmistakable."

"It's rare enough. But, after all, the press boys have to live. And unadulterated truth makes dull reading and sells few papers."

"Not always. You don't sound dull in this article, you sound like yourself: 'Mr. Mackay replied: Boys, I am very much pleased to meet you all, and I can only say that I deeply appreciate this unexpected present. I am afraid you have spent too much money on it, though. It is a beautiful album and I thank you very much. I received the silver piece at San Francisco and have it placed in my rooms there. I shall always treasure it very highly, and hand it down as long as my family lasts as a precious heirloom. You must convey to all the boys who were not able to be present here tonight, especially those at distant stations, my warmest thanks.

"'In your address you mentioned the cables. We have had war, but after war comes peace. We have peace now, and I hope it will continue for a long time. I think the success of the company has been due to the efforts and good work done by you and your colleagues on the other side of the Atlantic, to whom you must convey my earnest appreciation. I think the cables can be safely left to Mr. Ward and the staff.'

"They must have been pleased, John—the staff, I mean—by what you said."

"It was the simple truth. They're fine boys, all, from General Manager Ward to cableman Poole Davis of Bristol. Damn fine boys, every last one of them."

"And they say the same of you, only more elegantly and mostly in verse. I like best the poem written by cableman John Morrison of Canso, Nova Scotia:

"Tried chieftain, generous master, friend,
Whose words are deeds, whose thoughts are actions true . . .

"He's trying to say what all have felt who ever knew you."

"Why, Louise, you're not often one for blarney."

"It's not blarney. It wasn't blarney when Mary tried to say it the night the robbers broke in in Virginia. It's what Mémé and I and even the little girls felt on the night of the bad earthquake. I wish I did have the gifted tongue of the Irish to tell you what all feel or at least to tell you what I feel."

"You don't need to tell me about yourself or your feelings, my darling, I know."

John arrived in London in time to witness Louise's victory over the Manchester Press.

The action was brought before Baron Huddleston and Mr. Justice Stephen. Mr. Arbuthnot and Mr. Finlay appeared for the plaintiff and Mr. Marshall and Mr. Bosanquet for the defendants.

Louise's case was strong. Mr. Finlay, usually restrained in manner, permitted himself an air of triumph when he called on her after leaving court.

"They're beaten and they know it," he said. "Bosanquet will make them offer a generous settlement. And I think you should accept. You do not wish to appear vindictive."

On the fifth of December, Baron Huddleston in the High Court of Justice, Queen's Bench Division, approved the settlement. The defendants agreed to make a full apology, to pay costs as between solicitor and client, and to pay a substantial sum to a charity to be named by the plaintiff.

Sweetest of all to Louise were Baron Huddleston's remarks which were on record in the Royal Court of Justice.

"Yes. It is quite right if possible to put a stop to what Mr. Bosanquet has very properly styled 'gossiping scandal' of persons who are in a position to be and are libelled daily, and who feel it consistent with their dignity and public position to treat it with contempt; but when scandal attacks private individuals, the only way they can vindicate themselves is by coming into a Court of Justice. The paper has admitted they are in the wrong and apologized, and I think I may say that they are singularly lucky in finding a person like Mrs. Mackay, who is able to treat them so leniently. I therefore make an order embodying the terms agreed on."

John read the copy of the decision which Mr. Finlay sent to Louise.

"The judge is right, Louise, they got off easy at that."

"Not so easy but that other reputable papers will hesitate to publish the next malicious story."

"But only the reputable papers. There are still the fly-by-night sheets. There are still the little printers willing to turn out a scurrilous pamphlet on order. There's still the f-f-fellow who's responsible. D-d-damn him. If I could lay my hands on him either here or on one of his v-v-visits to the Bay . . ."

"John, you don't know for sure who he is. You can only guess."

"I can make a damn good guess."

"Still, you're not sure."

"No, but if the day ever comes that I am, the fellow better stay out of my way or I'll break his neck."

The suit proved to have been worth while. The English papers and the London correspondents of American papers printed no further disagreeable articles. The editors and writers had no wish to arouse the anger of a lady who was willing to bring them into court to face the strict English law on libel.

Occasionally a malicious story appeared in an obscure American paper or in an anonymous London pamphlet. Louise learned to be indifferent to those attacks, since her acquaintances were not affected by them.

John engaged detectives to identify the author of the anonymous stories. At the end of six months he had no evidence that would stand up in a court of law. But he himself was convinced that Bonynge was the man who was responsible.

In the summer John's solicitors inserted the following advertisement in the *Morning Post* and other London papers.

Caution £200. Reward. All kinds of slanderous reports are being maliciously invented and circulated in London society concerning Mrs. Mackay and family; the latest offense being the circulation of an extract from a scurrilous American paper, the editor and publisher of which are being at once prosecuted in America. We are authorized by Mr. John W. Mackay to offer a reward of two hundred pounds to any person or persons who shall, within one calendar month from the date hereof, supply sufficient evidence to lead to the conviction in England of the persons circulating here the false statements referred to—Dated July 8, 1890.

Johnson, Budd, and Johnson, 24, Austin Friars, London, E. C., Solicitors.

Sufficient evidence for a law court was not forthcoming. Several of her acquaintances told Louise that they thought her husband was correct in blaming Mr. Bonynge.

"Not, of course, that I know it of my own knowledge, but friends have told me that Mr. Bonynge has stated that he doesn't consider the stories libelous and he has hinted of further disclosures which he could, if he liked, make public."

"Would your friends testify?" Louise asked. "Would you?"

Oh dear no, the ladies said, they were not so brave as that.

Consuelo, who, since her father-in-law's recent death, was the Duchess of Manchester, offered to go into court if Louise needed her testimony.

"All I've heard is at second hand and I suppose that's no use."

"No use at all. And that's the only kind of evidence John has found, except for one printer, a wretched, scared little man who, the lawyers say, would not make a convincing witness in court even though they believe him. Practically everything John has discovered is what the lawyers call circumstantial evidence, and that alone they say is unsatisfactory. One thing is certain, all the attacks come from the same source. Some are so vile that John won't let me see them."

"I know," Consuelo said gently. "I've heard."

"But I believe they all tie together. For instance that first unpleasant little pamphlet, the one you showed me more than a year ago, has reappeared as a letter to the editor in a blackmailing Washington sheet called *The Working Woman*. That's one of the papers from which articles have been privately reprinted and circulated here."

"It started and continues in London, so it must be someone who resides here but someone with American connections, since extracts from American papers are circulated. And it must be someone who knows the West. The Nevada and California background in the stories always sounds authentic to me."

"It is. The turn of speech attributed to the anonymous old-timers couldn't be set down so exactly except by someone who has known the western country."

"It all fits Mr. Bonynge. What a pity you didn't invite them when Mrs. Phelps first suggested it five years ago. You had no reason at that time to dislike him, had you?"

"I had no reason to like him. I certainly had no reason to invite a C Street broker to my house."

"Why, Louise, that's the first snobbish thing I've ever heard you say."

"You never saw those curb-side brokers with their poor sick victims. If you had you'd not think me snobbish to want nothing to do with them. Perhaps it was a mistake not to make an exception of Mr. Bonynge, but I can't say, even now, that I regret it."

"I'm glad you're my friend, not my enemy. You quite frighten me when your voice gets hard like that."

"I grew up in a harder school than little Consuelo Yznaga. That's all. It needn't frighten you."

"If I were Mr. Bonynge, I should be frightened."

"Of me? He's been clever and cautious enough. I can't take him into court. But I think he would be wise to be frightened of John. John doesn't easily forgive an injury done to me."

It was not until the next year, on January 27, 1891, that John met Bonynge. The meeting occurred in the office of Mr. I. W. Hellman, the new president of the Nevada Bank. Bonynge, a stranger to Hellman, was consulting the bank president about investments in southern California. John entered and saw the man whom he held responsible for the attacks on Louise.

What happened next was inevitable. Louise knew this as she read the dispatches in the London press.

Millionaires at Fisticuffs. Mackay on His Muscle. Thus the papers headlined the description of the fight in which John had knocked Bonynge to the floor of Mr. Hellman's office. Some of the newspaper writers were amused that an elderly businessman would engage in a fist fight on his wife's behalf. Louise was not amused. Her eyes were wet when she finished reading John's statement in the London edition of the *Herald*:

"You may send this account of the trouble I had yesterday. It happened this way: Long ago I suspected that Bonynge was the instigator of the vile attacks on Mrs. Mackay, which appeared in certain papers in New York and London. Having had proof that this was true I determined to punish him the first time I met him. Yesterday, when entering the President's room in the Nevada Bank by the back door, of which I, as a director, have the key, I saw Bonynge sitting at the desk with Mr. Hellman. As I entered Bonynge turned and saw me. He had a malignant look, and made a threatening movement. I struck out with my right, and hit him in the left eye. Then I hit him again, and called upon him to put up his fists and fight like a man, but instead of fighting he fell and clasped me around the knees, like a coward.

"His blood poured all over my trousers and upon the floor. The clerks rushed in and removed him. The sound thrashing he received he well deserved for circulating those stories.

"I'm not so handy with my fists as I used to be twenty-five years ago, when upon Comstock; but I have a little fight left in me yet, and will allow no man to malign me or mine."

Long ago in Virginia the young Irishman had promised her that with his strength he would protect her. At the age of almost sixty he was still willing to protect her, even with violence if that was necessary.

In the months that followed the fight it became plain that violence had succeeded where detectives and solicitors and rewards had failed. From the day that John resorted to his fists, no more anonymous pamphlets were circulated, no more cuttings from obscure papers were sent to Louise's friends.

John had protected her as he had promised. Louise did not see the middle-aged, frock-coated capitalist whom the *City Argus'* cartoonist portrayed whipping a dog labeled "Bonynge." She saw the young, gray-shirted miner sitting beside little Mrs. Bryant in an open carriage and offering her the strength of his hands.

Chapter XXVIII

·····◆◎◆····

6 Carlton House Terrace

BEFORE HE LEFT London in December of 1890 John had arranged to buy for Louise a residence at 6 Carlton House Terrace. The mansion had been built by the third Duke of Leinster and had been purchased in the '80s by Mr. C. H. Sanford. The millionaire had poured money into the renovation of the house. The stairway alone had cost him twenty thousand pounds. He had given *carte blanche* to architects and decorators, and for two years the work had continued. Just as it was almost completed, Mr. Sanford had met with financial reverses. His house had been put up for sale.

"I'd like to buy it for you, Louise," John had said. "I know you've been wanting us to have a house of our own in London. I can close the deal in twenty-four hours if you like the place, and, at the price he's willing to take, it's a good investment."

Louise had been delighted with the house. Everything had pleased her: the majestic marble entrance hall and stairway, the dining room paneled in mahogany and satinwood; the drawing rooms, the fifty-foot ballroom opening on the broad terrace that overlooked St. James' Park.

"I suppose," she had said, "that if we buy this we should give up the Paris house. We're there so little."

"That's up to you, old lady. It's you that has the bother of managing two places."

"It's no bother; I enjoy it. Only, without the children the Rue de Tilsitt has seemed lonely. And it would be more sensible just to have a suite of apartments in Paris. But Eva loves the house. Her children were born there and—and I think it's a refuge for her."

"I know damn well it is. Poor little Eva. One's only got to look at her to see how things are going. I didn't need you to tell me of Ferdinand's gambling or Joe to tell me about his women."

"Ada tells me all Rome talks of his affairs. Only Eva has never said a word to anyone, not to Ada, not to Mémé, not to me."

"That's her pride. Be glad you gave it to her."

"I don't think it's pride alone. I wish it were. I'm afraid it's love."

"You mean to say she still loves that blackguard? My God, women and the men they choose to love! No man living can understand it."

"We don't choose, John. It happens."

"I know. I know. But why in hell did it have to happen to Eva? This miserable fellow with his gambling and his mistresses. Well, you stick close to her as much as you can. Get over to Paris when you know he's there with her."

"He has avoided us all fall. He never once came to Paris or London with Eva. He'll claim pressing business in Rome or Naples if he knows I'm coming."

"Go over unexpectedly. See what you think of things. You'll see more clearly than Joe or Ada or anyone."

"I have a perfect excuse. I'll get the alterations and decorations at Carlton House Terrace under way, then it'll be natural enough for me to run over to the Rue de Tilsitt to see what I want to take for the London house. Perhaps if I'd gone more often to stay with them in Italy . . ."

"It's better for young folks to be left to themselves."

"But I didn't stay away for their sake. I stayed away for mine. I couldn't abide being under Ferdinand's roof. I never could make myself like him and I detest all those relations of his except Amalia. I like her. But the rest of them fawning over Eva. The uncles make me sick. Like two old chattering monkeys dancing and bowing to an Italian organ-grinder's tune. Italians!"

"Come, Louise, there's good and bad in all nations. I learned that in the diggings. And you know it too. Joe's Italian, and your nephews and nieces and your grandchildren."

"They're different."

"The ones we like are always different."

"I love my grandchildren and the little Telfeners but I can't change my feelings about the rest of them."

"Don't change them but keep them under control. You must do that, old lady, for Eva's sake. And you must keep calm. You'll need all the calmness and strength you have to give her. Don't hurt her pride but let her know we're standing by ready to help."

It was late on a cold February night when Louise and Demoutier arrived in Paris. Eva had written her mother that she was in bed with an attack of grippe. This, Louise decided, gave her an excuse to appear unannounced. She would explain that she had not wished to burden Eva with preparations for her arrival.

The concierge greeted Louise's cab with cries of astonishment and regret. Madame should have ordered the carriage. Madame should have let them know.

The front door was opened by a footman. Ferdinand stood behind him.

Ferdinand kissed Louise's hand and expressed his pleasure and surprise at seeing her.

"Eva wrote me that she was not well, so I slipped over for a quiet visit."

"You will want to see her at once. I shall escort——"

The footman interrupted to explain that the princess had retired for the night; she had asked not to be disturbed.

"Don't be stupid," Ferdinand said impatiently. "When the princess gave her orders she did not know of Mrs. Mackay's visit. Naturally she will wish to see Madame, her mother."

"Not at all. I wouldn't think of disturbing her. Bring me a cup of hot tea. I'll have it in the Pompeian suite."

"Surely you are tired after your journey. You will prefer to go to your boudoir."

"Presently, Ferdinand. First Demoutier must have some refreshment. Then she will prepare my things. Meanwhile I will have my tea in the morning room."

"Since you insist." Ferdinand shrugged his shoulders.

Louise walked briskly to the closed door, opened it, and entered the softly lighted room. A girl was sitting on the sofa with her feet tucked under her.

Ferdinand spoke quietly. "This, my dear, is my mother-in-law, Mrs. Mackay, a delightful but unexpected visitor. And this, madame . . ."

"I believe we met in London," Louise said. This young American had had quite a little success in English society. Her red hair framed a small white face in which blazed the greenest pair of eyes that Louise had ever seen. As the girl rose, her slim, rounded body moved with the grace of a professional dancer. The satin and lace of her tea gown revealed every curve.

"I'm sure you did not realize the hour," Louise said. "Fortunately my maid is with me. Ferdinand, be good enough to ring for Demoutier. She can accompany this young person to her hotel."

"My dear madame, surely you can see from her costume that the young lady is not merely dining here. She is staying here."

"I see," Louise said. She saw that for Eva's sake it was best not to precipitate a scene. "I suggest that the girl retire now. In the morning I am sure she will prefer, in view of my daughter's illness and my own unexpected arrival, to move to a hotel."

The girl, who had not spoken, walked toward the door. Ferdinand followed her.

"Just a minute, Ferdinand. Let the young person find her own way. I wish to speak to you."

The girl left as a footman entered with a tray.

"Would you care for a cup, Ferdinand? Or would you prefer something stronger?"

"Nothing, thank you."

Louise dismissed the servant and motioned her son-in-law to a chair. "I think we had better talk. You cannot explain this young woman in any but the obvious way."

"I shouldn't dream of trying."

"I warned you when I paid your debts."

"I have not asked you since. I have let Eva pay. I imagine that quite soon she will be forced to approach you or her father for financial assistance."

"How dare you?"

"Eva's very fond of me. That's how I dare. And even if she weren't, there are the children. Drink your tea, madame, and be quiet and listen to me."

"How dare you in my house speak to me——"

"I regret that it is necessary. I am sorry you saw fit to arrive unannounced. But since you did, we may as well speak frankly. This cannot be such a great shock to you. You cannot really have imagined that I was ever in love with your daughter."

"I was never sure. But Eva accepted your word, the famous word of honor of a Colonna."

"Don't make me angry, madame, or that lame girl upstairs will suffer for it."

Louise held her hands tightly clasped. Be calm, hold yourself steady, John had told her. Father Manogue had told her.

"You are wise to curb your tongue, madame. Eva is unhappy, I grant you, but she could be more unhappy. And she will be if you make me angry. If you, madame, do not mind your own business, if you are rude to my friends as you were to my little American miss, Eva will pay. Listen to me. Eva minds my gambling, she minds my mistresses, but she cherishes her illusion that once we were in love, I as well as she. And furthermore she believes that though, shall we say, romance is over between us——"

"Ferdinand, you mustn't talk like this even to Eva's mother."

"Why not? Eva's mother of all people should be *au courant*. Romance, I use the word in deference to your curious American squeamishness about reality, romance is over. After all, now that I have two sons there is no further need for that sort of thing. But Eva believes that I am still fond of her. I think that without her illusions she would be more unhappy than she is now."

"She would be unhappy but she would survive. Eva is not made of soft stuff like you and your kind. She has known pain and hardship."

"Come, madame, that was a long time ago. For years you have surrounded her with your protection. In the world you made for her she has lived the life of a doll, and dolls break easily."

"You're wrong, Ferdinand. She's stronger than you think."

"And I, madame, am stronger than you seem to realize. Europeans are not sentimental fools about their women. We are less squeamish in many matters than Americans. If it becomes necessary, more than Eva's illusions can be shattered, more than her feelings can be hurt."

He rose and smiled and bowed. "Good night, my dear mother-in-law. I shall have a very good night indeed with my little miss. And I can assure you we shall leave in the morning. Eva does not know of my visitor. Your servants are too kindhearted, too devoted to her to tell her. I hope that, for Eva's sake, you will be equally kind, equally devoted, equally wise."

Louise sat for a long time staring at her clasped hands. She must keep quite calm, quite steady.

Presently she stood up. Her bones ached with fatigue. Every muscle was tense with strain. She must force her body to rest, so that in the morning she would wake refreshed, able to think clearly, to talk calmly as she sat beside her child's bed.

It was not a child who lay in the bed in Eva's girlhood room. It was not a girl. It was an ill, unhappy woman.

As her mother entered, Eva began to cry. "Forgive me, Mammy. I have been quite ill; the fever was high. Now I'm tired and I cry easily."

"It's all right. We needn't talk."

Eva wiped her eyes. She put her hand in her mother's. The confiding gesture was unchanged from the days when Louise had sat beside her daughter's bed at 10 North A Street. She must not be hurt again. Louise must protect her.

"Don't worry so, Mammy," Eva said. "There's no use worrying when there's nothing to be done."

"There's plenty to be done."

"You saw Ferdinand, didn't you? And the girl. Don't look surprised. No one told me. But I heard a girl laughing in the hall. Besides, it's not the first time."

"Don't think about it. They're gone."

"I know. Ferdinand left a message with my maid that he has been called to Naples. But when the money I gave him is gone he'll be back. Here or in Rome, he'll be back."

"Don't talk about it. Don't think about it till you're stronger."

"I don't mind speaking. Since you know. I suppose you all do, Father, Ada, and everyone."

"Don't mind our knowing."

"I don't mind for my sake. I wanted to protect the children. No, that's not all. I was protecting him. I suppose I still love him."

"You can't, Eva."

"I can, Mammy. And I should. I promised. For better, for worse. This is for worse, that's all."

"There's a limit to what one is expected to endure, Eva."

"Death is the only limit they put to the promises."

"I sometimes think a married clergy would show more sense. They don't know, those priests, what a bad marriage is like."

"But I did promise. And marriage is a sacrament."

"Separations are allowed, Eva. I'll go straight over to the Avenue Hoche this morning, or better still I'll speak to the nuncio."

"No, Mammy. Be calm. It wouldn't be right for me to leave Ferdinand. And you mustn't worry. I'll be given grace to walk."

"Grace?" Louise remembered the American girl's graceful body. She put her hand on her daughter's forehead. "Have you still some fever?"

"My mind isn't wandering." Eva laughed weakly. "I'm not talking about the kind of grace which you so lovingly taught me. I'm talking about the grace that makes even a hard path possible."

"Oh, Eva, those nuns gave you too much religion. Perhaps I should have let you be one of them."

"But I didn't want to. Oh, I did sometimes, but I wasn't called. The Sisters knew I had no religious vocation. And anyway I wanted to marry Ferdinand. I loved him and I thought he loved me."

"Of course he did."

"You never believed it. And I don't know who was right. Today Ferdinand would tell you that he never cared for me."

"Has he said so? Has he dared to say——"

"No. No, Mammy. But I know. I think he has forgotten, but it may be that I imagined his love. I didn't imagine mine. And it still exists."

"One can get over love, Eva."

"Can one? Maybe. I think one could grow tired, so tired that one would want to stop caring. So tired." Eva's eyes closed.

When Eva was again awake Louise turned their talk to practical matters.

"You mentioned the money you gave him. Are you pressed financially? You have a nice income, but still——"

"Nice! Mammy darling, nearly two hundred thousand dollars a year deserves a larger adjective."

"Is it enough? You said you gave him money. You haven't pawned your jewels?"

"I didn't pawn them. I sold some of them. I told Ferdinand that when the last of the money they brought is gone he will have to live within my income."

"To whom did you sell them?"

Eva named a jeweler.

"I'll send for him. You shall have them back."

"Oh no, Mammy, it would only start all over."

"I'll buy them back and keep them for you. And I'll arrange with my London bank to deposit an extra hundred thousand to your account. I'll not have you worried. And money is one thing, thank God, that needn't trouble you."

"Father has been too generous to me. Always. We mustn't take advantage of him. Remember, you told me that long ago. I'll not let my husband rob him."

"Don't worry now, but get well and strong again."

When Eva regained her strength she announced her intention of returning to Rome. She firmly refused her mother's offer to accompany her.

"No, Mammy darling, I must go alone. Later, come to visit us, or stay with Ada and Joseph if you'd rather. Now I must go alone. I must go home, bringing the children with me, and await Ferdinand's return as though it were the most natural thing in the world. You told me once that it's not what you have to begin with that counts in marriage, but what you have to go on with. I'm going on. Pray for me that I may succeed."

Louise returned to London. There was nothing more she could do for Eva. Eva wasn't a child. She was a woman of thirty. Later, Louise could go to Rome, ostensibly to visit Ada and Joseph. She could let Eva see, by frequent visits from both her parents, that they were standing by. And that was all she could do. She could no longer help Eva any more than she could help any grown woman, however beloved. She must stand, watching, outside her grown child's life, powerless to help her.

Louise was grateful for the new house. It came at a time when she needed an occupation.

By the end of May the work was practically completed. Louise was able to keep a promise she had made to Princess Louise. On the fourth of June, under that royal lady's patronage, a part of the house was opened to the public for a sale of work and a concert for the benefit of the Scottish Home Industries.

On the twenty-fifth of June, Louise gave her first reception. Smaller, more exclusive parties would follow. This was a party to show all of London Mrs. Mackay's fine new mansion. The guests need not be chosen for their congeniality; they were there to see the house, not one another.

Louise received at the head of the grand stairway. Later she joined her guests in the pink drawing room and in the ballroom and on the terrace. She went downstairs and accepted many compliments on her bookroom and on her lofty Henry II dining room.

Willie had returned from a visit to America to act as host.

"Big success, Mammy," he reported. "Your guests have nearly broken their necks craning them at your handsome ceilings. They've admired every tapestry, every piece of statuary, every painting. Lots of compliments for Cabanel's portraits of you and Father."

"You will notice I had the vanity to give them the places of honor on each side of the doorway in the pink drawing room."

"Poor Mammy, it wasn't a bit of use. The main attraction in the painting line is the Meissonier tucked away in a corner."

"Probably because they are astonished to see it at all, having believed the idiotic story that I had burned it."

"That's not the only reason. It's a good picture except for the hands. Clarie and I like it. Of course Eva has always said the Cabanel was better."

"Eva remembers me younger, as M. Cabanel was kind enough to paint me."

"Oh, Mammy, you look pretty young right this minute, all dressed up in your lace and brocade and those big diamonds in your ears."

"Thank you, Willie." It was curious, she thought, that she no longer minded the Meissonier. It was not because the disagreeable old man was dead, that would not have softened her. She had taken the picture from the bank vault to make sure it was in good condition. She could not mind it so much any more or she would not have decided to hang it in her new house. The portrait, except for the hands and the awkward, bony wrists, was more like her than when it had been painted. Perhaps she had hated it because she had secretly known she would grow to resemble it. Perhaps when she had been still almost young it had frightened her to have her middle-aged appearance so accurately foretold. Now it didn't matter; she was older than the portrait.

"I guess he was cleverer than I was willing to admit," she said.

"Meissonier? Well, he kind of got your expression. That's what Clarie and I think. But never mind him. He's not really the biggest center of interest."

"What is? My Don Quixote tapestries or——"

"No, Mammy. One of your guests: Mrs. Arthur Wilson. Pretty spunky of you to invite her."

"Of course I invited her. She was always kind to me before the baccarat scandal. Is she all right, Willie? Are people being nice to her?"

"They're being interested, especially the Americans. I saw Mrs. Robert Lincoln and Mrs. Harbord Taylor both having a good look. But I'm not sure that many of them are talking to her."

"Many of my guests were pleased enough to accept her invitations to Tranby Croft before that miserable card game. I'll not permit them to be rude to her now in my house. Go and find her and ask her to join me on the terrace for some champagne and strawberries. Bring her out yourself, but not too quickly. I'll collect some people at a table and in my presence they'll have to behave well to her. There's Lady Mary Lloyd. I'll start with her, she hasn't an unkind bone in her body."

As Louise sat with her guests she faced the open french windows. Through them she could see her splendidly decorated, brilliantly illuminated drawing room. Six Carlton House Terrace, she thought, was as handsome as 9 Rue de Tilsitt, and the furnishings were better than the first purchases she had made for the Paris house. She had learned a lot in fifteen years. When John came over he would be pleased. "Oh, it's grand, Louise," he would say as he had said at his first sight of the newly decorated Paris mansion. "You've done a fine job, old lady; I'm proud of you."

Willie celebrated his twenty-first birthday in London and then sailed for America. This trip was not a visit such as he had paid to New York the previous winter. This time he was going to settle in an apartment of his own at the Belgravia Flats. When he came again to Carlton House Terrace it would be as a visitor. Only for Clarie would the new house be home. Like Eva, Willie was grown up, but it was a little easier to believe of a boy than of a girl.

As she saw Willie off at the boat train Louise remembered the parlor suite at the Grand. Certain anniversaries, eighteen, twenty-one, thirty, wound time into a coil so that a distant scene was plain to see. She remembered the afternoon sunlight reflected in the polished rosewood furniture, and John's first mention of the Con Virginia, and Louise Althea in her smart feathered hat, and the baby Willie, a small sleeping bundle in her arms. Then, twenty-one years had seemed a long span. Twenty-one years had been as much of her own lifetime as she could clearly remember. She had planned for the grown-up Willie but she hadn't really imagined him. And here he was.

She kissed him. His proudly waxed mustache brushed her cheek. How odd for the baby to have grown a mustache.

"Why are you smiling, Mammy? Not very polite not to be sadder to see me go."

"I'm smiling at your having grown up. That always seems to a mother a ridiculous, unbelievable thing for a child to do. And I can't be sad at your going. You'll enjoy working beside your father. And he'll enjoy having you. He'll so enjoy."

Clarie, on his graduation from Beaumont, showed no inclination to continue his studies. He pleaded for a holiday.

"After Father gets Willie well trained, you know he'll put me to work too. Let me have some fun in the meantime."

John permitted the holiday. The boy was good at sports. Let him develop his aptitude for them. Let him enjoy himself for a while. "And besides," John said to Louise, "I can only train one of them at a time."

And besides, Louise thought, Clarie is the youngest and so to you too, though you'd never admit it, he's the baby, the one always young enough to be spoiled a little longer.

The holiday, Louise thought, was doing Clarie no harm. He worked harder at his sports than ever he had done at Beaumont. Cricket had been his first love, and his picture as captain of the Beaumont eleven hung in his room. Now his great enthusiasm was court tennis, a rather pretty game, Louise thought, and racquets, which seemed to her almost as exhausting to watch as to play.

In the winter of 1893 Eva rented a villa near Rapallo. She invited her mother to visit. They would have a chance to be together, she wrote, and with the children, in a way that was never possible when Louise came to Rome.

Louise enjoyed the visit. Her little grandsons reminded her of Willie playing long ago on a Mediterranean beach. But Bianca was her favorite. She had not, as far as she could read her own heart, had a favorite among the children and she had been thankful. She had pitied the children whose mother loved best the pretty one or the clever one, the easy one or the difficult one, the baby or the eldest, the son or the daughter. But among grandchildren a little favoritism, provided it was concealed, could be forgiven. And forgiven or not, Louise could not help it. Bianca, now in her sixth year, was Eva again, a prettier, sturdier Eva. Bianca laughed more easily; Bianca could run and skip. Bianca was not timid. She held her own with her older brother and his friends. But the wide-set eyes were Eva's and the generous shape of her mouth. Her beautiful little nose was like her father's. At least, Louise thought, he had given her the one good thing he had.

Ferdinand came to Rapallo for a few days. He expressed his regret that his duties in Rome and Naples prevented his spending more time with his family.

Neither before nor after her husband's visit did Eva speak of him to Louise. With the children she talked of Papa. She urged Andrea and Bianca to write to their dear papa, and in the three children's prayers Papa was mentioned first in the long list of those whom the Lord was asked to bless.

When they were alone Eva talked about her children and Ada's, about the book Mr. Murphy had based on Colonel Hungerford's recollections.

They reminisced about Eva's school days at Neuilly when the house on the Place de l'Étoile was newly purchased.

"Is 6 Carlton House Terrace really as beautiful, Mammy?"

"I think it is in a different way, though it's not the same to me. But then the Rue de Tilsitt isn't the same any more. I think of it with children in it. And now the children are all grown. I get lonely when I go over. Even you, Eva, it's two years since you've been there. And Willie and Clarie prefer, when they go to France, to rent a country place for the riding and shooting. I told the agents a year ago I'll sell when I can get my price."

"There's no use keeping it for me, Mammy. I—I don't find it easy to get to Paris. And, of course, Ferdinand is right when he says the children should grow up in their own country."

Louise asked no questions. She spoke of the charms of the Italian Riviera. "Perhaps someday you should own a villa here, Eva."

They talked of Theresa Fair. Though her death had occurred over a year ago, the pain of it felt as fresh to Louise as it had on the day the cable had come with the news.

"And it still doesn't seem true," Louise said. "She was the only friend of my grown-up years. All the others, even Consuelo Manchester, are, compared to Theresa, acquaintances. I can't believe I've lost my friend."

"Poor Mrs. Fair. She hadn't a very happy life."

"You mustn't think of the sad part. Think of how she was when you were little."

"I remember her then too. But I was thinking of the time she came to Rome with Tessie and Birdie. She seemed so sad and different from Virginia City days."

"But those are the days she'd want to be remembered in. She was happy then. And gay and pretty with bright, silky hair and a real wild-rose complexion. She was as pretty as one of those Irish ballads your father likes to hear you sing."

"Poor little Birdie," Eva said. "She's young to be left."

"Tessie'll look after her. John likes that Hermann Oelrichs she married. He's a bit older, of course, but with Theresa gone and Jim Fair worse than useless as a father, it's a good thing to have a man to look after the girls. We say, 'Poor Theresa,' but she was spared sorrow. Jim made her unhappy, but he could never hurt her as it would have hurt her to see young Jim die of drink. At least she missed that by a few months. And there might have been more for her to bear. I hear only bad reports of Charlie. She should never have been weak enough to leave the boys to Jim's handling. But she had happiness out of the girls. She was proud of Tessie's grand marriage and her high position in New York and Newport and she had great hopes for little Birdie. Still, I guess it was a mercy she was taken. Her sons would have brought her too much sorrow."

"You and Father are lucky in your sons. And I'm lucky, too, to have brothers like Willie and Clarie."

"Willie will be over soon on a quick trip. Your father is putting more and more responsibility for the European end of the business in his hands. Try to go up to Paris while he's there."

Just before Eva's lease was up Louise returned to London.

On the morning of her mother's departure Eva clung to her.

Her eyes filled with tears as they embraced. "I mustn't cry, Mammy. Don't let me. The children will think . . ."

"They'll think only that you're sorry to see me go."

"But you'll not go far, not too far. Of course sometime you'll want to see Willie's establishment on Fifth Avenue, but you won't be going for a while, will you?"

"No, my darling, and if I do, New York's only a week away."

"London's closer. Stay close, Mammy. Please stay close."

"I will. And remember, wherever I am I'll always come quickly if you call me."

"That's the first thing I remember, me calling and you coming."

"I'm still listening, Eva. You've only to call."

Almost immediately after her return from Italy, Louise received a cable from John telling her that he had been shot and slightly wounded by Wesley Rippey, a half-crazed old man who attributed his miserable financial condition to the machinations of the bonanza kings. The bullet had passed between two ribs, doing so little damage that John had been able to walk the short distance from the scene of the attack to the Palace Hotel. There was, he said, absolutely no cause for alarm.

For over two weeks cables came almost daily to Louise telling her of John's rapid recovery. Then for several days there was no word. If John had returned to work he might in the first press of business have neglected to cable. But surely, Louise thought, he would by now have sent a message to tell her that his doctor had allowed him to resume his normal life. She cabled to ask if anything was wrong and if he needed her. The reply that came on the following day was signed Richard Dey. It informed her that Mr. Mackay was doing well, that there was no cause for alarm and no necessity for her to come to California.

The message puzzled her. If John were well he would have answered her cable himself. If he were really ill he might have said "Tell her not to worry." But he would want her with him and he would have sent for her.

There was nothing in the news dispatches about a change in John's condition. Nothing could be wrong, she told herself; nothing could suddenly develop at this point in a normal recovery from a bullet wound. She knew: she had seen enough such wounds in Edmund's practice thirty years ago. Still, she was frightened and uncertain what to do. There was no use cabling Mr. Dey. If he had been told not to worry her he would obey orders. She made herself think calmly of the sensible course to follow. Then she addressed a message to Sam Rosener asking him to tell her the truth about the situation.

She told her secretary to take the cable to the office and to see that it was marked urgent and dispatched immediately.

"And find out," she said, "when the next fast sailing is; I may want you to book passage for Mr. Clarence and me."

She could not reach Willie. His business in Paris was concluded and he had already sailed for home on the *Majestic*.

Before evening Sam Rosener's reply arrived. John was dangerously ill, not from his wound but from another cause which the doctors had diagnosed as an inflammation of the appendix vermiformis. "Get on the first boat," the message concluded.

Louise and Clarie sailed two days later on the *City of Paris*.

Four years before the voyages on this ship had been delightful. A luxurious steamer cut off from the cares and worries and even from all news of the land had seemed the perfect setting for a holiday. Louise had kept as a souvenir the program of the ship's concert at which she had sung and Willie had played the violin.

On this voyage the sea was as calm, the ship as luxurious, but the days and nights with no news had been an ever-increasing strain. As the ship approached the harbor, the strain became almost unbearable. Clarie sat with his mother in her cabin. Neither could think of anything to say.

A steward knocked. He brought a telegram that had been delivered to the ship at quarantine. It was from John. The inflammation had subsided, he was making a fine recovery. All danger was past.

Willie was at the pier. By the time he had arrived in New York, John was recovering so rapidly that he had telegraphed Willie to wait and accompany his mother and his younger brother on their westward journey.

Louise and her sons arrived at Oakland in John's private car, the *Corsair*. They were accompanied by a newly purchased Skye terrier which Willie had insisted on bringing as a present for Birdie Fair.

When they stepped from the car Birdie was in the group that was waiting to welcome them and to accompany them on the ferry to San Francisco. The Michael de Youngs were there, and Sam and Fanny Rosener.

Louise heard her voice break as she tried to thank Sam for his cable.

"That's all right, my dear. All's well now. But I couldn't think what delayed you. I knew John had sent for you some days before I got your message."

"Louise, it's been a long time," Fanny said as they boarded the ferry.

"You don't change, Fanny, nor does Sam. If it hadn't been for Sam, I might—I might——"

"Don't think about it. As Sam says, all's well now." Fanny lowered her voice. "I suppose Dick Dey never sent off John's cable. Horrid man. I've never liked him. Nor did Theresa, and how right she was, poor soul. But say nothing to John, Louise."

"But if Mr. Dey is not to be trusted?"

"In business he's all right. Sam would tell you that. And it's only business dealings John has with him. John isn't so young any more, Louise, and he's been pretty sick. It would be hard on him now to break in a new man."

"What are you women whispering about?" Sam asked.

"Can't you guess?" Louise smiled and glanced at Birdie and Willie.

"Sure, Sam," Fanny said. "Theresa and Louise always had their hearts set on such a match. But don't let the young ones know the idea was their mothers' or that'll be the end of it."

Birdie was a fashionable young lady. The tomboy had disappeared. She was small and slim. Her shining black hair and eyes and her soft husky voice were her father's. Her smooth fair skin was Theresa's. Her manner, too, was like her mother's. Birdie had the same warm smile and the same quick laugh that rang out unexpectedly, like a child's.

Louise watched the graceful little figure as she knelt beside Willie to admire the shaggy mop of a dog. Even in this undignified attitude her son and Theresa's daughter were a handsome couple.

John was waiting for Louise at the door of the suite at the Palace. "They let me get dressed in your honor," he said. He was pale and a little thinner. "Boys, take our guests to the main parlor. We'll join you in a few minutes."

He closed the door and turned to Louise. "My dear. I—forgive me. I'm not so steady on my legs yet." He walked to a sofa and sat down. "I knew you'd come as soon as you got my cable."

"Your cable?" She did not want to distress John. She hastily turned the question into a statement. "That cable, of course."

John had heard the uncertainty in her voice. "Dick!" he shouted. "I told Dick to send it off. I was pretty sick. I don't even remember your answer. But they told me you were coming. It seemed a long time until I heard, but I kind of lost track of the days there for a while. I think it was Sam who told me. That's a funny thing. Dick!"

"Yes, sir."

"What about that cable I gave you for Mrs. Mackay the day the inflammation started?"

"Oh, John, don't fuss at the poor man. I was frightened so I cabled Sam. The old friends come first to mind in trouble."

"Sure, they do. And I guess things were pretty busy round here. I just want to be sure you got my cable."

"You must know I did. I'm here."

She watched the color return to Mr. Dey's face. If John had been himself he'd have noticed that something was wrong with his secretary. For a moment Mr. Dey had been deeply frightened. And yet to act as he had, he must have counted on her protecting him for John's sake. He was useful to John and John was accustomed to him. John depended on him in his California affairs. He particularly depended on him in his endless private charities. And Louise was sure that Mr. Dey dispensed John's kindness to the old-timers with meticulous honesty. He would take pleasure in the role of a rich man's almoner. She looked at him curiously. Why had he tried to keep her from John? Mr. Dey's eyes met hers. Now that he was certain she did not mean to betray him, fear had gone, but dislike was still here. She recognized it. She remembered how he had looked at her at the Everett House on the night of Mrs. Stevens' party. She supposed he could not forgive her for the move to the East, the move to Europe. These moves had left Mr. Dey behind. He had no part in the affairs of the cable company; John had kept him in San Francisco. And so, Louise thought, he hated her who had turned John's face to the East and had thereby diminished the reflected glory in which Richard Dey lived his vicarious existence. That was it, this man lived at second hand. It was not only because he disliked Louise that he had not sent John's cable and had later sent one of his own; it was that, thinking John was going to die, he had wanted to be chief mourner. "I," said the dove, "I'll be chief mourner." He didn't look like a dove, he looked like a crow, she thought in angry distaste.

"You can run along, Dick," John said. "I've got Mrs. Mackay to look after me now."

Louise put her arms gently around John and kissed his forehead. "Say, I'm not all that fragile, old lady."

"Of course you're not. But I've been so anxious."

"Nothing to fear now, my darling. But I don't mind telling you I was scared myself. There's about a week there that's pretty hazy in my mind. But in a few days I'll be out of here. And we'll see old friends and have a real holiday before Willie and I have to get back to business."

Louise managed to extend John's needed holiday for more than a month.

It was a quiet holiday, spent mostly with the Roseners, the De Youngs, and a few other old friends. Willie and Clarie with Birdie and Tessie and Tessie's husband, Hermann Oelrichs, were lavishly entertained and entertained in their turn.

John and Louise watched with pleasure the development of Willie's and Birdie's interest in one another.

"Don't push it, Louise. You might only put them off," John said. "But sure, you've sense enough for that. And they're young; they've plenty of time."

"I'd like it. And not just because of Theresa. I like Birdie herself. I always have since she was a little thing. But in her ways, in that friendly warmth she has for the whole world, she's very like her mother."

"Like her father too."

"I never said Jim lacked charm and Birdie has it all, much more than Tessie, though Tessie is the handsomer of the two sisters."

"Poor old Jim. He had other good qualities, though you'd never admit them."

"Theresa never denied them. And she'd want me to see the good and forgive the bad, but it's for her sake I can't."

"I haven't asked you to forgive him or even to see him. But suppose those two young ones decide to get married, what'll you do?"

"I'll be polite to him at the wedding, but more than that you cannot ask."

By the middle of May, John was restored to health and anxious to get back to work. "And Willie's got to get back in harness too. He's had holiday enough."

"He's young, don't be too hard on him."

"I'm not. But I've a right to think of us. If I'm ever to retire I've got to get Willie in shape to take over all my business affairs. You know what I'm going to do soon as you and Clarie leave? Take him up to Virginia. I think it's not a trip you'd care for."

"A poor ghost of a town it must be." She shivered.

"Pretty near."

"What can Willie learn of business there?"

"He can take a look at old Mount Davidson and the deep shafts and the steep trails and the railroad Sharon built so painfully. And the water flumes and Sutro's tunnel. He can go down in the mines. He can learn how hard the money was to come by. He's got to learn that a fortune doesn't come easy. Nor is it easy to hold on to. There's no use preaching to a boy his age, but he's a bright lad. He can learn a lot from the Comstock, from the men who licked it and the men it licked. It's all history now. And a better history for an American boy starting out than he can find in most of the books."

"He'll make you proud someday."

"Sure, he will. And it's not too far off, that day when you and I can retire to the side lines and watch him."

Louise, on her return to London, tried to distract herself with the activities of the season, but Eva's letters were disquieting. They said very little. Eva gave news of the children but none of herself.

In August, Louise went to Italy. Colonel Hungerford had not been feeling well and this gave Louise an excuse to visit her father and be near her daughter.

"I guess it's just my years catching up with me," the colonel said. "The doctors can't find anything wrong."

Eva was pale and she seemed thinner. She did not speak of her domestic affairs and Louise asked no questions.

Once when they were alone on the loggia of the Hungerfords' villa Eva put her hand in her mother's and said in a low voice, "I'm glad you're here, Mammy. I feel safer when you're with me." Then she jumped to her feet. "Now, isn't that a silly thing in a woman my age! I must have a touch of Roman fever." She laughed and turned the subject.

While Louise was in Rome, John was operated on unexpectedly in New York. There had been another inflammation of his appendix and, though this time it was slight, the doctors decided that the wisest course was to operate without delay.

In a few weeks, John cabled, he would be able to travel and would join Louise at Carlton House Terrace. She, in the meantime, was to stay with Eva.

In September, Eva was obliged to go to Naples to visit her father-in-law. "You go to London, Mammy," she said, "and wait for Father."

"According to his last letter it will be quite a wait. Till Christmas, most likely. He's deep in some sort of reorganization of the Postal Telegraph Company."

"Go anyway," Eva said. "Perhaps I'll be able to visit you later. And it will do Grandpa good. He loves England at this time of year. Some of his old California cronies are always passing through London in September."

Colonel and Mrs. Hungerford were still with Louise at Carlton House Terrace in October when the telegram came from Eva. The message was brief; it said only that she and the children were on their way to London.

When Eva arrived Louise was shocked by her appearance. She must have lost ten pounds. When Eva lifted her veil to embrace her mother Louise saw that the dark eyes were deeply circled. She pushed back a curl that had come unpinned and fallen across Eva's cheek. Eva winced under the gentle touch. Louise withdrew her hand and saw the wide, ugly bruise on her daughter's swollen cheek.

"Not now, Mammy." Eva lowered her veil. "Later we can talk."

The children were delighted with the house they had never seen. They ran up and down the marble stairs. Marco slid down the smooth balustrade. Bianca climbed on the tall base of a statue and stared curiously at the veiled stone face.

"My darling, you never brought them all the way alone!" Mrs. Hungerford exclaimed.

"It was for a treat, Mémé," Bianca said. "Mamma told us that for once we would go off for the night with her, without even Nurse. But it wasn't just for the night, that's the surprise."

"And I was in charge," Andrea said, "because poor Mamma was tired from packing."

"She packed our portmanteaus herself because the trip was a surprise," Bianca explained.

"It was much better than a picnic," Marco said.

"I can imagine." Mrs. Hungerford caught Marco's hand and held him firmly. "You just stay off that balustrade and the three of you come with Great-grandpa and me. We'll leave Mamma and Granny to have a nice cup of tea."

Louise sent for tea and sandwiches. "You should have a proper meal, but I want you to have something quickly. How long since you've eaten?"

"Oh, I ate. I'm really too tired for food. If I could just have tea."

"You'll have tea and you'll have food. They can bring it to the bookroom. We won't even go upstairs till Mémé has the children settled down."

"I'm sorry not to have brought Nurse. You see——"

"It's all right. We can easily get someone. And until we do, Mémé and I can manage. We didn't always have nursemaids, you know."

When the refreshments had been served and Eva had eaten a little, Louise gave orders that they were not to be disturbed.

"Rest a little, Eva. Take off your hat and lean back."

Eva covered her cheek with her hand. "I'm sorry you saw this. I tried to hide it with powder."

"Don't talk until you want to. Just rest and feel safe."

"But am I safe?" Eva started forward. "Can he make me go back? And the children, can he take them?"

"No, my darling, your father and I won't let him. You're quite, quite safe."

"I was so frightened. I've known for a long time that I should leave him. Even my confessor said so. For the children's sake."

"Don't try to tell me yet."

"There isn't much to tell. There were women. So flagrantly that as the children grew older they'd be bound to realize. Ferdinand is always sober, but sometimes his women were drunk. I tried, Mammy. Truly I did."

"I'm sure you did."

"But then I became frightened. It was the night before I left. That's why I left. I was so frightened that I didn't dare try any longer. He demanded money. I refused. I couldn't bear to ask you and Father to pay any more of his debts. He became angry."

"Was he drunk?"

"No, he never drinks too much. And it wasn't that kind of anger. It wasn't any kind of anger I ever saw before. He laughed a little bit and moved quite slowly, quite easily toward me, like someone in a ballroom approaching a lady to ask for a dance. And then this"—Eva put her hand to her cheek—"this happened, and I fell to the floor. He stood and looked at me. He was still laughing a little. 'A small first lesson,' he said. 'There will be others.' And then he turned and walked out of the room. I was so frightened, Mammy." She began to cry.

When Eva's sobbing ceased she spoke again. "I'm more frightened for the children than I am for myself. If they should make him angry? They're so little. Suppose he hurt them."

"He can't reach the children here."

"He said he could reach them anywhere. I spoke once about a separation and he said any Italian tribunal would give him the children and I'd never be permitted to see them. That's why, after he—he frightened me, I ran away with them. I didn't tell my maid. I gave her and Nurse the day off. I packed just those little bags and told the major-domo we were going to spend the night with friends near Ostia. I didn't even dare go near the safe for the jewels I have left. A servant might have seen and warned Ferdinand that I was leaving. I left all my silver and my wedding presents. All the beautiful things you and Father gave me. I'm sorry, Mammy."

"Things don't matter, Eva. What counts is that you and the children are safe."

"Are you sure?" Eva sat stiffly on the edge of her chair.

"Perfectly sure. Your father's lawyers will take charge from now on. Don't worry, my darling. You're home again."

Chapter XXIX

• • • ◦ ● ◦ • • •

Willie

FOR ALMOST TWO years Ferdinand refused to consider a legal separation. In the meanwhile, John's lawyers advised patience. The Prince of Galatro had assets in Rome. There was the princess' handsome residence and its furnishings. There were the jewels and other valuables she had left behind. The prince could live quite comfortably on the proceeds from the sale of these possessions. For the present the princess must remain with her mother. It might even be wise for her to take her children to New York for a brief visit with Mr. Mackay, Jr. This might indicate that she was thinking of settling in America. Oh, he knew, the lawyer explained, that the princess wished to bring her children up in their native land, but for the time being she must keep this wish to herself. She must make it perfectly clear that she had no intention of returning to the prince or to the jurisdiction of the Italian courts. When his money ran out the prince would be forced to be reasonable. Then and only then could the princess appear before the Italian tribunal for a legal ratification of the separation agreement.

In September of 1895 Ferdinand consented to a legal separation and to Eva's having custody of the children. In return it was agreed that he should receive an annual income of twelve thousand dollars.

When everything was settled Louise decided to join Lady Mary Lloyd, who was holidaying in Normandy. September in Paris had been hot; the cool sea air would be a refreshing change.

Willie had rented for the summer the Duc de Gramont's place in the Sarthe. Louise had promised to visit him before he returned to the States at the end of October. He was proud of his château, of his horses, and of the miniature race track he had constructed on the property. He was delighted that his father had permitted him to extend his vacation for an extra month.

Lady Mary and Louise found the seaside resorts, with their half-empty hotels, rather bleak and depressing. They left the coast and settled in a comfortable inn on the outskirts of a small sheltered village.

Louise was tired after the strain of the last weeks in Paris. Once Ferdinand agreed, the legal negotiations had been simple. But the end even of an unhappy marriage was, Louise had discovered, a painful process to witness. It had not been easy to look at Eva's white drawn face as she read and signed the papers the lawyers gave her. At the beginning of the marriage there had also been lawyers and papers. Eva, her mother knew, must be remembering the beginning.

Louise was grateful for the quiet country retreat. She had been wise to refuse Willie's invitation to join the young house party with which he was now surrounded. She was too tired to be with the young.

Lady Mary was a little older than Louise and comfortably resigned to middle age. Her companionship was restful and undemanding. Louise wanted no entertainment more strenuous than to walk across the meadow to admire the innkeeper's apple orchard or down the lane to buy a spool of thread or a paper of pins in the village.

Sun-warmed, windless October days like these had been called Indian summer in the Atlantic states, Louise remembered. Only the cool nights and the sharp wind at dawn reminded her that at the edge of this extra, unexpected little season, the end of autumn was waiting.

The early evenings and the quiet routine of the days were soothing. Louise began to feel happier about Eva. At least she was safe and she had her children. And though to Louise all of Eva's youth seemed wasted, Eva herself still believed in her early happiness with

Ferdinand and so possessed it. Her memory of the first years of her marriage was unspoiled by bitterness. Eva was curiously incapable of bitterness.

"What are you thinking about?" Lady Mary asked. The ladies were walking slowly beside the far edge of the orchard.

"About Eva. And thanking God I'm old enough to know there are more years than the young ones, and other joys than the romantic ones."

"Poor Eva. And yet, you know, I only half mean that. Your girl has a serenity about her that makes it difficult to pity her. Though when one thinks what she endured from that scoundrel of a husband!"

"He spoiled most of her young years, but she's safe from him now. And she has her children. She hasn't everything I wanted for her, but at least she has a part of it. And at my age one knows how much better even a small part is than nothing at all."

"One learns, as one grows older, to expect less, which is just as well, since less is invariably what one gets."

"There are pleasures too, you know." Louise gestured at an almost perfectly symmetrical tree laden with crimson fruit. "I can get real pleasure looking at that tree, at the tree itself, I mean. When I was young I saw only my own feelings in anything beautiful. I saw my sorrow or my joy, my hope, my memory. Now I can see the thing itself, the tree, the branch, the fruit."

"I'm something of a collector of the compensations of age. That's one I hadn't thought of. The young do rather live inside themselves, which isn't very comfortable unless one is perfectly happy."

"I envy them a little when I suddenly remember what the good part was like, but on the whole I'm content to admire the apple trees."

Louise picked an apple from a low bough and slowly ate it as she and Lady Mary walked in comfortable silence through the orchard toward the inn.

The taste and the fragrance reminded Louise of Mr. Duhme's store. When he had given her one of his apples it had been like this one, just an apple, round and handsome and good to eat. In childhood, too, objects were clearly outside oneself. It was in later youthful years that everything became an extension of oneself. She smiled, thinking of Clarie who at twenty-one was absorbed in his picture of himself as a young man about town. She remembered the

Paris Exposition and the little boy staggering under the weight of a mechanical fish. The toy had been first a longed-for object, then a beloved possession outside himself. Now his possessions were part of a dream. His flat in Paris, his trotting stable, the moor in Scotland which he and Evelyn Fitzgerald had rented, all these were part of his self-portrait of Clarie Mackay, keen sportsman, gay bachelor, experienced man of the world.

A man in dark city clothes was standing in the courtyard of the inn. As he came toward them, Louise recognized an assistant manager of the Paris office of the Commercial Cable Company.

"Eva." Louise spoke the name aloud. Her heart seemed to contract into a tight knot of fear as she ran across the grass. What could be wrong? The lawyers had been so sure. But something must be wrong for this man to have been sent all the way from Paris. Ferdinand had the money, that was what he wanted. He didn't care enough about Eva to hurt her. But Eva must be hurt. From the pity in the man's tired face Louise knew that Eva must be hurt. She stared at him, waiting for his message.

He spoke slowly, painfully, as though he were out of breath. He had, he said, been traveling since yesterday. The final telegraphed message had reached him at Trouville. They had told him at the Roches Noires that Madame was here. He had had to wait. The first train from Trouville had been this morning.

"Never mind all that, monsieur. Give me your news."

"Monsieur Willie," he said. "Monsieur Willie."

They stared at each other for a short measureless space. Then Louise heard his voice ringing in her brain. The man stopped speaking and still she heard his voice repeating: Monsieur Willie has been killed in a riding accident. Monsieur Willie has been killed Monsieur Willie Monsieur Willie Monsieur Monsieur Monsieur. The voice was a jangle of sound ringing in her brain always louder, always faster, until she pitched forward on the grass and heard nothing at all.

John, in San Francisco, had learned the news in a series of cables sent hour by hour. Louise heard the details little by little in her room in Paris.

Though the negotiations for the sale of 9 Rue de Tilsitt were practically completed, Eva and Clarie had arranged to reopen the house so that Willie's body could come home.

Louise refused to continue to take the quieting drugs her physician had prescribed.

"They don't make me sleep," she said. "They only make me dream and hope that all is a nightmare."

Slowly they told her. Clarie sat beside her while Willie's friend Ned Lynch, who had been present, told the story of the fatal accident.

At luncheon on the eighteenth of October, Willie announced to his guests that he planned, for their afternoon's entertainment, a race on his new course.

Young Digby did not like the suggestion.

"I had a nightmare last night," he told his host.

Willie laughed at him. "You dined too well, so of course you had a bad dream."

"No, listen to me. Whether it was the wine I drank or not, listen to my dream: I was watching a race. Among the riders was a jockey wearing black and silver, your colors, Willie. His horse fell and he was killed. I saw him fall. I knew with that queer, close certainty one has in a dream that he was dead."

"Well, I'm not wearing my colors this afternoon, old boy. Besides, dreams go by contraries. Yours probably means that I'm going to beat you fellows in this little race."

At three o'clock the race began. Louise knew the De Gramont place. The meadow where Willie had built his race track was on the edge of a wooded park. The underbrush and young trees had been cleared away. The old trees stood tall and thick and strong enough to support the roof of a cathedral. The duke's guests had always admired the contrast between the sunny meadow and the dark, quiet wood beside it.

As Willie reached a curve on the **side** of the track near the wood, a distant shot rang out. His horse **shied** and bolted, out of control, between the trees. As the frightened horse swerved Willie was thrown head first and crushed against a tree.

He was unconscious when his friends carried him into the château. After the doctor came he recovered consciousness for a little while. He tried to stroke the head of Reinberg, his dog. The animal, Ned said, refused to leave its master.

Willie, lapsing in and out of consciousness, lived for six hours.

"He sent for us," Ned said. "He knew who we were, he recognized our voices."

"Couldn't he see you?" Louise asked. "No, of course."

Head first against the tree, Ned had said; of a fractured skull, the death certificate had read. When Clarie and Evelyn Fitzgerald received the body at the Gare Montparnasse it had already been embalmed and sealed in its coffin.

"That's why," Louise whispered. "That's why you wouldn't let any of us, not even Clarie, see him. Because he couldn't see. Because his eyes and his face were crushed against the tree."

Downstairs the coffin was still sealed beneath its white velvet pall, beneath its burden of flowers. Louise tried to think of the chapel she had told them to make for Willie. It was carpeted and draped in black and silver. Thirty lighted candles surrounded him. Two nuns knelt beside him, day and night.

She tried to sit up. "Get Demoutier. I must dress. I must go down. I must see."

"No, Mammy." As Clarie stood up, Willie's dog stirred beside him. "You can't see him. Please, Mammy."

"Please, Mrs. Mackay," Ned said.

The boys looked frightened. She mustn't frighten them. When she tried to sit up it was the room, not she, that moved.

"Please, Mammy," Clarie said. "We've done everything you asked for Willie. The façades of the house are draped in black velvet and silver. I myself put your Parma violets on the casket."

Willie had always liked violets. He wore them often in his buttonhole. He always sent them to his mother on Christmas morning. She tried to think of the violets and the other flowers. She tried to think of velvet and silver, of burning candles and of the tall white moiré cross above the mourner's prie-dieu. She must not think of the sealed bronze box. She must not imagine the broken body, the face. Willie's face.

"If you would take your medicine, madame. It's late." Demoutier was beside the bed. "The doctor has said that Madame must get some sleep."

"All right. I may as well. It doesn't matter. Asleep or awake, it's the same nightmare."

Willie had died with none of his own beside him. Now his parents tried to do all that could be done for the beloved dead.

The funeral was held at St. Ferdinand des Ternes in Paris. In New York there was a Solemn High Requiem Mass at St. Leo's.

In the States and in Europe the main offices of the Postal Telegraph and Commercial Cable companies were closed and draped in black on the day of the funeral.

Louise and John were kept busy with all that was left to be done for Willie. They planned the building of a magnificent mausoleum at Greenwood. They arranged that Masses should be said in perpetuity. They collected his obituary notices and pasted them in two thick black-bound volumes.

They brought his body to America on the *Touraine* in a stateroom which had been transformed into a chapel.

Sitting beside each other in the main cabin of their suite they sorted the letters and cables and telegrams of sympathy.

They read and reread Birdie's letter to John.

453 Fifth Avenue

Dear Mr. Mackay,

I am heart-broken at Willie's death. I little realized how much I cared for him until now when it is too late. The thought of him dying never entered my head so the shock was awful—I always felt I had Willie to turn to if I was in trouble and now I have lost my best and dearest friend—I only wish dear Mr. Mackay there was some way of comforting you but I know there is none—you loved him too dearly but I hope you will accept my deepest sympathy.

Sincerely yrs.

Birdie

Oct. 20th.

They must keep busy. They must put off the day when there would be nothing left to do for their son.

On the morning of the twelfth of February Louise left the States on the *Majestic* on her return journey to Europe. Now there was nothing left to do for Willie. His body waited at Greenwood for the completion of the mausoleum.

Louise, veiled in black, stood on the deck. She lifted her veil and kissed her hand repeatedly to John and Clarie on the pier. Father Ducey of Saint Leo's was with them. He had known Willie and he had given the eulogy at the New York Mass. He would, Louise hoped, be a comfort to Clarie in the strange city. Some considered him too worldly, too fashionable a priest. The archbishop was said to have criticized his smart carriage and tandem pair. Louise had found Father Ducey kind and tactful. He had realized that she and John wanted no pious words of consolation. He had offered none. He had done what he could to smooth and simplify the arrangements for Willie.

John found it difficult to speak of Willie's death. Even with Louise he had said little, and his occasional references to their sorrow had come slowly and painfully. Louise knew that men often found it easier to talk to one another than to any woman, however loved. But John had now no associate with whom he had the ease of friendship he had enjoyed with Jim Fair. With Jim Fair he might have been able to talk of his grief. Neither separation nor estrangement had altered the affection between the partners. John had explained to her often enough that a partnership made and kept in the diggings was closer and more enduring than the friendships formed in softer, easier circumstances. When in the autumn of 1894 Jim had died, Louise had not wept for him. Now she wept that he was gone and John left alone in the man's world, the business world, in which his days were spent.

She was grateful for the pressing concerns of his business. The Commercial Cable was absorbing the Postal Telegraph. This was an intricate matter in which John was compelled to take an active part. He was also obliged to keep a watchful eye on the construction on Broad Street of the new Commercial Cable Building which represented an investment of over two million dollars. He would, she hoped, find distraction in his forced attention to his affairs.

Her eyes lingered on Clarie. He looked young and lost. He had loved Willie and he had looked up to him. Four years had been a high pedestal between the brothers. Clarie had accepted the fact that Willie was destined to take their father's place. Willie, he had always known, would someday be head of the family and of the business. Now Clarie, while he mourned for his brother, must try to take his place. Poor little Clarie, Louise thought pityingly. John, absorbed in his grief, walling himself in silence against companionship, could not see how hard the boy was trying. For a long time Clarie's place beside his father would be a lonely and a difficult one. As the ship moved from its pier, the three figures grew smaller until they were indistinguishable in the crowd that surrounded them.

Louise turned her thoughts to Rome, where Mémé was waiting for her. Colonel Hungerford was dying of a tumor of the liver. The doctors could not say whether his ordeal would be long or short. Willie had scarcely been placed in his temporary resting place when the cable summoning her to her father's side had come. "Grant, we beseech Thee, a place of refreshment, light and peace." The liturgical words might someday comfort Mémé. Her Daniel had had a long and full life. There were no words that Louise could say for Willie with more than her lips. He had had so little.

"Eternal rest give unto him." He was too young for rest. Mechanically she finished the prayer. "And let perpetual light shine upon him." She remembered the Duc de Gramont's sunny meadow. It had been summer when she had seen it. That was what Willie should have, the warm sunshine of this world. He was too young for the bright light of eternity.

Her heart felt heavy and dry as a stone. It could offer no prayers. She lowered her veil and walked slowly toward her cabin.

For more than a year Louise moved restlessly from city to city, from hotel to hotel. The London house, fully staffed, stood untenanted.

After her father's death in Rome, Louise tried to console her mother, but it was Mémé who offered consolation to her, and Louise could not accept consolation, not from Mémé or Ada, not from Eva or Clarie, not from John. She and John knew each other's bitter grief too well to try to lighten it with words.

Clarie was gradually becoming a comfort to his father. Louise saw that John was slowly giving a part of Willie's place to his younger son and she was grateful.

"It's hard on the boy," John said, "him not having been trained for business, but he does his best. In the end I believe his best will be pretty damn good."

Louise visited Eva at her newly purchased residence, the Castella Costa in Santa Margherita. The grandchildren, Eva said, would be a distraction. They were the new generation with whom Louise could look ahead, not always back at sorrow and loss.

Marco was too much like Willie.

"Granny! Granny!" he would shout. "Here I come!" and he would run toward her, confident of her welcome, of her delight in his company. His voice was Willie's as he pounded up the stairs of 825 O'Farrell Street, calling "Mammy! Mammy!" Marco's dark good looks were wholly Italian, but his boisterous merriment and his voice were Willie's. Louise had only to close her eyes and she was back with Willie in O'Farrell Street, in the Everett House, in the Rue de Tilsitt.

She fled from Eva's villa to the Hotel Métropole in Monte Carlo, but the Mediterranean held too many memories of a three-year-old Willie playing on its shore. She went from Monte Carlo to the Hotel Vendôme in Paris. Here there would be nothing to remind her.

In the sitting room of her suite there was a clock in the shape of a gilt and bronze chariot, complete with horses and driver. Just such a clock, she remembered, just such a clock had been on the mantel of a hotel in Nice more than twenty years ago. Willie had admired it and had begged to be lifted up to see it, to stroke the horses, to touch the wire-thin reins.

Louise began to cry. Her sobs shook her so that she clung, frightened, to the arm of her chair.

"Hold yourself steady," Father Manogue had said. Slowly and painfully she controlled herself.

She had known such destroying grief before, she told herself. She should have learned to bear it. Its wound could not have for her the terrible unfamiliarity that it held for John. She should be stronger than he. But it was John who had been able to go on with his life and she who had shut herself inside her sorrow.

Because she remembered sorrow she should have remembered, too, that one had no right to mourn the dead at the expense of the living. She should, before now, have put away her grief for John's sake, and for Eva's and Clarie's. And for Willie's, she realized in amazement. By clinging to her sorrow she was destroying every memory of him but one. It was the dead Willie she was clinging to. It was the dead Willie with whom she had fled for a year and a half from one empty place to another. If she was to remember the living Willie she must learn to put away her grief before it hid him from her entirely.

Willie had enjoyed every one of his twenty-five years. He would want them to be remembered as happily as he had lived them. He would want her not to mourn but to remember. He would not like to have the recollection of his childhood pleasures bring tears to his mother's eyes.

She walked determinedly across the room to the mantelpiece. She reached out her hand to the clock and touched one little gilt horse. Her tears fell, but she did not sob. She held herself steady and, slowly, her tears stopped.

She remembered the little boy quite clearly now. He had laughed with delight because the reins were so tiny and the horses were just like real. He had suddenly leaned forward and tugged hard on a gilt tail. The clock had fallen and its face had cracked against the marble hearth. Willie had scrambled from his mother's arms and had righted the chariot and the horses. He had dragged them across the smooth marble and he had laughed triumphantly.

"Look, Mammy! Look!" he had shouted, confident that she would be as pleased as he that the useless ornament had become a splendid toy.

Chapter XXX

Katherine

Louise was still at the Vendôme when in the early summer Clarie arrived for his long-promised vacation.

"You look well, Mammy," he said. "Better than in a long time."

She had lightened her mourning. She had removed the bands of crepe and she was wearing pearls and diamonds at her throat and in her ears.

"For the child's sake," Mrs. Mock and Theresa had said.

Clarie still seemed to her a child. In many ways he was only a boy. He deserved to have his mother look as young and pretty as she could manage. Perhaps because he was the youngest he would always seem to her more a boy than a man. Perhaps she would never entirely believe in the grown-up Clarie. Her lips quivered as she studied his new, carefully trimmed red mustache.

He stroked it proudly. "Notice my mustache?"

"Clarie darling, who could fail to notice it?" She laughed helplessly. "Forgive me, but you look exactly as you did when you were four years old and dressed up as a policeman. I must get out the portrait to show you."

"Well, don't get it out now. They say a girl admires a fellow with a mustache. I don't want anything to spoil the effect of mine."

"Is there a girl, Clarie?"

"There is; my girl. At least she isn't yet, but soon, I hope, she'll be my girl. We met on the ship coming over. She's Katherine Duer and she's as beautiful as her name."

Louise remembered the name of Duer. The *Home Journal* had mentioned it often and she had read in Mrs. Ellet's book about Lady Stirling and her daughter Lady Kitty Duer. This modern Katherine Duer had been described by the papers as the loveliest of the young Duchess of Marlborough's bridesmaids.

"I know the name," she said.

"And I want you to know the girl. She and her mother are staying in Paris for a few weeks. I'm taking her to dine at the Tour d'Argent tomorrow night. Beth and André Poniatowski will chaperon us. I'd like to call for Katherine a little early and bring her to see you."

"So it's Katherine already?"

"Well, things go fast on shipboard, seeing each other all day and evening. I'm glad I saw her first on a ship. She's tall and she has a proud way of holding her head so that she always seems to be standing on a high place with her face in the wind. She's like a figure on the prow of a sailing ship, if you can imagine a carved figure being slim and graceful as a reed, as well as proud and brave. I'm sure Katherine's brave, you can see it in her eyes."

"Why, Clarie, you sound positively poetic."

"She makes a fellow feel poetic. I never cared much for Shakespeare and all that at Beaumont, but looking at her I could. The Dark Lady of the Sonnets must have been like Katherine. She's different from most modern girls. Oh, she's gay and full of fun. Well, when I tell you she's a friend of Birdie's you know she'd have to be. But Katherine has something the others haven't. She's as elegant as one of Charles Dana Gibson's girls but she's more romantic, more mysterious, you'll see, Mammy, tomorrow evening if that's all right. I don't suppose you want to go out, even to a little dinner."

"I'm beginning to go out again, but tomorrow evening I'll leave you to your young selves. Later I'd like to give a dinner to which I can invite her. Eva will be in Paris next week and I think Amalia Torlonia and her husband. And I could ask Egidie."

"All that married set would be fine. But as far as bachelors are concerned, I want to keep her to myself while she's in Paris. It's bad enough that she's going to spend over a month visiting friends in England."

"We can go to Carlton House Terrace. It's ready and waiting for us."

"No good. She's booked solid with country visits and Scotland and all that. But she told me when she's sailing home and I've taken passage on the same ship. And I've got these weeks in Paris. That'll give me a head start on young Manchester and young Wilson and the rest."

"We'll do what we can to make her stay in Paris an agreeable one."

"And may I bring her to you tomorrow?"

"Of course you may. I'm very anxious to see your Dark Lady."

Because Clarie was so obviously in love, his mother discounted much of his description of Katherine. When on the following evening Katherine entered the room Louise caught her breath. This girl had real beauty. Louise had seen it only a few times, more often on the stage than in the nearness of reality. She could picture Katherine on a stage; she could see her standing straight and tall in the warm glow of the footlights. The audience would see first the dark, deep-set, expressive eyes and the smoky cloud of black hair. Later they would notice the perfection of feature, the smooth olive skin, the slender column of her neck.

Katherine held herself like an actress, Louise thought, or like a queen. Then she smiled shyly and moved a little awkwardly as she bent to take Louise's outstretched hand.

Louise felt the cool, long-fingered hand tremble as it clasped her own. The girl must be nervous at meeting Clarie's mother. She was young, not more than nineteen. For all her distinction and elegance of dress, her poise was not secure. She had not yet grown up to her beauty.

Louise drew Katherine to the sofa beside her. She admired the pale mauve orchids that were pinned to the décolletage of her cream lace dress.

"Clarie sent them, Mrs. Mackay. He sent more than those. Where's my hat, Clarie?"

"In the hall. I'll get it."

"I shan't put it on till just before we go to the restaurant. I want the flowers to stay fresh. Clarie bet me on the boat that he could send me more orchids than I could wear. But he lost. They're my favorite flowers."

Katherine took the hat from Clarie and held it out to his mother. The gauzy brim was wreathed and lined with sprays of orchids.

"Mamma thought real flowers on a hat were rather *outré*, but I don't see why, especially in Paris. I know they wouldn't do on Washington Square or Murray Hill."

"No one will know they're real, my dear," Louise said. "And even if they do, it won't matter, they're so pretty."

As they talked, Louise noticed how often and how softly Katherine's eyes met Clarie's. When they looked at each other they lost the thread of their sentences. Louise, appearing not to notice, set the polite conversation going again.

They spoke of Birdie, of Newport, of the New York horse show, of the opera.

"Do you know, Mammy, that one of Katherine's favorite operas is *Mignon*? She happened to mention it when she heard me whistling '*Connais-tu le pays*.' Isn't that a coincidence? I told her how when I was a boy I learned from you to love it."

"A nice coincidence," Louise said and thought that young people in love had an aptitude for creating such coincidences.

As she smiled and talked she felt an unfamiliar little pang. So it was true, a woman was jealous of her daughter-in-law. Perhaps she would not have been jealous of Birdie, but Birdie was like herself. In loving her, Willie had loved his mother a little. This beautiful stranger was nothing like Louise; and she was a stranger.

Louise talked and hid her thoughts. It was a very small pang; it should be quite easy to hide.

When they left Louise walked with them to the entrance hall of her suite. Katherine stopped before the mirror and lifted her hat, placing it like a May queen's bright flowered crown on the dark waves of her hair.

Louise looked up at her and smiled with genuine pleasure. She was content that Katherine should be the next Mrs. Mackay.

While Katherine was in Paris, Clarie saw her every day. They rode in the Bois, they dined with friends and with Louise. Clarie took her to tea at the Pré-Catelan. He organized for her pleasure a boat trip on the Seine. He escorted her to the races.

Katherine, in the Bois in her brown riding habit faced with sky blue, or at Longchamp in a pale, embroidered frock and a softly plumed picture hat, was too vivid, too conspicuously lovely for Clarie to be allowed to keep her to himself.

"You might as well try to hide a bird of paradise in a flock of sparrows," he said to his mother.

Clarie's most persistent rival was Guy de Lubersac. Louise was glad that Clarie had so eligible a rival. A man liked to feel that a race was hard to win.

Clarie would win, she thought, and not because of the fortune to which he was heir. Katherine was her parents' only child. They had spoiled her and denied her nothing, so that she had never been aware of any need for money. And she was, as Clarie had said, romantic. She would not fall in love with wealth, though, no doubt, she would enjoy spending it.

Louise studied the young couple and she was certain that it was Clarie himself, not his possessions, that drew Katherine to him. At nineteen one could be dazzled as easily by a title as by a fortune, but Katherine turned always from the Count de Lubersac to Clarie.

Though to his mother he seemed a boy, to Katherine, four years younger than he, he must seem a man. He was not quite as tall as she but he was sturdily built. Katherine, for all her height, had a fragile quality like the tallest spray of her favorite flower. Standing broad-shouldered beside her, Clarie looked strong and capable of taking care of her.

After Katherine left for England, Clarie suggested to his mother that they take a trip together.

"We can go to London," Louise said. "You'll be bound to be invited by some of Katherine's friends."

"No, I'd rather wait till the ship, where we can be alone. Even if she got me invited to Blenheim and those places, I'd never get a chance to see her. So for the rest of the summer you and I are going to have a holiday. It's been a long time. What do you say to Trouville and then Homburg? Will you come, Mammy?"

"Of course I will."

This would be the last holiday with Clarie, she thought.

Katherine and Clarie became engaged on the homeward journey. Clarie wrote the news to his mother and added that for a while the engagement would be a private one. Mr. and Mrs. Duer advised them to wait and John agreed. They were young, the parents said, and should take a little time to be sure of their own hearts.

"And, of course, there's the difference in their religions," John said when he joined Louise for a short holiday at Biarritz.

"Why, John, I never thought you'd be the one to care about a mixed marriage."

"I don't, but Clarie and Katherine ought to think about it. I've seen a difference in religion make trouble between man and wife, real bad trouble. It's not always as easy for Catholic and Protestant as it was for Mémé and the colonel."

"Marriage is never easy. I think if it breaks over religion it would have broken anyway."

"And, of course, they're lucky that they'll not have their elders making difficulties about it. You won't because of your father. And Mrs. Duer has a sister who's a convert. And, too, her people were from Baltimore originally; they don't feel about Catholics down there as some do in New York."

"And Mr. Duer?"

"He's as easygoing as myself on such matters. So, luckily, it'll be up to the young folks entirely. And they seem untroubled by it. The fact is, they're not troubled by anything. They're walking on a cloud, the pair of them. I think the engagement will be announced any day and that'll be a happy day and a lucky one, in my opinion, for the Mackay family."

"She's very beautiful."

"She is that. And unspoiled. You'd think her lovely head would be turned by all the attention she's received, but not at all. And she's no fool. I could tell that when I talked a bit about the cable business and old days on Comstock. I tell you, Louise, I'm proud of the boy for winning a girl like that, damn proud."

On New Year's Day of 1898 Joseph Telfener died after a short illness at Rome. Louise hastened to her sister's side. She felt a hot anger that it was the good, kind Joseph who was taken, while Ferdinand was left to flourish.

Louise was still with Ada when in February word came that Katherine's and Clarie's engagement was to be announced on the eighteenth. The wedding would take place in May.

Katherine wrote to ask if Inez Telfener could be one of her bridesmaids. She was, she said, inviting Inez instead of her older sister because Clarie had told her that Edna's engagement to Don Giacomo de Martino was soon to be announced.

Louise was touched that Katherine should include one of Clarie's faraway Italian cousins in her bridal party. She persuaded Ada to give her consent.

"And you must go over with Inez, my darling."

"But my mourning." Ada wept and touched the edge of her veil. "And poor Joseph so lately, so lately——"

"Joseph would want you to go. He would want Inez to have this little honor, this little pleasure. And how can the child accept if you refuse?"

"But I'll look a poor black crow of a wedding guest, and you can't ask me to put off my black."

"Of course not. But you must lighten it for the occasion. You must leave off your crepe and put on your pearls and diamonds."

"If you ask me to, Louise."

"It's not for me I ask, it's for our children, for your Inez and my Clarie."

The wedding date was fixed for the seventeenth of May.

Louise arrived in New York on the *Lucania* on the thirtieth of April. Ada, Inez, and Eva were to sail directly from Italy.

It saddened Louise that her mother had not felt equal to the journey. After her husband's death Mrs. Hungerford had aged. Before that, despite her white hair, the years had seemed to touch her lightly. Now, suddenly, she was old.

On the afternoon of Louise's arrival Mrs. Duer called on her at the Waldorf-Astoria.

Katherine's mother was a pretty, blue-eyed, light-haired woman. She had a lazy, infectious laugh and a soft slow voice which she must have inherited from her southern mother. Clarie, Louise decided, was lucky in his future mother-in-law. She was gentler than the crisp New York ladies whom Louise remembered.

Mrs. Duer suggested that they take a drive. "I have the carriage waiting and there'll be many changes for you to notice. Oh dear, whenever one returns to New York there are so many changes."

Each time Louise came to New York it startled her. She kept always her childhood memory of the city. When, in the spring of 1895, she had come over with Clarie to celebrate his twenty-first birthday, it had still, as in previous visits, been the New York of 1853 that she had unconsciously expected to see.

As she drove with Mrs. Duer on Fifth Avenue, she admired the Renaissance Vanderbilt mansions that seemed to be rising on every block. She glanced with pride at St. Patrick's twin spires, but it was the old St. Patrick's she remembered, and the brownstone houses, and Broadway, bright with omnibuses and the harbor and rivers, crowded with ships whose masts seemed tall as Trinity's spire.

"I wish," Mrs. Duer said, "that you'd be kind enough to come with me to Twenty-first Street. I'd like to tell you my plans for the seventeenth and it's so much easier to explain when one's actually in the house."

"I shall be delighted."

"And the guest list. We must go over the guest list. I'm quite beside myself with it. I believe Willie Duer is related to everybody in New York. And then there are my brothers and sisters and nephews and nieces. Hattie Fearing and George will come down from Boston, and Louisa and Jim Wadsworth from Geneseo. And there are quite a few of us in New York too: my cousins Nellie and Jimmie Speyer and——" She laughed. "Still, we're not as many as all those Duers and Gracies and Kings of Willie's, which is a good thing. It keeps him from fussing at the size of the wedding. Oh, and there are Katherine's friends, all that new, young crowd, the Harry Payne Whitneys, the Belmont Tiffanys and Alfred Vanderbilt and Willie K., Jr., and the young Tommy Hitchcocks and the rest. So attractive they all are but, dear me, so numerous. And you and I must go over the list. Clarie gave me several names that he knew you and Mr. Mackay would want, the Levi Mortons and the Ogden Mills and a few others. You must look and tell me if you have any additions."

"Fortunately my additions are safely in London and Paris."

"Well, perhaps it is fortunate. As you can see my house is really rather small."

The carriage had stopped at 17 West Twenty-first Street.

Louise remembered when houses like this one had seemed to her the largest and most imposing in the world. Up just such steps as these she had walked with her mother. The familiar shape and pattern of the Duer residence, as she entered it, still seemed handsome to her. The high-ceilinged drawing rooms opening one into the other had been her first picture of elegance. They were a little narrower than she remembered but they were still elegant. They had style, they had a cramped, old-fashioned, New York distinction that the vast new mansions would always lack.

"The ceremony is to take place at this end of the main drawing room," Mrs. Duer said. "Both rooms will be done all in white flowers, with apple blossoms against the walls. Just here, where Archbishop Corrigan is to stand, we'll have a sort of grotto of lilies. Thorley is doing the floral decorations and he suggested American Beauties for the hall and dining room. They're all the rage of course, and they make a fine show."

"And they'll be becoming to Katherine. Not many girls can stand beside them."

"She is striking, isn't she? I've never quite understood how I produced anything so dramatic. But the Duers have always had a gift for drama, in their looks as in everything else. Now upstairs in the library—if you'll come this way."

Louise, as she followed her hostess up the stairs, did not say that she knew the way. The library would overlook the street. At the back would be the bedroom where the lady of the house waited for her seamstress.

"And here is the list. Sit here beside me, dear Mrs. Mackay, and look it over. I naturally want to be sure it meets with your approval."

"Of course it will. Still, I'm interested to see it."

Louise studied the list. It included new names, many of them friends of Katherine's and Clarie's, but the core of the list was the old New York which long ago she had determined should open its doors to her children.

Here they were just as she remembered them. Mr. and Mrs. Bayard Cutting, Mr. and Mrs. Elbridge Gerry, Colonel and Mrs. William Jay, Mr. and Mrs. Edward King . . .

Here were the names that she had seen in the *Home Journal* and in Mrs. Ellet's book, that she had heard at Mrs. Stevens': Beekman, Bronson, Livermore, Lispenard, Livingston, Loomis, Turnure, Van Cortland, Van Rensselaer, Warren, Winthrop, Whitehouse . . .

Even though she cared less about them, even though their world itself mattered less, she felt a profound satisfaction that they should be present to see her son marry the fairest of their daughters.

"A very nice list," she said and returned it to Mrs. Duer.

"How I'll ever feed them all properly, I don't know. But Walter

Bussell of the Newport Casino is serving and he's experienced at this sort of thing. He suggested small tables. We're having Lander's orchestra, they're very gay and modern. Oh, they'll do *Lohengrin* solemnly enough, but after the ceremony they'll give a cheerful tone. One needs that so at a wedding, I always think, so many old people one's parents knew and relations one has avoided for years."

"I'm sure it will be charming."

"I hope it will. Up here I'm going to have nothing but pink and white flowers. They'll lighten the gloom of all those law books of Willie Duer's. I'll put vases of sweet peas and moss roses everywhere. Now let's go down and have a cup of tea in the drawing room. Of course all the banisters will be done with smilax, and we'll have potted palms and ferns on the landings. Do you really think it will be pretty, Mrs. Mackay?"

"I think it will be lovely."

"I should like it to be perfect. I'd like to give Katherine a day she can remember always. She's my only daughter, so you can understand."

"I understand."

The weeks before the wedding were filled with festivities. Katherine's parents and relations entertained John and Louise. John and Louise gave a dinner at the Waldorf-Astoria in honor of Archbishop Corrigan and Mr. and Mrs. Duer.

Mr. Duer was a tall dark man with courtly manners and a shy, warm smile. John liked him and said he was a clever man as well as a charming one.

Katherine's presents included handsome jewels. Louise had had made for her in Paris a deep diamond collar with large pendant diamonds. Clarie gave her an emerald and diamond necklace and a toilet set of gold and turquoise.

John's present to her was the deed to six hundred acres of hilly and wooded land overlooking the Sound near the village of Roslyn on Long Island, and the promise that she could build any kind of house she desired.

"She told me she'd rather build than buy," John said to Louise.

"Doesn't she know the old saying that fools build houses for wise men to live in? Well, I know enough not to start my career as a mother-in-law by giving unasked advice."

"You also know a present is no good if it's only to the giver's liking.

Katherine had her heart set on that hilltop. Let her build what she's a mind to on it."

The wedding day was fair and mild.

Louise put off her black for the occasion. She wore a gown of pearl-gray crepe de Chine and a small bonnet trimmed with point lace and silver. At her waist was the bouquet of violets that Katherine had sent her.

When she and John entered the Duers' drawing rooms the guests were assembled between white satin ribbons which formed an aisle. The improvised altar and the two prie-dieux were placed against a curving mass of lilies. The tall windows were open. On the walls the apple blossoms stirred in the breeze.

Mrs. Duer entered. Her gown was of sky-blue satin, trimmed with cream Chantilly lace and silver sequins. She took her place beside Louise.

"Everything is perfect," Louise said, "just as you hoped. Katherine will remember."

The laughter and the conversation of the wedding guests was not quieted by the arrival of Archbishop Corrigan accompanied by Father Ducey and Father Connelly, who would assist him in the ceremony.

When Clarie entered with his best man, followed by his ushers, there was a louder ripple of talk. What Louise could hear of it was complimentary.

Then came the bridesmaids: Evelyn Byrd Burden, Lila Vanderbilt Sloane, Daisy Leiter, May Goelet, Katherine Neilson, and Inez. There were many admiring comments as they moved forward to the slow tempo of the march from *Lohengrin*. They were pretty girls, and so seemed even prettier dressed alike in white lace over turquoise-blue silk. Their headdresses were of blue aigrettes and they carried bouquets of gardenias.

The loudly chattering guests were suddenly still, every head turned, the music of the orchestra was the only sound as Katherine came through the far door on her father's arm.

Her dress, cut with a long train, was of silver brocade, draped at the bodice with soft malines lace. Her tulle veil was held back by clusters of orange blossoms. Her bouquet was of white orchids. Her only ornament was a pearl and diamond pendant which Clarie had given her on the eve of the wedding.

The details of the beautiful costume Louise would see and study later. Now it was only Katherine herself whom she saw, whom all saw.

The wedding breakfast was as gay as Mrs. Duer had hoped. Louise looked often at the bridal table where Katherine and Clarie sat with their attendants. The names of the best man and the ushers, like those of the bridesmaids, were a mixture of old and new: Columbus Baldwin, Walter Martin of San Francisco, Fred Betts, Williams Burden, Philip Lydig, Frank Lyon Polk. Their world, Louise thought, would be a new one which they could fashion to their liking. It should, if one could judge by their handsome laughing young faces, be a happy one.

When all was over and the bride and groom and the guests had departed Mr. Duer took John up to the library to have a drink and a cigar. Louise and Mrs. Duer were left in the drawing room.

"It was perfect," Louise said. "The flowers, the music, the champagne, the food, every single detail. But after the details are forgotten, not one of those who were present will forget your girl as she came through the doorway and walked toward the altar. They may forget what the veil and the dress were like, but they'll always remember Katherine."

Chapter XXXI

····——◆◉◆——····

Coronation Season

QUEEN VICTORIA DIED on the evening of January 22, 1901. When Louise heard the news she could not keep her thoughts in the present. Everywhere in England, she supposed, and in Europe and America, the death of the old Queen must have set people to remembering. Few were left who had known a time when Victoria had not been Queen.

For longer than my lifetime, Louise thought, and remembered the crooked length of Pearl Street. She remembered 9 Grand Street and the colored embroidery silks on the table in the lamplight, and *Godey's Lady's Book.* In its pages there must have been references to the fashions of Victoria's court, but Louise remembered best an American lady's golden cloak trimmed with sable. Before Grand Street there was the dim memory of a memory of the barbershop on West Broadway and the rich smell of pomade and the giant chair that towered like a throne. She remembered quite clearly the ship on which she and Mémé and Grandmother Visera had sailed from New York on the beginning of their journey to Downieville. There had been so many journeys since then, and so many places. And so much time, Victoria's time, which had now run out.

She and John had come a long road in the old Queen's time, Louise thought. It had been, on the whole, a good road. There had been sorrow, but it wasn't only on an upward path that one met sorrow. And they had known happiness. She remembered the beginning of their happiness in the house on the corner of Howard and Taylor streets. Such a fine house it had seemed. And their first trip abroad. Even their anxiety for Eva had not diminished the excitement of that first European journey.

Through Clarie and Katherine their happiness continued. A daughter had been born to Katherine. Louise had gone to the States to see her. The baby Katherine, whom they called K, was like her mother, with black ringlets and dark inquiring eyes which appeared enormous in her little face. Louise remembered more vividly than the child or her parents the look on John's face as he held his grandchild. He would not love her better than Eva's children, but this was the grandchild of his flesh. This was the continuation of his life into the new generation. K, Louise knew, would always have a special place in her affection because of the look she had brought to her grandfather's face.

Louise thought of Andrea and Bianca and Marco. They and their mother had spent the last two summers with her at a house she had rented in Kent. Ada had also come from Italy with her younger children. All the cousins, here and in America, were growing up, safe and happy, in the world that she and John had made for them.

John, at seventy, had still not retired. That must wait, he said, until he brought his most recent project to a successful conclusion.

This project was to lay the first cable across the Pacific via Hawaii and Guam to the Philippines. Clarie was working closely with his father. John at his age shouldn't be working at all, Louise thought, but she could not regret the project that brought him closer, day by day, to his younger son.

She thought of Clarie and Katherine and of their new residence, Harbor Hill, which she had not yet seen. Clarie had sent his mother copies of McKim, Mead and White's sketches of the various elevations and they promised considerable grandeur, but grandeur was becoming to Katherine.

In June of 1900 Louise had given her first large entertainment since Willie's death, a dinner and concert in honor of her son and daughter-in-law, who were visiting London. She could still see Katherine standing beside her at the head of the stairs. In Katherine's dark hair, boldly adding to her height, was a tiara of diamonds and turquoises. Her gown of satin white as marble was skillfully cut and draped to display her tall, slender figure. Louise smiled as she remembered. Grandeur would suit Katherine. The architect didn't exist who could design a residence imposing enough to overshadow her. In the years since her marriage the girl had grown up to her beauty.

Once she had begun again to entertain on a grand scale, Louise continued. Six Carlton House Terrace was not a house in which to be alone. But the excitement of receiving the elite, even royalty, had ebbed. Perhaps she had lost the habit of it, or perhaps, in the end, one tired of a game at which one could not lose.

For her latest scrapbook she had collected more items about Katherine than about herself. It pleased her that the young Mrs. Mackay was taking her proper position in society.

She must, she thought, start a new album with the coronation. The final clipping in the completed album was from the New York *Herald*. The headlines read:

MRS. MACKAY'S
DINNER DANCE

One of the Most Brilliant Social
Events of the Season at
the Waldorf-Astoria

ORCHID DECKED TABLE
Foyer where the Guests Were Re-
ceived and Adjoining Corridors
Turned into Electric Bowers.

It might have been a party of her own, Louise thought, as she reread the description of Katherine's elaborate entertainment.

John had promised he would retire when the cable was laid and in operation. Louise was willing to retire, too, and let her daughter-in-law take her place, but before she did she would like to see the coronation season. She would persuade John to take her to the coronation. They would, she was sure, be able to arrange for two tickets to the Abbey. That would be a fitting ending to their long upward journey.

At the beginning of the summer of 1902 the arrangements for the laying of the cable were completed. When, at the end of June, John came to London he told Louise that three ships carrying the first sections of the cable would shortly leave England for California.

"Once Congress licked that public-ownership bill, we were in the clear. I explained our project personally to President Roosevelt and he was delighted. We're building without a government subsidy. I hope the Navy Department will let us use the Pacific soundings they made in '91 but if they don't it will only delay us a little. We should lay the California end of the cable down about the first week of December. That'll be quite a sight, Louise. There'll be maybe thirty thousand people watching the ceremony. Will you come to San Francisco to see it?"

"Of course I will."

"Then say by July of next year if all goes well we ought to have the cable operating."

"And then, John?"

"Then, my dear, the world will be ours to choose from. We'll keep this for a town house, but for most of the year we'll find a quieter spot."

"The Riviera?"

"If you like. But I've been looking into southern California. It's got the finest year-round climate there is. There are some lovely little villages along that coast. You remember, J. P. Jones built a grand place for himself at Santa Monica. That's not far from Los Angeles."

"Mr. Hellman always speaks well of Los Angeles, though I notice he left it for San Francisco."

"It's not a place for young people, Louise. But we're getting on. I hope you'll take a fancy to that part of the world. I guess the truth is I'd like to die in America."

"I don't want to die anywhere. But I'll spend our old age wherever you say. And we needn't keep Carlton House Terrace. I'm retiring as well as you. And I gather that, in Harbor Hill, Katherine and Clarie have as splendid a residence as they'll ever need."

"They sure have. Katherine has even grander ideas than you and, if you'll forgive me, Louise, that's going some. She and Clarie have built themselves a white stone palace fit for a king on that hilltop of theirs. It's beautiful, I'm not denying that, mind, and I said they could have what they liked, but I was sure taken aback by the size and the magnificence of it. I told Katherine if she had a dozen children she'd have to tie bells round their necks to find them in the place."

"It may seem a little large for them now, but since they were set on building, I'm glad they did it once and for all. And I like to think that when old Mrs. Mackay retires, young Mrs. Mackay will have a suitable mansion in which to take her place."

"Well, if it pleases you . . ."

"It does. Mostly because its very size and magnificence make it seem true that we're going to let the young pair take over for both of us."

"Soon as the Pacific cable is laid down and in working order."

"I'll go to the San Francisco ceremony with you. But, first, will you go to the coronation with me?"

"Hell, Louise, we went to one coronation."

"I'd like to go to this one. Let Mamie Hungerford have this last little triumph with you there to witness it."

"If that's what you want, old lady, by God you're entitled to it."

Ada and Eva came to London soon after John's arrival. It pleased Louise to have them present at her dinner and concert for Princess Louise. This, she thought, might be the last of her lavish entertainments at Carlton House Terrace. She wished that Clarie and Katherine could have come over for it, but they were busy with the landscaping of their Long Island estate, and Clarie's horses would soon be running at Saratoga.

At noon on Tuesday the fifteenth of July, Louise and John saw Eva off on her return journey to the Continent. Afterward, Louise went to a luncheon party and John went to his office in the City. He was impatient at the government's delay in the matter of the Pacific soundings and he sent off a long cable to Mr. Cook, the Commercial Cable Company's lawyer in New York. He then went to luncheon with Mr. Ward, vice-president and general manager of the company, at the Winchester House.

When Louise returned to Carlton House Terrace, she found Mr. Ward waiting for her. John, he told her, had not felt well at luncheon.

"He complained of the heat, Mrs. Mackay, as well he might. It's the hottest day we've had this year. He consented to be put to bed and I took the liberty of sending for the doctor. He's with him now."

"You think it's just the heat, Mr. Ward?"

"It may well be, but he may be coming down with a summer cold. As we were driving here in a cab, he complained of a chill. I'll leave you now so you can go to him, but before I do I'll tell you one thing that I know will please you. As we were leaving the office to go to luncheon, he said, 'I think I've worked long enough. I'll just see to the laying down of the American Pacific Cable and then take a rest.'"

John's temperature alarmed the doctor. This was more than a summer cold. It could be pneumonia. He suggested a consultation.

On Wednesday John was no better, but on Thursday and Friday he seemed to improve and the doctors were guardedly optimistic. One could not be certain, they said, there was still the possibility that one lung was congested, and at his age the heart, they said . . . But it was encouraging that the patient's breathing was easier and that his fever was down.

On Saturday John's condition grew worse. He complained of no pain and he slept a great deal.

The doctors talked anxiously together. They said little to Louise, and the medical phrases they offered her were as devoid of meaning as they were of comfort.

Doctors were always mysterious, Louise told herself. She listened to John's heavy breathing. It had been worse than this on Wednesday and he had got better.

Ada called her sister out of the sickroom. "You must send for a priest," she said.

"Really, Ada, what a thing to suggest!" Louise exclaimed impatiently. "You know John is never much of a one for religion. And when he's sick, of all times!"

"Of all times," Ada repeated gently. "You must, my poor darling."

The pity in Ada's eyes mirrored the fear which Louise had refused to acknowledge.

"Very well," she said. "Send for Father Forster. Call me when he comes, Ada. I must take him in to John myself."

When, hesitantly, Louise brought the priest into the room John stared at them. For a moment she thought he was going to be angry.

Then he smiled at her.

"That's my girl," he said. "I always told Pat Manogue he needn't worry about me, that you'd see me safe on my way. I hope, Father, I don't need you as bad as I think I do, but thanks for coming around."

Louise left John alone with Father Forster. She beckoned the doctor and nurse to follow her.

When a little later the priest called her back into the room, she kept telling herself: This needn't be the end. The last rites don't mean—they don't necessarily mean . . .

Mechanically she obeyed the priest's directions and tried to keep herself from thinking of the finality of the sacrament.

After the priest had gone John reached for her hand.

"Thanks, old lady," he said and fell asleep.

On Sunday, John was conscious for only a few moments of the day. Louise sat beside him.

He was unconscious when at six-thirty in the evening he died.

Louise never remembered very clearly the days that immediately followed John's death.

Presently the doctors told her that she had suffered a heart attack. It was, they thought, due to shock. She must remain in bed, they said, and leave the funeral arrangements to her daughter and to her son, who would soon be in London. After that she must go to Bad Nauheim and place herself under the care of the great German heart specialist.

It was not shock, Louise knew. If her heart was damaged it was because she was almost fifty-nine years old. She had suffered shock before. She had known grief. Grief, she thought wearily, should not be a stranger to her, except that it was always a stranger, it was always different. She wept. She did not sob then or later.

There was no hysteria, no wild anger in her grief for John. She cried softly and tiredly and often unexpectedly when she was not alone. Like Ada; Ada fingering her crepe veil and weeping for Joseph.

John's death had been quick and without pain. She thought of Jim Flood's long-drawn-out suffering and knew she should not begrudge John the easiness of his going.

She listened when Eva and Clarie told her of their arrangements for their father. Seeing their anxiety that she be pleased, she praised them: Yes, it sounded as though they had made a most beautiful chapel of the ballroom. Yes, St. Mary's in Cadogan Square would have been her own choice. Yes, he should rest at the Notting Hill Franciscan convent until the doctors would let her take him to Greenwood.

"Yes, Eva. Yes, Clarie. Thank you, my dears."

John had had the priest before he died. For that she was grateful. But she could not keep her mind on the arrangements which his children were so lovingly making for him. Her thoughts kept going back to the old years. She could see as if it were now instead of then: John, unknown to her, standing in Mrs. Mock's parlor with the Rosener brothers; John helping Eva down the steep steps of the Fairs' porch late on a Christmas afternoon; John flushing and stammering with anger at Mr. Sharon's contempt for the Irishmen. There were so many years to remember. On November twenty-fifth, they would have numbered thirty-five. She remembered the announcement in the *Enterprise:*

"The union of so estimable a couple and the devotion of a thousand worthier friends make every wish of joy and prosperity which we would utter superfluous and so we simply offer the congratulations which all who know them must extend to two so worthily mated that none can say which made the better choice."

Thirty-five years was a lifetime. And the lifetime for her and for John was over.

Chapter XXXII

Old Mrs. Mackay

THE DOCTOR AT Bad Nauheim, intending to be encouraging, had frightened Louise. One could, he had assured her, live for a long time with a heart condition like hers. If she was careful she could count on thirty years or more.

The English and French doctors agreed with the German specialist. In addition, they pointed out, there was the all-important factor of heredity. Mrs. Mackay came of a long-lived family.

How would she manage? Louise wondered uneasily. They had all depended on her, her father and Mémé, Ada and Eva; and she had depended on John. It was his strength she had given to the others. How would she manage without him?

Louise learned to manage alone. Old Mrs. Mackay, she had called herself to John, only half meaning it. Now she slowly learned to play the part.

For eighteen years, except for occasional visits to Clarie and Katherine, she remained in Europe. It was easier to grow old in familiar places. She kept her London house, but she spent most of the year in Paris where she had rented an apartment on the Avenue du Bois.

The years went quickly. Time and her world contracted at an ever-increasing rate.

Her mother's death in 1908 was not a shock. Mémé had been in failing health for so long. Her death was a release not from pain but from the burden of living.

Ada's death, two years later, was a greater sorrow. Poor little Ada, she was too young to die. How odd, Louise thought, to have reached an age where fifty-three seemed young.

Few of the old friends and acquaintances were left. There was Lady Mary Lloyd. There was Alice Hubbard. Louise did not like Alice much. She seemed always to have sprung full-panoplied from the brow of Mme. Ritz. But she was Louise's contemporary. There were fewer and fewer of those.

There was the church in the Avenue Hoche. Louise went to St. Joseph's Church and Father MacDarby came faithfully to call on her. His visit added one more little engagement to her week.

The invitations to the large engagements still came and Louise pasted them in a scrapbook but she did not often accept. It was easier to reminisce to Father MacDarby about her acquaintance with such famous princes of the Church as Cardinal Manning and Cardinal Vaughan, or to talk with her secretary, Mr. Stopford, about her secular titled friends, the prince who had been for so few years a king and his princess, the Lornes, the Duchess of Manchester and the rest.

She joined with Clarie in giving to the University of Nevada a School of Mines in memory of John, though she did not share Clarie's sentimental feeling of obligation to that state. She hoped the poor boy was not counting on its enduring gratitude. Still, John had a fondness for the place; he might be pleased. She was pleased that a statue of John by Gutzon Borglum was to stand in the university grounds. She might almost make the journey to see it. But no, Nevada was too long ago, too far away.

Clarie sent her a photograph of the statue. She could imagine it, standing tall and strong, in the blinding Nevada sunlight. John was dressed in miner's clothes, the shirt open at the neck. He was wearing just such a shirt of gray flannel the first time she ever saw him. He would like to be thus remembered. For the sculptor to have put a pick in his hand was, she thought, to paint the lily. But John, no doubt, would be delighted.

Pleasant things happened in those years.

Katherine's and Clarie's third child was a son. He was named John William for his grandfather and his uncle. Katherine called him

"Boy" as Birdie did her Vanderbilt son. These girls and their fads! The fads never lasted long. In the end, young Willie K. and Clarie would see that their sons were allowed to outgrow the childish nickname and be called Willie.

Early in her widowhood Louise had been given a Pomeranian puppy by Clarie. To Louise, an old lady and her dog had always seemed a sight as dreary as it was inevitable, but she had not wanted to hurt Clarie's feelings and she had become fond of the animal. From then on she had always one and sometimes two of the handsome, alert little dogs. They were good company, she discovered, and thought that the ways of old wives, like their tales, were usually based on wisdom. The shrill barking annoyed others, she supposed, but it pleased her. She was growing extremely deaf and the barking, faintly heard, warned her of a knock on the door or of an approaching footstep. Her Pomeranians helped her to avoid some of the humiliations of deafness.

In 1905 Eva's daughter had married the Count Jules de Bonvouloir. He was a good-looking, good-tempered, witty Frenchman. And he was kind, Louise learned as she watched him with his sisters as well as with Bianca and his mother-in-law. During the war it turned out that Jules was also brave. Bianca, deeply in love with him and anxious for his safety, was still proud of his decorations won under fire.

The war years were lonely ones. Louise was separated from Eva, who worked in an Italian hospital. She was grateful for Bianca's presence in Paris.

In March of 1919 Eva died of influenza at Santa Margherita.

Louise, almost unable to believe this final sorrow, sat beside her as she lay dying. Not Eva, not her daughter. She should be lying there while Eva sat beside her.

Eva put her hand in her mother's. "Don't feel bad, Mammy," she said, "I'm not frightened. I always told you I wasn't worldly."

Eva was not frightened. She knew she was going to die but she was calm and smiling. Louise did not understand her daughter's serenity in the face of death, but it comforted her a little.

When Eva was gone there was nothing to keep Louise in Europe.

At the beginning of the war Katherine and Clarie had been divorced in Paris. Katherine had remained in France and had remarried.

Clarie had tried, ever since, to persuade his mother that once the war and the submarine danger were over, she must come home and be the mistress of his estate in Roslyn. He even promised to buy a town house, instead of renting for the winter as he had always done. He had his eye on a suitable house just off Fifth Avenue on Seventy-fifth Street. There would be room in it for many of her possessions. The ballroom was made to order for her tapestries.

Louise decided to go. Bianca was happy with Jules. Their sole disappointment was that they had no children, but the fact that they had only each other seemed to draw them even closer together. Bianca did not need her grandmother nor did the Colonna boys; they weren't boys any more, they were men.

Clarie's children were younger. Perhaps, as he said, they needed their grandmother or, at least, would like to have her. She was not sure she could help him with them, they were nearly grown up and she was almost a stranger to them. But, for Clarie's sake, she would try.

K, Ellin, and Willie were tall young strangers. Louise had seen them as babies and as children. The last time had been in the summer of 1914. In six years they had outgrown childhood, even the boy who was now thirteen.

Mrs. Duer had died in 1903 and Mr. Duer not long after. Louise was the only grandparent the children knew. They were frightened, she thought, by her great age, and they were sorry for her. They tried politely to hide their pity, but she saw it in their eyes and knew it embarrassed them.

Poor things, she wanted to tell them that in the end, for everyone, two alternatives were left: one could be old or one could be dead. And, if one's mind was clear and one's health reasonably good, it was better to be old. But she could not mention death to them. They would not know where to look if she spoke the awkward word. Death for them was far away, beyond any visible horizon; for poor Granny it was a natural expectation.

She could not tell them that looking back on a lifetime was in some respects better than looking ahead. They wouldn't believe her. They had their three beautiful futures practically untouched; poor Granny had only the past. They would not understand if she told them that one never had the future safe until it became the past.

Her past was unalterably hers; their futures were as they might be. She knew the past; they could only dream the future, poor young things. How absurd they would think her if she were to tell them that the old found any reason to pity the young.

Sometimes the grandchildren asked her about the past and she told them a little. They could not listen for long; they had too much to tell. As they grew accustomed to her and, she believed, even fond of her, they talked to her and she listened. That was her role: to listen, to comfort, and to explain to their father.

Poor Clarie appeared to them so fierce when he was trying only to protect them. He had not yet learned that no one, not even a parent, can make another's life safe. She listened as he told her his hopes and his plans for his son and daughters. Sometimes they talked of the past, but more often, with Clarie as with his children, she listened.

There was one person who listened to her, the pretty, young auburn-haired trained nurse, Miss Mary Finerty. The children called her Finny. She had come to them when Willie was eight years old.

Clarie had always been a great one for protecting his children. Louise would never forget the retinue that had accompanied them on their arrival in London in 1913: two Canadian trained nurses, a Danish governess, an American tutor, a French courier, and a German maid.

Now the girls had a chaperone, Miss Josephine Noel. Louise liked her and approved of the careful manner in which she charted their social course. Willie had a tutor. They had outgrown Mary Finerty and Louise had inherited her.

With age one's infirmities increased at a steady creeping pace and Louise was grateful that she had someone as gentle and tactful as Miss Finny to care for her.

The New York heart specialist recommended to his patient abstemiousness in her diet. The nurse protested only mildly when Louise disregarded the doctor's instructions. Miss Finny, wise, Louise thought, beyond her years, knew that a hearty appetite and a good digestion were small but agreeable blessings for an old lady, particularly for one who, for her figure's sake, had denied herself for many years. Miss Finny was too sensible to think one should do without any blessings that were going.

Louise looked back wistfully at the sumptuous meals she had

offered her guests: the mushrooms under glass, the plovers' eggs in jelly, the mousse of chicken, the crusted *pâté de foie gras,* all the delicious rich dishes which she had allowed herself only to taste. Now when she felt like it she stuffed. Fortunately, Clarie, like his mother, had always an excellent chef.

Mary Finerty was kind and she had quick, competent hands, but above all, she listened. Her Irish blue eyes seemed to grow even larger when Louise described the party for President Grant or the first one for the Prince and Princess of Wales.

"Oh, Mrs. Mackay," she would say. "It's like something you'd read in a book."

The nurse understood the early pages of the book as the sheltered grandchildren never could. Mary Finerty had been born and brought up in a mining town. The Scranton mines held coal, not precious metal, but there had been fortunes made and lost, and there had been terrifying disasters. And Mary Finerty also understood that a living must be earned. She was interested when Louise told her that she had earned hers by going out to sew.

"Though I was never as clever as my mother. She did the most beautiful embroidery you ever saw, Miss Finny."

Louise described the piano lessons that Father Manogue had arranged for her to give.

"He became a bishop later, but I always think of him as Father. Those piano lessons! He meant it in kindness and I was grateful, but it was the hardest work I ever did in my life. I was never really very good at the piano."

Remembering out loud was a pleasure that the old were not often given, Louise thought, but Miss Finny gave it generously. Louise spoke of little Marie who had died in Virginia City and of Theresa Fair.

"I think Mrs. Fair was the most absolutely pretty woman I ever saw."

She spoke of her father. Sometimes when Louise and Mary Finerty had luncheon alone, Louise stopped on her way from the dining room through the great central hall to look at the gilt and glass case in which Colonel Hungerford's sword lay on a bed of antique velvet.

"You know, Miss Finny, Mr. Mackay does many things to please me, but it pleases me the most that among all his beautiful possessions my father's sword should have a place of honor. And Mr. Mackay didn't do it for me, he did it for his grandfather long before I came over."

Louise returned to Paris for a visit in the summer of 1923. She stayed at the Plaza-Athénée. Demoutier and one of the granddaughters and Mary Finerty were with her.

The granddaughter enjoyed a Paris that Louise had never known. She lunched at Larue. She dined and danced at Ciro's and the Club Daunou. Her beaux seemed to be mostly young Americans who worked at the Guaranty Trust or Morgan Harjes.

Mary Finerty listened to Louise's account of the Paris she had known. She admired the landmarks that Louise pointed out, the Opéra, the Madeleine. She listened, wide-eyed, to Louise's description of the Trocadéro when it was new and overlooked the Exposition of 1878. She drove up the Champs Élysées with Louise and the chauffeur waited while they walked slowly beside the iron railings that enclosed the gardens of 9 Rue de Tilsitt.

In Paris, as on Long Island and in New York, Mary Finerty took care of Louise and listened to her stories of distant times and places.

Louise reminisced to Mary Finerty, she reminisced with Demoutier. Once Demoutier had been younger than she, now they were two old ladies. Demoutier was titular maid, she selected Louise's costume for the day or the evening. She dressed her hair. She performed all the small, easy services, but most of the work was done by her *seconde* whom she herself engaged and whose name Louise could never remember.

When Mme. Demoutier and Mrs. Mackay reminisced they said little.

Demoutier, hooking one of Louise's black dresses, would say, "Ah, the costumes Madame had in the old time. There was one Madame wore to court the year we moved into Carlton House Terrace. It was sky blue with a pale yellow train and Madame wore her turquoise and diamond parure."

Louise, standing beside the table where she kept her royal photographs, would read an inscription aloud.

Demoutier, straightening the family photographs on the bedside table, would touch the embossed silver that framed John's picture and say, "There was no one like Monsieur. He was good as good bread."

The old ladies needed few words in which to remember together.

Clarie's friends were thoughtful in their attentions to his mother. She liked best of the ladies who called on his account Mrs. Goodhue Livingston. She was a pretty woman and she was amusing. And Louise could hear all her little anecdotes. Mrs. Livingston took the trouble to speak slowly and distinctly, without shouting. She was a kind woman as well as an entertaining one and did not condescend, as some others did, to Louise's age or to her deafness.

Mrs. James Gerard was another faithful visitor. Her father, Marcus Daly, and John had been friends. Mr. Daly had left his children to John's guardianship. Molly Gerard had not forgotten John nor his kindness. Louise could feel that Molly was her own visitor.

She had other visitors who were her own. Whenever they were in the East the De Young girls came to see her at Seventy-fifth Street or at Harbor Hill.

Alice Hubbard came from Paris and was invited to stay. Louise was amused by the startled expression in a granddaughter's eyes when she heard Mrs. Hubbard address her hostess as Louise.

To the other visitors, even to her own, Louise was always Mrs. Mackay. If the grandchildren ever thought of her Christian name they thought of it in the full dignity of Marie Louise. Antoinette they had never heard. M. L. M. were the initials they saw entwined on her Sèvres china and on her Comstock silver. It was a pretty monogram and Louise always used it, but not since Louise Althea had anyone called her Marie Louise. Now in her old age one of Clarie's children returned the name to her. K, the first to be married, called her first baby Marie Louise. Louise was pleased that her first great-grandchild was named for her; she was glad that K had given the baby almost the whole of the beautiful name that Daniel Hungerford had selected for his daughter.

Louise's favorite visitor was Birdie Vanderbilt. Birdie remembered so much and she seemed to like to listen and to talk about the old days. She was always a warmhearted little thing, Louise thought, and no doubt enjoyed giving an old lady pleasure. But Birdie had had much unhappiness in her marriage, so perhaps she too found pleasure in recalling the years when she and Clarie had been young and Willie had been alive.

Birdie's children and Clarie's were the same age. Muriel, Consuelo, and Willie Vanderbilt were each a few months younger than

K, Ellin, and Willie Mackay. It pleased Louise that Theresa's grand-children and hers had been friends since they were born.

Louise often said that she wished Miss Finny might have seen one of her entertainments in Paris or London.

"I can imagine it, Mrs. Mackay. The way you tell it, I can imagine it very well."

"Seeing is different. Not only the beauty and the extravagance—and, dear me, I was extravagant—but the excitement. There's an excitement one can't describe about a great reception or a ball, particularly when royalty is present. Mr. Mackay's father used to say we all got buck fever when royalty entered the door."

In the summer of 1924 Clarie told his mother that he planned to give on September sixth a dinner and ball in honor of the Prince of Wales, who was visiting America.

"Now you'll see, Miss Finny," Louise said. "You'll be with me as you always are when I appear at one of Mr. Mackay's parties. You're my ears, you know, and very much prettier than that unsightly trumpet affair you and Mr. Mackay are always urging on me."

In the prince's honor Clarie illuminated his house and grounds more spectacularly than he had ever done before.

Beside every driveway, as far as one could see into the woods, thousands of colored lanterns were hung. The brilliant clusters, carefully placed, seemed to belong on the thick-leafed branches as though they were a natural autumn bloom that had replaced the dogwood of spring and the rhododendrons of summer.

On the broad white stone steps and terrace that led to the front door, the bay trees and orange trees glowed with tiny lights. Concealed floodlights illuminated the Renaissance mansion and the south terraces and the formal gardens and terrace beyond the west wing. The lighting was not garish, it seemed only to extend and intensify the brilliance of the young moon. In the fountains the Paul Manship figures seemed alive beneath the tall, widely curving sprays of water. The replicas of the horses of Marly, at the far edge of the terrace, were white against the sky. On every side of the house the trees that edged the lawns were hung with pale blue lanterns that seemed to shine with the moon's light, not their own.

Inside the house in the two-storied hall where the ball would take place the only floral decorations were American Beauty roses in their usual vases. Louise noticed approvingly that Clarie had not tried to improve on the magnificence of the vast room. The tapestries, the suits of armor, the musicians' gallery where Paul Whiteman's orchestra would play, the ancient battle flags that hung on their outthrust staffs just below the ceiling, all these were ornament enough.

In the stone Renaissance room and in the smaller Gothic room there were vases and bowls of flowers. Clarie had not allowed a florist's elaborate arrangements to detract from the beauty of the sculpture and the paintings and the medieval stained glass.

In the dining room, on the table at which eighty guests would sit, were Louise's candelabra and her towering epergnes filled with fruit and roses. Between the french windows the punch bowl, on its pedestal, held American Beauties.

On the north terrace was a large marquee in which supper would be served. The combined imagination of Clarie and Frank, the head gardener, and Mr. Smythe, the florist, had turned the temporary structure into a pavilion of flowers. One could believe that it was, like the conservatory in the west wing, an integral part of the house.

Clarie accompanied his mother in her motorcar so that she could see the lighting effects on the Front and North and Fern and Farm drives. Afterward she walked slowly beside him on the terraces and through the house.

"You approve, Mammy?" he asked.

"It's perfect."

"Any more suggestions?"

Louise had made only one suggestion concerning the arrangements for the evening. She had asked that the granddaughters be placed beside the guest of honor. She had had her turn long ago; let them be hostesses to the prince.

Now she said: "You'll be delighted with my suggestion when you watch your girls tonight. I'm going to let Ellin wear my pearls. Not being married, she hasn't as yet sufficiently handsome jewels."

"And have you any little touch of your own to add to my preparations?"

"Just one. I'd like to bring downstairs the photograph the Princess of Wales gave me of this boy and herself when he was a baby. I'll not place it conspicuously—in the Gothic room, I think, on a small table."

When the prince arrived Clarie brought him to the Gothic room where Louise was waiting to receive him.

He was a slight, fair boy who looked younger than his thirty years. He might, Louise thought, be the son of his grandparents, he was so like them in appearance and in manner. He was spoken of as such a modern young prince in his tastes and in his amusements. To her he seemed completely Edwardian. He was as tactful as his grandmother too. He instantly noticed her photograph and commented courteously on it.

There was much at Harbor Hill for a young man, even a prince, to admire. Louise supposed that he had been taught to appreciate or at least to recognize the best in painting and sculpture. He probably also had some knowledge of tapestry and armor. He had perhaps seen the Pembroke armor in its original setting.

The prince inquired, however, about only one object, a small figure of a man in miner's clothes. It was Clarie's copy of the Gutzon Borglum statue.

As Clarie and the prince spoke of the statue, Louise thought of John and of what he would say of the evening's splendor.

"This is how you planned it, old lady," he would say. "Your boy's at the top of the heap, just where you always meant him to be."

During Louise's years at Harbor Hill, Clarie gave one other party that equaled in magnificence his entertainment for the Prince of Wales.

On the thirteenth of June in 1927 the house and the grounds were again illuminated. Beside the driveways colored lanterns hung in the trees; in the gardens the fountains played. In the dining room the most imposing pieces of the Comstock silver were displayed.

The guest list was almost identical. Most of the girls who had vied for the prince's notice were married but others, just as eager, were present to take their places.

This time the dinner and ball were in honor of a young American who had lately flown the Atlantic. The fashions in guests of honor might change, Louise thought, but the occasion never varied. For a hero or for a prince the excitement was much the same.

As she talked with the guest of honor at dinner and watched him later, she realized that what the grandchildren called a celebrity wasn't very different from royalty. This boy was like royalty, not only in the attention he attracted, but in his response to it. He was quietly courteous and occasionally he flashed a quick attractive smile, but he was withdrawn. He did not allow himself to be entangled by the guests who crowded around him. Several ladies spoke to Louise of his charming shyness. Shyness, she thought, was too soft a word for his reserve. It seemed to her more like an armor in which he concealed himself as he warily felt his way along an unfamiliar path.

She wished that John could be here tonight. This guest of honor would, she knew, interest him more than the other. John always said that it was the man himself that counted. One could not know the man behind the boy's guarded face, but his daring lonely flight would have impressed John.

John had never been impressed by royalty except on her account. He had wanted her to have success in the world of her choice and he had been proud of her when she achieved it. Her world was slowly receding, perhaps even ceasing to exist. John, she thought, would be more at his ease than she in this queer new world where an airplane could fly across an ocean and its hitherto unknown pilot be more widely acclaimed than the heir to an ancient throne.

The end came for Louise a little more than a year after the party in honor of Colonel Lindbergh.

On the morning of September fourth in 1928, Mary Finerty recognized the nearness of death. The doctors whom she summoned dismissed her fears and regretted that she had gone so far as to put in a telephone call for Mr. Mackay in London. When the call came through they told him that there was no cause for alarm.

"Just another very mild little heart attack," they said, "or it may even be only indigestion."

Mary Finerty had seen too many people die not to know the meaning of the unfamiliar gentleness in Louise's voice.

"I've never really thanked you, Miss Finny," she said, "for all you've done for me."

Then she talked a little of happenings long ago. Mary Finerty noted the change in these spoken memories. Today they seemed to be simultaneous rather than in sequence, as though the past were a circle instead of a straight line.

Mary Finerty, in a low voice, called Demoutier into the room.

"Look how she's picking at the bedclothes, Mme. Demoutier. They always do that."

"I know," the old woman whispered, "I have often seen it."

They concealed their anxiety from Louise, but she knew when

Miss Finny sent for the married granddaughters that the nurse was frightened and Willie, too, she thought, must be frightened for her. He was too much in love with little Gwendolyn Rose to spend his days anywhere except with her, but today he stayed home with his grandmother.

The grandchildren, when they went into her room, tried to hide their anxiety, but Louise saw it. It pleased her that as she talked to them in her accustomed way their strained young faces relaxed.

Louise did not feel hungry for lunch, but at five o'clock she asked Mary Finerty to ring for tea.

"And bring my paper," she added. This was the hour at which she always read her Paris *Herald*.

Ellin went home and K explained with elaborate casualness that she was spending the night.

Louise understood. Port Washington, where Ellin had a house, was only twenty minutes away, but Southampton, where K lived, was too far for her to be quickly summoned.

Could Miss Finny really be right, Louise wondered, and this be the end? Could the last of all her journeys be as easy as this?

She would know if Ellin came back and if Miss Finny brought Father Martel to her.

At a little after nine in the evening there was a sudden change. Mary Finerty had been waiting for it but she had not expected it to come so gently and so quickly.

She sent Demoutier for K and Willie and the doctor. She told Willie to telephone Father Martel. If he was out on another emergency, Willie, she said, must try the rectory at Manhasset.

"And hurry, Willie. There isn't much time. After we get the priest you better call Ellin."

There was no time. Before a priest or Ellin could arrive, while K was still untangling her rosary, Louise's heart stopped beating and, without pain, without even realizing it, she died.

It has taken a long time, dear Granny, to find your story and to write it down. There were so many people to talk to, so many places to visit, so many books and newspapers to read.

Many people remembered and helped me. Mostly it was their parents' recollections that they shared with me, and as they spoke, I heard not their voices and turn of speech but their mothers' and fathers'.

When I was in Nevada, Frances and Bill Berry of Reno drove me to Yuba County in California to meet their old friend Mrs. Delahunty, in Whiskey Diggings. Her husband was Father Delahunty's nephew and her mother, Mrs. McMahon, was related to Father Manogue. She remembered.

"My mother," she said, "and my husband's mother fashioned your grandmother's mourning garments when Dr. Bryant died. They often spoke of little Mrs. Bryant, so lost and unhappy, and so pretty, poor young thing."

Mrs. Delahunty told me about Poverty Hill and we drove there and then to La Porte by way of Brandy City. There's nothing left of Poverty Hill. It's buried under the tailings of abandoned mines. But

La Porte is, I think, unchanged. Even the names of the families are the same.

I went to Sausalito to see Louise Althea's daughters, Miss Louise Howland and Mrs. Charles Gunn. They had written down their mother's recollections of her journey to Downieville first on the John L. Stevens *and later on a burro up the steep trail with Mrs. Meier's bureau roped to the back of the mule ahead. The daughters had gone to see the Meiers' store in Downieville and they described the beautiful scale on which the gold dust was weighed. They told me about the rich assortment of merchandise that had been offered for sale in their mother's time when your grandmother and your mother worked for Mr. Meier.*

"Everyone called Mrs. Mackay's grandmother Madame," they said. "She was a French lady and there was no one who could make prettier hats than Madame, not even at the Bay."

As they talked, I knew that no more than you had Louise Althea forgotten your childhood years together.

I was staying with K at Lake Tahoe when I met Mr. Hellman's daughter, Mrs. E. S. Heller, and I saw my grandfather through her father's eyes. It was Grandfather, she said, who persuaded Mr. Hellman to move from Los Angeles to San Francisco.

Mrs. Gertrude Atherton was very ill when I saw her before she died, but she remembered a little and tried to tell me about your days at 825 O'Farrell Street. And when she talked about Jim Fair it was almost as though you were speaking.

In San Francisco I met Mr. and Mrs. M. A. Hirschman. His father was the jeweler, Adolph Hirschman, whom you and Grandfather first knew in Virginia City. Mr. Hirschman showed me the silver cup you sent him when he was a child.

The Lyman brothers, George and Edward, who grew up on the Comstock, remembered Grandfather in their boyhood days. He had always, they said, been very kind to them. He would, I think, be pleased by their kindness to his granddaughter. Dr. George Lyman showed me the books in his library and explained them to me. I had no knowledge at all of western Americana and he shared his own wide knowledge with me. He arranged for me to do research at the Bancroft Library at Berkeley and at the State Library at Sacramento and he told me how to go about it.

Mrs. Leo Meininger, who was Emma Rosener, the youngest of

Mr. and Mrs. Sam Rosener's daughters, remembered more than anybody.

She told me about the hard years in Virginia City and about the extravagant ones at the Bay.

"Momma used to say," she said, "that when they went out shopping in San Francisco together, Mrs. Mackay never asked the price of anything."

Before her marriage Emma Rosener worked at the Nevada Bank. She was in Mr. Hellman's outer office when Grandfather and Mr. Bonynge met.

She talked about Richard Dey. "Momma never liked that man or trusted him," she said, and shook her head as she told me about the cable Mr. Dey sent and the one he didn't send. "But, luckily, your grandmother cabled Poppa and Poppa told her to get on the first boat."

She gave me a mirror and some beautiful little gilt boxes that you had bought at the City of Paris for her mother. And she showed me a tinted photograph of herself and her sisters wearing the lace- and embroidery-trimmed frocks you sent them from Paris in 1876.

I talked often with Mr. and Mrs. James Gerard. They remembered Father and Uncle Willie and Mrs. Fair's daughters as though they were all still young, as though there had been no years between.

The Dominicans still have a convent building at Benicia but there is no longer a school there. I went to their school at San Rafael. The Mother Superior took from the safe the red ledger in which are the records which were kept in Mother Goemaere's own hand. We turned the pages until we came to your name.

"Marie Louise Antoinette Hungerford de Downville. Entrée le 15 Janvier 1857. Agée de 13 ans."

I never knew your whole name before that and I can tell you now that until then I was never quite sure that you had told the exact truth about your age.

I went to Downieville. Only the Catholic church was left of the buildings you knew, but looking across the Yuba from the old hospital site I could see the faint outlines of the terraces where the Italians planted their vineyards.

I have Captain Bunker's painting of Downieville as it was in 1859. Since then the trees have grown back on all the hills and, from the *trail, the little town is almost hidden at the bottom of a smooth, deep, green cup.*

I went to Virginia City. It's filled now in the summer with tourists. All along C Street there are souvenir shops and bars. I think the bars must be almost as noisy as you remember. St. Mary's and Mr. Piper's opera house have been rebuilt, but the Gould and Curry office is still there. They call it the Mackay house because Grandfather stayed there whenever he went to Virginia after the fire of '75. The Geiger Grade must have been smoothed and widened but it still seemed to me a steep and perilous road as I drove down it and thought about Grandfather and Mr. Sharon. Old Mount Davidson hasn't changed. It still casts its long, early shadow over the town. The wind still whistles harshly across the divide between Virginia and Gold Hill.

I read as many contemporary writers as I could, trying to know your time as you and they saw it. I liked best in the early years Major Downie and R. M. Daggett and, later, Ludovic Halévy and Mrs. John Sherwood. I suppose that's because they liked you best.

I detested Garland Harris but I was glad to find his handwritten account of his years as justice of the peace. You would be pleased to know that both his penmanship and his spelling were very bad.

I read Mrs. M. M. Mathews' book, and while she must have been pretty frightening as a maid even though she stayed with you such a short time, Ten Years in Nevada *is good reading. Mrs. Mathews had that wonderful freshness of vision which lunatics seem to share with children. Her description of Virginia City is the most vivid I have found.*

All sorts of people who went to the diggings kept diaries or later wrote their memoirs. I think I came closest to your point of view and your mother's in the Shirley Letters.

I shared your pride when I read about Colonel Hungerford in the Piute War in Thompson and West's History of Nevada, *and in the official records of the War of the Rebellion about the commendation he received after the battle of Fair Oaks.*

Then there were the directories. I believed you when you used to say crossly "They'll bury me in Brooklyn but I wasn't born there." Still, I was pleased to find in the New York Directory of 1843 the address on Pearl Street exactly as you had given it to me. In the Washoe directories I found you at 10 North A Street and the Hun-

gerfords at Cedar Ravine. I couldn't find Mrs. Mock's address but I read about her in The Big Bonanza by C. B. Glasscock.

The newspapers I needed are scattered. There are early western files in so many places. I read what I could in Berkeley, in San Francisco, in Pasadena, in Sacramento, in Washington, in New York, in Worcester.

At the University of Nevada I read the file of the Territorial Enterprise that Father gave them. I first saw the huge stack of volumes when he had them brought in for you to see before he sent them West. You turned some of the pages and stared down at them, but whether you were reading or remembering, I didn't know. Then you shook your head and walked away from the table on which the volumes had been placed. You returned to your favorite chair and picked up your Paris Herald.

I have your books of letters from all sorts of people: Queen Isabella, Meissonier, Cardinal Vaughan. And I have your London scrapbooks. The earlier ones were lost, I suppose, when the house at 9 Rue de Tilsitt was sold. I am grateful for the way in which you collected your clippings and I am astonished by it. I could never have been so detached. You kept everything: compliments and criticisms, pretty sketches and grotesque cartoons. There are accounts of balls and royal functions, of cable-rate wars and libel suits, of garden parties and directors' meetings. Your clippings came from every kind of paper. The collection includes the Wasp, the Argonaut, the Court Circular, the Electrical Age, Truth, Town Topics, the American Working Woman, the San Francisco Examiner and the Chronicle, the New York World and the Sun and of course your favorite, the Herald of New York and of Paris.

Do you remember when Harold Ross, the editor of The New Yorker, told me to ask you to write your memoirs? I said I would help you. You started to make notes in the flowing pointed hand you learned at St. Catherine's and never forgot. You wrote out two things: "Mrs. John W. Mackay was educated at Benicia," and, on a separate piece of paper, the Enterprise's announcement of your marriage to Grandfather, which you knew by heart.

I got married and the project was abandoned. Now I've tried to carry it out by myself. The events, even the least of them, are all as they happened, and the people and the places are as they were. I know I have described your journey exactly as it was, but I can *only hope that in my book you are as you were, that this is how you felt and thought and spoke.*

I am less certain than when I began whether you would be pleased or not. As I have put your story together, I have realized how little I knew you. You might easily tell me that I still don't know you. You would smile as you said it and try not to sound impatient.

You always knew your grandchildren better than we thought and better than we knew you. And, of course, you knew then what we are slowly learning, that no human being ever knows more than a little about another.

Dear Granny, I have done my best. Here it is with my love.

Ellin

Lantana, Florida
March 1956

Acknowledgments

BESIDES the kind friends and relatives whom I have named in my book, many people have helped me.

My deepest thanks go to the librarians. Every place I went, from the Huntington Library, which was the first, to the New York Society Library, which was the last, I met with kindness and consideration. Experts in other fields, such as Classical Music and Horses, have made me feel foolish every time I opened my mouth. Among the librarians I found only courtesy and patience. I could ask all the questions I liked and they never made me feel ashamed of my inexperience as a researcher.

My gratitude goes out to every name I write on this list as well as to any that, through temporary forgetfulness, I omit.

Bernice Baumgarten	Warren Howell
Leah Rappeport Cogan	the late Richard Carley Hunt
Thomas B. Costain	Elaine Douglas Kahn
Mrs. John Fulton	Edward Nally
Norbert Guterman	Margaret Leech Pulitzer
M. A. Hirschman	Leland S. Rosener
Terence Holliday	Timothy Seldes

There are two people whom I should like particularly to mention. One is the late Eleanor Bancroft, who was Acting Director of Bancroft Library, University of California, Berkeley, California, and the other is Caroline Wenzel, Supervising Librarian, California Department, California State Library, Sacramento, California.

They were generous and untiring in spending time with me, in guiding me, and in answering my long and frequent letters of inquiry. To them I owe very special and most loving thanks.

American Antiquarian Society, Wooster, Massachusetts
    Clarence Saunders Brigham, Director

Bancroft Library, University of California
    Frank S. Brezee

Beaumont College, London, England
    Reverend Lewis Clifford, S.J., Rector

California Historical Society
    Mrs. Rogers Paratt, formerly Director

Huntington Library and Art Gallery, San Marino, California
    Lyle H. Wright, Head of Reference Department and Reading Room

International Telephone and Telegraph, New York City, New York
    Colonel Sosthenes Behn, Chairman
    Forest L. Henderson, Executive Vice-President (of American Cable and Radio)
    Eleanor McGonagle, Librarian
    Dorothy O'Keefe, formerly Secretary to Sosthenes Behn

Mackay School of Mines, University of Nevada, Reno, Nevada
    Jay A. Carpenter, Director

Museum of the City of New York, New York City, New York
    Grace Mayer, Curator of Prints and Photographs
    V. Isabelle Miller, Curator of Silver, Costumes, China, and Furniture
    Jerome Irving Smith, formerly Assistant Librarian

Nevada, University of, Reno, Nevada
    James J. Hill, Chairman of Department of Library Science
    Austin E. Hutchison, Professor of History

Newport Historical Society, Newport, Rhode Island
    Mrs. Peter Bolhouse, Executive Secretary

New York Genealogical and Biographical Society, New York City, New York

    Arthur S. Maynard, Librarian

New-York Historical Society, New York City, New York

    Wayne Andrews, formerly Curator of Manuscripts

    E. Marie Becker, Reference Librarian

    Geraldine Brand, Chief of the Reading Room

    Betty J. Ezequelle, Assistant Curator of Maps and Prints

    Lewis J. Fox, Reference Assistant

New York Society Library, New York City, New York

    Mrs. Frederick Gore King, formerly Assistant Librarian

    Helen Ruskell, Assistant Librarian